SODOMIES I

Aldo Busi was born in Montichia[...]
Goethe, John Ashbery, Christine St[...]
well as *Alice in Wonderland*. He is t[...]
Standard Life of a Temporary Pantyhose Salesman. An English translation of
his other work, *La Delfina Bizantina*, is forthcoming. Aldo Busi lives in
Brescia.

by the same author

Seminar on Youth
The Standard Life of a Temporary Pantyhose Salesman

ALDO BUSI

Sodomies in Elevenpoint

TRANSLATED BY STUART HOOD

faber and faber
LONDON · BOSTON

English translation first published
in Great Britain in 1992
by Faber and Faber Limited
3 Queen Square London WC1N 3AU
Originally published in Italian in 1988
as *Sodomie in Corpo 11*
by Arnaldo Mondadori, Milan
This paperback edition first published in 1993

Printed in Great Britain by Clays Ltd, St Ives plc

English translation © Stuart Hood, 1992
© Arnaldo Mondadori, 1988

Stuart Hood is hereby identified as translator of this work
in accordance with Section 77 of the Copyright,
Designs and Patents Act 1988.

A CIP record for this book
is available from the British Library

ISBN 0-571-14279-6

2 4 6 8 10 9 7 5 3 1

to the sub-god

I like the look of Agony,
Because I know it's true –
Emily Dickinson

I am suspicious of the ease of methods that draw upon the feelings. To furnish one's own feelings is not up to the author but to the other.

Paul Valéry

I would be so solid to love – for example, from my lips you would harvest little clusters – spherical, vocal, damp – and to the typewriter beat of the old organ, the heart, could pass night after night listening to concerts of pure rhetoric that would be almost like spring storms. And just think what these absent drops could focus on to the paper for you, setting ablaze the Academy of distance, the Arcadia of practical sadnesses, while waiting for new architectures of rheum to crumble under the tap suddenly turned on by each awakening. I would not talk to you simply of love, it is not merely a question of love – what is involved in this story is the detailed flow of the blood which becomes ink and *its story* would be told through the pressure of fingertips on cellulose flesh.

In this fine love story, which is all the more devastating the less there is of it, I figure less and less and neither more nor less than all the others, including those excluded.

~~

'Do you have the time, please?'

The voice, so fresh, adolescent, comes from the other side of the netting that lines the parking area on the autostrada just on Vicenza West. The outline of a boy picked out by the headlight of a motor-scooter in neutral.

I smile at this trick which I have never been able to use – to ask the time and to be there, ready, something to be lived, escaping from between the hands of the watch.

'Six o'clock exactly,' I say and it has been dark for half an hour. The engine cuts out. I am coming back from a literary prize giving which will take place tomorrow – I went by invitation (twenty-four hours early) and out of haste to be over and done with such a phoney engagement I have ended up with not getting over and done with it – because tomorrow I am certainly not coming back here: my lack of inclination has overcome all my enthusiasm. I was anxious to see who a Venetian bank gives prizes to and with what official blessings – the writers and poets who had entered the lists belong above all to that trustworthy class of communists

1

tolerant of Church and Capital, with Gastronomy as the main conversational course at table.

Besides, the banks never give prizes – they only acquire *futures*, the futures – already so scarce – of writers, poets, critics, journalists. I intended not to miss the appointment so as to study some patterns of behaviour in public – above all of my own – because *I* am always the centre of my interest, *I* what I submit to the jury of my irrevocable judgment of myself – whereas I pardon almost everything in the world, because the world is what it is and is indivisible and cannot help it and interests me only as it reacts to me and to the secret sentences I shall pass on myself, piling up verdicts as if I were laying in a supply against future fits of mental lethargy. But I am not sorry to have got the days wrong – you don't always have to be in a place to say what it is like. A sung Mass is a sung Mass – what can a literary prize given by a bank or an association of industrialists sponsoring *culture* be like? A sung Mass broadcast by cable so as to save the most precious and distant ewe-lamb lost in the thickets of *freedom of thought and speech*.

'Thanks,' says the sing-song voice. He cannot be more than fifteen. He has put his foot on the rest; hand and elbow imprint on the dark the flash of the movement on the handle-bar that turns on the engine – he is about to leave – the motor starts up again.

'Come on – let's get it out and warm ourselves up a bit,' he says all in one breath, ready to escape.

'Here it is,' I say, and insert it in a tear in the netting. The boy gets off his moped, unbuttons his flies, begins to speak in Venetian dialect, breaking up the phrases, panting out short obscenities as if reciting them for the first time and from memory. I give a little laugh – my excitement stops halfway – I don't like little boys and then these live barbs of wire round my prick, a crown of thorns. I whisper to him what he believes to be adult dirty talk, we suck each other off – I am a little puzzled by the drop of eau-de-cologne, undoubtedly taken from his mother and all of a piece with the tenderly ridiculous convictions one has at his age about personal cleanliness. I hear him standing there, tense, with his whole body against the wire-netting, breathing in the light exhaust-gas of the moped with its engine still running, and now he wants to kiss me through the mesh of the netting. The taste of the frost on the rust between our tongues, he floods my mouth with spurts of saliva, the boy gives a long, rigid sob, clings to the netting with his hands, shakes it violently, how much repressed energy is discharged in that kiss between prisoners. I let it happen like a marionette bent on playing things out to the end, on leaving him either a pleasant memory or no memory at all, willing but not involved.

'Tell me when you come this way again, please, I beg you. I'm called Pierluigi,' he says. 'Sunday? Monday? I live down there – down there . . .'

There must be an isolated house down there or else the mental horizon of solitude.

Yes, I too have been like that – trembling, with my heart in commotion. I would rattle off my particulars to shadows on the other side of something, I was willing to put up with anything so as to be in love with something, to beg for a date, wanted to run today and tomorrow together, and went to all the dates I made for myself with the false complicity of sceptical or already indifferent adults. Nothing disappointed me to the point of not falling into the same trap I would set for myself the moment I got out of it. I was too shy to talk of love, I went on about sex, which I did anchoring in it rage, desperation, the need to be loved and the desire for vendetta, for social revenge and for others *down there*. My prick was the perfect diagram of my brain – they were fused and intimately opposed, at war. I overflowed and there was no limit which intelligence or the evidence of facts could invent to dam my animal abstraction. I was prey to an agonizing fantasy. I was dying for a halo of reality which might show me a crumb of sympathy, but would even make do with anyone who could simulate interest because he thought it was the only way to make me clear off. And now these people around me, this order achieved because accepted in its artificiality and convenience, this intellectual plenitude cleft by the beautiful unreasonableness of desire, this *reality* in which I feel sufficient to myself is much less concrete than those shadows and that furtive chaos. But I would no longer change it. And I throw that back above the red jewel of the fleeing moped a safe blessing, an amorous wind to enwrap the boy and give him the warmth he will continue to

3

dream of, to protect him from those like me, to love him for himself.

Yes, I am moved, but by myself, not by him, and by the easy wisdom of the loser.

～

I am sitting in a bar and thinking that if I am admitted in time I shall manage to pass the New Year in hospital, so I won't need to think – and shall do research into some handy illness.

Woman with a flabbergasted look a metre and a half away from me. Oh, I know the pangs of women in love with the wrong man – more good-looking, younger, often with his head somewhere else and for this reason all the more unattainable, desirable, despicable, the shifting sand that was needed . . . She sits there in the alcove, resting on her thick peasant's calves, her spectacles thick but with an elegant, slightly baroque frame, the famous downcast glance which attempts indifference, sipping at a complicated cocktail which says much about her intimate need for simple and traditional things with a touch of the prohibited . . . And only after a quarter of an hour do I notice that she is not here alone and that there is a link between her and the shady, skinny person who is whispering with a big man on the stools at the bar. She sips an infinite number of times without swallowing a single drop from that clepsydra, which is the colour of clotted blood (raspberry), touches her ears with her first finger, looks elsewhere, at an imaginary fixed point, without making faces or signs of impatience, motionless, in her thick-set body of a woman who wanted more for herself and who has the money – she does – under the floorboards to permit herself an adventure fiercely stoked. She is ageless, stuck around thirty, shiny complexion (as if groomed with wax), without resonances – no joys either past or present play on the porcelain face cast in a pleasant but perverse little fixed smile. She is the voluntary slave of a dream far beyond her oneiric system: a slim youth, tall with intensely black and somewhat static eyes like an oriental, a triangular face, a brown mole at the furthest left-hand corner of his bright pink lips, long eyelashes, like a doll. The woman reminds me of other unhappinesses without outlet, a state of lingering in the most bloody suffering: to love an object turned to

4

you only in profile, to love a man – to love half of him – who exudes charm until the way you delude him with what he might get out of it is finally settled in a legal document, an outburst of weeping, a flight, love! *true* love at last. Someone to be attracted by playing on his guilt complex because by dint of thinking of what he could do with the money he will take off you, he has also built up a kind of sincere feeling towards you and, moved by an impulse of authentic pity for himself and disgust with you, he will give you a caress which, without even brushing against you more than is necessary, will lacerate you beyond words.

She puts up with this, thinks that with time her special powers of understanding will overcome all the boy's resistance to ugliness and her being past her prime, that he will not be able to do without her, a secure, sheltering featherbed which an ambiguous and well-fucked man needs when he has already given all he has to God knows whom and wants to be adored while he sleeps and recharges, and in his sleep will allow her to formulate over him a renewed promise which once again he will not keep because (apart from women) he also goes with men and this enrages her – excites her beyond all bounds. When the squall is over – for they are always quarrelling – she or he will tell the other that the *true* relationship is the one there is between the two of them, that no one else counts, the other women don't count, passing fancies – and while she will always be on the point of laying her head on the pillow and putting his hand on her breast, the telephone or doorbell will ring and he will have to run off somewhere . . . She will also play the educational card – she will play the diplomat even if it is not her profession – he will pretend to let her play it because while she *teaches* him and he *learns* he doesn't have to waste precious energies in bed with her seeing that afterwards he has another sudden appointment. Getting up from the calf's skin laid out in front of the fireplace in the two-roomed penthouse flat with usual services and rocking on her robust Gothic calves she will tell him once again that she is the daughter of a rich pork-butcher, a hateful man who kept her under his thumb until four months ago and made her eat salami even with her coffee, year after year, Mass and Communion every week, but that she is still a respectable woman and that she wants a child from him even by artificial insemination . . .

Women who live with their eyes flooded with red, the eternal internal conjunctivitis . . .

Her impossible toy boy has now made her a brusque sign as if to say he will be back later, and he goes out with the big fat man with whom he has been talking *sotto voce*; she gets up from the settee and goes and sits on the stool which her beau occupied before going out. Another cocktail, Iole? Of course, it's such a cold evening!

She smokes badly, she doesn't know how to take things in her mouth, the skin of her lips sticks and is now bleeding, she puts out the cigarette, shrugs, smiles to the barman, pulls her tartan skirt well down, adjusts her pure silk blouse under the little bolero which is patterned with gold and silver embroidery. Until a few years ago she must have gone to the private chapel to teach the catechism and to make sweets for the first communicants, she has blossomed very slowly and there has emerged an acrid little bloom, itching, almost dry already, which no one will ever water again, or not the person she says.

For three quarters of an hour she has remained with her eyes glued to the glass of the door (it was raining a little too) without moving, without speaking to anyone, without a smile, and prodigiously insignificant to anyone but me. But I know the neutral ways in which fatal passions mask themselves, and unhappiness is more enjoyable if one isolates it completely, immersing it in the pleasures of the others around you. She remains so motionless, concentrating so much on a feigned indifference the better to act it out – her unhappiness; so as not to have to share her own unadorned but resounding drama with anyone.

When he comes back he is pale, nervous, with too many things to hide all at once, a lie that doesn't come off, his hair and clothes without a drop of rain, he sits down beside her. She does not say anything and does not even give him much of a look, extends first finger and thumb and removes something that was hanging on his chin, which she shows him: a peculiarly curly hair. He turns away and begins to talk to the person on the next stool. She gives a sudden movement of her pelvis because of her skirt and bodice, goes over to her alcove, discreet, hopeful, more sad and more grateful than ever.

6

As for me, alone here and certainly with less existence than this full-time dreamer, to silence *the voice of the blood* is linguistically no mean task. But it has never found anyone it could force to listen to it after it lost its falsetto . . . and I could not continue to pitch it so as to give it fantasies to vibrate to in a *solo*. Now the exaltation of the *blood* lies all in this mental rejection where I leave a chink not inaccessible to the death of the living being that is attempting to live less. To break down platitudes – or even taboos – means to renounce the only possible beautiful thing in life: the age-old sedimentation of clichés. There is no other liveable life outside of them, that a writer knows. To attack the platitudes of the world means to remove from beneath it the only piles on which it rests – with this difference that it doesn't notice and you are the only one to collapse under it. It takes centuries to produce new platitudes and no one manages to live through the time he requires to make up for his own inadequacy vis-à-vis the society which is his contemporary – vis-à-vis its commonplaces and therefore its racisms and exclusions in its language. I have thousands of proofs of this and I no longer wear myself out to proclaim the contrary. I prefer to let myself go on respecting the subtle, cruel and stupid harmony of the world which relegates me to the margin of its rites, which are the more powerful the more trite they are; which persecutes by excluding me from its age-old rhetorics; and the world – and not I – is always right in the apparent life of its organization of movement. The world boasts of the insensible erection which is to be found in its cradle; I have to find a sensibility in the impotence which I am creating for myself so that, while wishing to castrate it, I can continue to carry on in the only way I know: rotating on myself so that I too can be a semblance of a world.

The usual recurring infection of the urinary tracts – that criminal of a urologist who at fifteen went up my urethra with a twenty-centimetre stethoscope and ruined me for ever, creating stenoses, galloping infections, urethritises which, with a knowing, punitive enjoyment of my *unnatural* confessions, he treated by pouring in liquid silver which caused me multiple burns inside and out and then gave me a final telling-off . . .

'What do you feel then?' asks the doctor in charge of the ward at his first inspection.

7

'Nothing special – it's this permanent drip in spite of all the antibiotics. There's no way of stopping it. I feel as if I were dripping away with it . . .'

My imagination has dried up where things requiring a limited investment of time are concerned but comes to life once more when it is on the track of technical complexity (of the deployment of forces organized during years of psychological definition within me before being committed to writing): a narrative tapestry which is the history and interpretation of my time and the history of linguistic style up to its latest breaking-point. I remember that on occasions like this (in basements, trains, lavatories, with little free time and, yes, spells in hospital) I used to indulge in brief jottings – sometimes in rhyme, alas – or the verbalized immediacy of a *sensation*. The results always convinced me – everything was destined for glory and I killed time with the physical refinement of the dilettante who takes pleasure in being the designated victim of enforced sincerity, which ranks only a little below eternity. Now to write like this *en passant* costs me a physical fatigue greater than any ambitious project, such as learning a hundred Chinese ideograms or taking up again the third – the third last – novel in my pentalogy, *The Byzantine Dolphin*. To me writing is a duty, exactly as it will be to stop – but in that case what a relief to be able to keep one's promise with a palimpsest.

'But what will you do when you've written all five of your novels?' I pretend I am asked by the gorilla-like attendant who is arriving with mop and pail.

'I shall play the writer's widow – I'll look after his interests in the various publishing houses of the world – go to accept memorial tablets and attend the unveiling of a municipal monument.'

Today I find facility difficult and almost as unbearable as the idea of a biography. What little conviction has remained to me even in rendering credible a terrifying case-history (discharges, hepatitis, haemorrhoids, polyps in the throat and nose, sprains, fractures, deafness, verrucas, heart . . . *heart*?) that, documents in hand ('But this is an archive!' exclaimed the orderly), speaks for itself and says nothing. And this business of homosexuality too – untenable. Whether it is declared, whether it is struck out, omitted or neglected by pure oversight, no one entirely believes me. I declare it from a spirit of ontology, with a straightforward scientific complex for having preferred (complying with the flexible intellectual rigidity which I have imposed on myself since childhood when faced by non-suits like sex – how I hate the term *sexuality*, the petty-bourgeois termite *eroticism*) the routine of a banality swollen by problems of *representation* to a cursed and parvenu talent that does not suit the neutral casualness of my condition, which is lived arbitrarily as if it were a choice.

Buñuel says that sex without sin is an egg without salt. Has he never drunk a raw egg newly laid? Salt robs it of savour. But sex, according to common opinion, is like the theatre: however experimental it may be – lower, draw back or raise the curtain – it remains bourgeois.

Everything that is formalized around sex is wrong. The most disgusting mode of discourse is the amorous one. Its expression makes official certain modes of behaviour to the detriment of all the others which are silent. One ought to be able to enjoy the freedom to be ill without anyone – those who instrumentalize the word for political, that is to say normative, ends – putting pressure on one to get *better*. Unfortunately one must always go on talking a great deal and talking to every generation of sexual beings in the name of those who are mute, so as to nail down the official order and the social state when faced by silence.

'Busi,' I make the nurse say who has come to shut the window, which up to now has let in a strong-smelling mist of bleach. 'Come on, say something to us – an aphorism!'

'What strikes me most about high rates of unemployment is that they are inevitably accompanied by very low needs for anal relations – an unemployed man clings to everything – even to his own shit to the detriment of other people's.'

'But that is not an aphorism – that is a press statement from the Catholic trade union,' and now she really turns to me and says; 'Get ready because you've got to go down and do a urine cocktail with olives.'

(?)

'The part up top doesn't only serve to make the part down below function.' They are many, the illusory merits attributed to the part up top. In war, for instance, the Vietnamese had only one marvellous weapon: their legs and the thing that dangled between them must have been the hammering peal of bells that incited them to run without ever stopping. With it they kept the rest going. Not even in sex, in politics and in economics and in art is there a vice-versa. It is the part up top which has every interest in remaining ignorant of the fact that it is an artificial emanation.

The Standard Life of a Temporary Pantyhose Salesman has drained me of a good deal of hate and, on rereading it, the only thing that leaps to the eye are the misprints. From a personal point of view it seems to me to be centuries old. I should like to know *who* wrote it and who this Angelo Bazarovi is who claims to be my *alter ego*, this monster of fascinating moral utterances which, to my male regret, no longer concern me, having been replaced (unbeknown to me) by moral utterances which are certainly worse, more conventional, indeed more *principled*. We become bourgeoisified through weariness too, and so as to impart an affected drawl to misanthropy, with which I am as fed up as I am with the collection of people which has transcendental aspirations to *comradeship*. It will be a rest to take up *The Byzantine Dolphin*, once more, an objective novel at last. I shall be able to construct a world that doesn't concern me (*sic*) and once the moulds are finished and done with there will be no need to destroy them in order to tell the story of what it was like: it will suffice to describe it, one piece of papier-mâché after another, and just for once I shall not be there under those ruins of the *memory* of the novel about myself. With *Seminar on Youth* and *The Standard Life* I have managed to create for myself an emergency exit to slip out of autobiography; with *The Byzantine Dolphin* I shall succeed in not even entering it.

Here in hospital I am not too bored. Laclos is a sublime bed-fellow, one who had it in mind to write a new French grammar and snored in forms that were both martial and metrical. I think that *Les Liaisons Dangereuses* is superior to *A la Recherche – Le Temps Retrouvé* apart – as far as linguistic inventiveness goes and above all in plot, whopping stories. The use Laclos makes of oxymoron is unique in its expressive power and superior to anything I have read up to now: only those things which are of great concern are denied and by this process are axiomatically affirmed, giving the illusion that they necessarily shine with their own light and not because of the cunning rhetorical play of the ordering mind. The moral of the book leads to various conclusions: that every moralist hides a libertine and that it is a waste of energy to be a moralist unless one has at one's disposal a secure amorality to defend and champion. Laclos' novel is writing which introjects itself sentence by sentence and the book, therefore, like *Tristram Shandy*, requires to be read as a whole which is already organic in each single sentence, for each sentence is a novel. With books like this one could spend several lives on a desert island, sure of having at one's disposal an infinite library; each time, articulating the sentences in ourselves in a different way because they are changed by our being changed, we would read a different book about different epochs in a system of perception which is *ours*, discovered by re-reading, or rather by reading. This is the rare magic of the great objects in literature: to be a single unembraceable form from the part to the whole and from the whole to the part, not to have in them an easy, commercial taste for mystery, to be a composite language, to have nothing special to reveal with uncoded messages (note that in both Laclos and Sterne the contents too are just as revolutionary as the style in which they are immersed . . .), but to be for the reader a constant source of revelation of *themselves*.

Les Liaisons Dangereuses is a mirror-image of Machiavelli's *Prince*: in terms of content, in the latter, the ends prevail over the means; in the former, the means (the mean means) are the only possible end of man's actions because every end is consciously absurd and of slight importance from the point of view of human chances of happiness and common sense. In Laclos *the end* is only the pretext to *divert* whatever separates from the common and unique goal of all things human – ridicule and death. What is important in Laclos is 'the eroticization of the will' (Malraux), not whether it aspires to an end or not: the intellectual abyss between the two guiding principles cannot be filled. Machiavelli's *Prince* has a *vulgar* conception and vision of desire: it is believed really to exist, and by existing has the possibility of being pursued and therefore the object through which to realize desire would really exist. To Machiavelli power is what counts in life and, by the fact of desiring it, he makes it exist outside itself, going so far as to establish naïvely a distance and therefore a *goal*. Machiavelli, out-

11

and-out specialist in *reality*, chops it into short, medium and long terms – like a business manager – sure that, should it not exist or not in a satisfying manner, it can be made to exist in the desired modes, because the desire for power can never be crossed by doubt as to its own vanity. The ambiguous greatness of Machiavelli consists in having considered the non-object *par excellence* (political power) to be so concrete and real that it can actually be projected, which is like saying that one must not be content with making smoke-rings with one's cigarette but play at ball-games and also give the feeling of the ripples on the water of the swimming-pools – and in fact he tells us that if the Prince acts thus and thus, if he avoids this and that, and if by chance or in a contrary case etc. etc. . . . . All this, in its stupidity (which is not so much philosophical as military), would lead to perdition any statesman or landowner with balls who wanted to win rather than to follow an intellectual theory about the art of winning and how to ward off bad luck until the government is under attack etc. as if to sit on a throne were an art and not a momentary abominable act by the incautious victor. Machiavelli sins from being naïve in wishing to separate politics from morals, the end from the means, the content from the form, simply because one cannot take away the bottle and make the wine stand up on its own – not to mention the possibility that one has a lot of wine but only one bottle; the wine although *contained* is much less precious than the *container*. So Machiavelli decides once and for all that means are means and ends are ends. But what people in later centuries have forgotten to underline in Machiavelli's perfidy is not that he examines *reality*, it is that unsuspectedly, he is inventing one from the ground up (no more or less than if he had been commissioned to do a romantic novel for a series on *the feelings*), and in this, his secret operation, he shows himself to be much greater than emerges from his having been relegated for centuries to the narrow confines of a kind of political or pedagogic perspicacity, however wide-ranging (the more the dolts claim to be *historical* and *great* the more they fall for it and have fallen for it: there are always any number of political pricks who interpret *The Prince* as a scientific treatise and not as a Renaissance vaudeville written by a depressed second-rate courtier brooding over absolute vendettas so long as there is a politician on the face of the earth). The reality which Machiavelli analyses as the premiss for the action of the Prince is a reality which is no sooner described than it is no longer there; untrustworthy, phantasmagoric, obsolete, all the right little instruments inapplicable even before they have grown cold. Reality, oh sire, has simply disappeared – but Machiavelli takes good care not to tell him. Concentrating a possible prince on the *end* he proposes, Machiavelli in effect removes him from his own most ambitious project: to dominate the Prince by giving him a false *end*, that is to say an end split by the means to attain it.

Rarely does the word teach anything that is not already known. So why does Machiavelli go to such lengths to teach things which, given the times, must have been the prerogative of the Florentine street urchins? One answer: to be freer to weave his words so that they might rule the world present and to come – words as the *end* of power and not some highborn criminal or other.

Machiavelli celebrates in the secret of his own accidie the autonomy of the word from political power, which wants to bend it to itself, and not the autonomy of political power (its impunity) from morals. In him the word is the end of all possible ends, not power, which Machiavelli tricks by giving it the illusion of supremacy over the word – it too being considered one instrument among so many others – and of action as opposed to thought, of content as opposed to form.

Laclos pushes things further: he denies an end to the word itself. He distrusts it, he does not leave in its hands the fate of the world, which it does not possess. Laclos by a linguistic tactic of progressive zero settings, which reveals his imperial and lucid strategy, which is inexorable and indifferent to the repetition of the same ridiculous and mortal destinies in the world, defeats even the illusory notion of desire by confronting it with the time required to realize it. The desire for the thing to be possessed (a woman, for example . . .) is already entirely one with the thing to be possessed already possessed: the distance from thought to action and to the word, from desire to its realization (the *end* in Machiavelli), has already been covered from every point of view even before the man takes or reveals a single step. The formulation of desire already gleams with the pale light of an ultimate awareness which renders ridiculous, dead and buried, both its success and its frustration. Everything has already happened before taking on any form or *that* form and is once again ridiculous and is once again dead – the soldier who becomes a general so as to forget that he is already dead the day he enlists. There is no salvation in the way one arrives at one's own death and desire is itself the psychic larva of our absurdity and of the corpse which we carry about inside our *living* body. The times are ripe to begin considering *The Prince* and *Les Liaisons Dangereuses* as two breviaries of aesthetics; the first an attempt at the ultimate militarization of the failed word, the second an attempt – a perfectly successful one – to silence the word itself.

In Laclos the soap-bubbles of human ends do not have time to burst *later* – they are born burst. Thought does not translate itself into words, but bursts in words and each word makes the preceding word burst until it leaves a *zero* text behind it. It is his poetic expedient to escape, in a manner that is not ridiculous, from ridicule and death: not allowing them to find anything on which to train their batteries of initial and final contempt, not even a last word, the ultimate bulwark of man's illegitimate desire to perpetuate himself, to *be*. Laclos leaves behind his own writing in a semantic field abandoned by any desire and therefore by any means and any end. The grandiose nullity of exemplary lives.

P.S.: What a pity about the end of the Marquise de Merteuil! Such a sensible woman, who does so much good to the timid and undecided, forced for ever and ever to show her inner self which has become her exterior, a creature too special to be inside out like that! But it is the destiny of great spirits to be completely annexed by the world according to its own scale of things, the world is only a minimal and necessary part of them, and to fail to make it understand after centuries of distance that theirs were not crimes but martial modes of behaviour and that there was nothing else they could do. It would be like saying that now they are inventing an *unconscious* to enable me to explain and make myself known to the masses, whereas I am simply too correct and too much of a shopkeeper to have one.

~~

I no longer take up positions against priests and military chaplains – I salute them politely because if one salutes them one may as well do it well; but from time to time I let it be understood that I do not welcome confessions. The vulgarity of any demonstration of the existence of God to someone who has two hours to get to sleep before the patient in front shits himself.

Peter Handke – *Falsche Bewegung* 1974, later the Wenders film *Halt Who Goes There!* ('No false moves'), which I would translate as *What a Lot of Apparent Movement!* ('for nothing') – is written in a style that is *sachlich*, terse and lean – ideal for anyone wanting to learn German. But this plot, with its intentional affinity with Goethe's *Wilhelm Meister*, doesn't hold water from the very first ever so clever little pages: 1) no confrontation with the world of work. Wilhelm has always been kept by his mother, who is even prepared to sell her supermarket so that her son can write *in peace* (how shameful! one writes as one can); 2) his mother is too clever not to put a halt to the ideological depression of her son (who is very annoyed because the world, just imagine, doesn't do what he wants) and yet this same mother says on a bench in a railway station that she has no advice to give, and it would never enter the head of any intelligent man to get rid of a parent who is so good at saying goodbye in order 'to go and write' somewhere else – as if one place were preferable to another. He could do it perfectly well at home and meantime give a hand with the wholesalers; he would learn the value of the money which is always found ready on the bedside table and would sometimes choose a character who would not take it for granted in full settlement of every chapter . . .

Personal aversion to novels which talk about the protagonist's desire – it is truly promethean in a white-collared sort of way – to become a *writer* and produce a book, as if writing were a profession like being an architect or a *bohémien* and not a leap in the dark. I who have translated *The Sorrows of Young Werther* know only too well the trepidation with which I waited for this spoilt boy (and I'm sure Goethe was with me in this) to commit suicide and stop being a damned nuisance with his romantic protests of an angry young man with ready cash. It is an old habit

15

of *high* (*sic*) literature never to make the narrating *I* work – as if to tell one's story excluded the need to earn one's bread or the unlucky fate of having to stamp a card and submit to a timetable so as not to compromise the ease with which the hero moves around. And so here we are again dealing with a narrating subject who is affluent but not fluent, who does not have to answer to any employer or to any economy of plot. He is given the usual liberal profession so that he will more easily move from page 10 to page 11, from city to city and at any time of the day or night (according to the need to pad things out in terms of landscape and meteorology), from caprice to depression, from anguish to sociological distress over the fate of the humble or to the melancholy of everyday encounters (he, in a train, sees her in another train opposite and they end up meeting but when on earth?), and always with that waitress ready with the cup of consommé, which serves as an ashtray, between a line of Communist writing and a chapter in Concorde, or moving around silver cutlery at a little funerary dinner for some neo-Rosa Luxemburg . . . I hate characters in novels who are socially *free*, exempted from answering to the law of money because they always have so much. I mean that their whimsical and *intimiste* cages are too big for anything essential to happen – so that almost everything happens by chance, something inconceivable both in reality and in any respectable novel – people who meet *by chance* in New York – 'Fancy meeting you here!' – eat *by chance* in the same restaurant with the excuse that since the most expensive one in the city is on page 48 and a chef is needed to keep the ranges going till 5 in the morning it takes less time to find them embracing by the sea and we have the dawn and the right light etc.

Besides a writer who writes of himself as one disgusts me: 'The writer, now in the evening of his years, revisits as a writer the city where he was born and which was precisely the place that gave him his origins as a writer.' It is only in and around Weimar that such calamities can happen. In proper cities people are born people, and so much the better if they don't go back to collect the signs of divine predestination but to bring bags of pasta and *cotechino* to nubile, ferocious, analphabetic aunts.

All the writer's anguish, which precedes writing and

accompanies it, must not leave a trace on the page which the writer finally de-liberates. From a writer (and from anyone else) I do not want anguish – I want results. What do I care for the giddiness of the bricklayers putting up a multi-storeyed building? I am interested in the house and thereby also pay for their fits of vertigo and possible accidents – whereas their fits of vertigo do not touch me if I have invested everything in the house and because of trivial problems of the trade it doesn't progress. I shall always be able to put up a plaque to the fallen – but my house, first and foremost. As if to say, I want the book but you can keep your dedications, very properly, to yourself. This because, owing to some sublime animal convention, we tend to consider the finished object not the effort it entails and the person as the origin of goods and not a sweat-box of effort because, as far as the latter goes, the man has had the good intentions and not the customer. To each his share of troubles, but we are interested only in the unborn child, who will have his own burden, without taking on that of his mother. Otherwise change profession – but I insist: How can writing be a profession? I realize that it can be – a whole lot of querulous authors live on royalties, live very well on their obscure ills and inability to cope with life: they get as fat as porkers. Not to speak of those who precisely as other people make mortadella with pistachios specially added – trying to meet the taste of the public, which is undoubtedly an advantage in industry and in handicrafts but a vice if one is a writer. A writer never takes into consideration any sort of horizon of expectation in the reader, in society – not even in himself: let's say his ideology. If a writer has to put himself in the reader's horizon of expectation, that reader must be himself: so let him write *how* and *what* he would like to read.

(Many people wonder about the reasons for a novel's success – but there is no reason for success, only for failure. It did well and that's that – the mortadella was ready at the right moment, long live mortadella! – and that is what happened with the Brown-shirts who from one day to the next went to the top of the hit parade of the consensus, thanks to their original monstrosity. Tomorrow there will be another masterpiece of mortadella, of a perfume, of a washing-powder, of a *novel*. What do you imagine 5, 6, 7 million copies of a book are compared to the billions of coloured Tampax or chequered mortadellas that are sold in the world every six months? And remember too that these are like medicines – they are bought by the basketful and end up, uncut, in the rubbish.)

In Handke's little novel obviously it is the project itself which involves the admission of 'artistic suffering' (but how much more moving are the sufferings of the miners in Lawrence or the inartistic ones of ballerinas everywhere) – but, I repeat, it is intolerable that a self-styled writer should reduce his mother to selling her shop so that he can get on comfortably with being comfortably tormented and with writing about his own (existential and political) incurable state. There is no comparison between having an ideological depression after ten years in factory or office and having it as a full-time job without needing to slave for it either, before or after – and these depressed privileged people have no idea of the difference – they bundle all the differences together, giving pride of place to their own, which are not weakened by the wear and tear, physical or moral, of being confronted day by day by the need to work *against one's will* in order to survive. I hate intellectuals who have *become bitter at the way things have gone*, who have nothing else to do but suffer with their leather-bound chequebooks in the inside pocket of their pure tweed sports jackets. Handke's characters – or those of that bourgeois pornographer, Moravia – all look like this to me: they suffer and suffer and never get any further forward or only get *forward* in one dimension. Meanwhile Handke with his twenty or more published books (the intensity of the suffering – just as in those of Thomas Bernhard – is proportional to the number of pages necessary to bring out another little Christmas present) could have set up a small but flourishing business – Delusion & Weltschmerz – with shares quoted on the stock exchange. This way of writing is very American of the Fifties and Sixties (and that not only because it is a question of a film treatment rather than a novel) and makes me think of someone who is perfectly healthy or totally ill, that is to say normal, that is to say an insignificant person without contrapuntal humours or comic contretemps. All Handke's novels are of 120/180 little pages, all filmable, all translatable without difficulty – beware of simplicity which is not baroque and of existentialism which is miserly. If one can understand them right away they are not worthwhile and underneath it all there is sleight-of-hand. It seems to me that there is nothing to learn or to unlearn from a thoroughgoing, rigorous monolithic *cupio dissolvi* – the oil is virgin but it conceals the second frying and it is odd finally to come up against an act of self-destruction which throws nothing of itself away . . .

I would opt for an academic-sarcastic style in the manner of Thomas Mann to describe the shallow ideological tension of our days of self-annihilation and the culture of violence. In Handke stylistically there is no polarity, counterpoint, diversity of registers – or of points of view, that is to say *the other bell*. If the death-bell tolls from the beginning you can be sure that it will go on like this to the *end*; it would be better to take oneself off to a funeral right away rather than read the book where what is really wanted is a fine ending with the depressed couple getting spliced and setting off for Monte Carlo at last. The novels of Handke – and of Bernhard – lack the narrative fervour of self-questioning; they have no *imprinting* to contend with on the plane of language – there is no dialectical clash between form and content – as people used to say when they were not afraid of being brief and clear instead of precise and obscure as nowadays.

In Handke and Bernhard the content contains itself by itself and always in the same way and in every *new* (*sic*) novel; and that seems to me to be excessive, as is the critical assessment of it. When one uses the same style *as a writer* in all one's books, one can no longer talk about style: they ought to say that they have lost control and can only go on copying themselves to infinity; precisely because they are accustomed to put mustard on frankfurters, they also put it on ice-cream, on cheese, in stew, even on mayonnaise, until without noticing they will put it on mustard. It is excessive – as in these sick people here who lack the self-control of elaborating a façade, of stylistic *lying* – their faces are the unstuck daguerreotypes of all the rottenness of their guts; they are incapable of hiding anything, they do not simulate, their dialogues are blandly *sincere* (that is either stupid or whining), they do not keep death in check by repelling it with the divine masquerade of life. They simply let themselves go. They are as they are. Already dead.

Looking at them I cannot help thinking of the duodenum, the colon, the pancreas, the tattered liver, and what use it is to have a face if it is a perfect reflection of the rotten guts it expresses.

That is why I very much like a man from Trieste, of my own age, with whom up to now I have not exchanged a word – always shaved, elegant, smiling, an inveterate smoker and drinker of coffee. If he has cancer there is no sign of it and you would not think he had it – so he bears it well and from it derives valuable hints in terms of hospital fashion: camel-hair dressing-gown, silk scarf, blue moccasins. All the others who have it and don't know how to dress it up – if only out of courtesy towards those who don't wish to be bored by arrogant corpses *in fieri* – have absolutely no style, so legible that you pass them by without even cutting the pages. Let them read themselves by themselves. Death is not a good reason for suddenly becoming *true*, at the expense of surrounding conviviality, if *truth* is inevitably synonymous with *decadence*. To dissimulate death at the point of life takes as much theatricality as to simulate life at the point of death. Style does not allow abandonment to the *self*. Heaven help you if you are *true* when you still have an infinite amount of breath to do better with.

End of the urine cocktail – a Martini with an extra-refined flavour of prick.

Hate, as distinct from love, circumscribes its own identity. Tell me whom you hate and I will tell you who you are; tell me whom you love and I will be as wise as before.

~~

I was saying then that the man in the bed in front of me gives off into the ward an acrid smell of *treated* faeces – phlebotomy, enema, a five-year course of thin broths. He dirties himself on average once every two hours, he cannot move, his thighs are locked, he used to run a drinks stall in a barracks in the south, for four years he gave the military salute banging the same heel against the same shoe until, one fine day, both his femurs . . . Servility, while it takes you off the unemployed list, inevitably leads to paralysis.

He lifts up his trunk, using an iron triangle which hangs from the head of the bed. He does it at 12 noon and at 7 at night (three

20

minutes) then he falls back finished and I see him no longer, continuing to give off the same monosporic stench without peaks or lows – of wasted thighs. He has some plans for the future – to get his heart into a condition to undergo an operation and then to open a bar *outside* the barracks. This is not a smell of death – I know it well, I had a grandfather like this; he will go on for years infesting the wards with shit and plans for the future.

Yesterday evening, a little before midnight – impossible to sleep, a stench of farts and snoring, an instigation to crime – I talked with a patient younger than me: cancer of the right testicle and consequent removal – a year ago. He has a business distributing video games and it serves him right for turning young people into idiots. But I told him that, in the days of Byzantium, mothers who were clever and farsighted removed these little trifles from their sons at birth and so they were certain to make a career at court. He was not aware of a North American plant – my memory is a blank – used to cure troubles with the genitals. I got the magazine in which I had read the news and he was delighted. He seemed to set great store by it.

At 2 in the morning the entrance hall was already shut and I was in a side corridor on a little wall smoking when the man from Trieste arrived, a cigarette, absolutely fed up with a fellow invalid from the same room – a petulant little old man who doesn't give a damn for others, who sleeps by day and at night reads the papers accompanying his reading – out loud – with interjections of surprise, of indignation, of incredulity, and never ceasing to crunch biscuits and swill Lambrusco. The man from Trieste has breath that smells of I don't know what – of sawdust scattered on a floor sprinkled with bleach. I tried not to be targeted by it and listened in profile, turning my neck in response to his movements and attempts to be more incisive by coming closer with his purplish lips. Another thorny story: having joined the Naval Academy very young, then a young second-in-command on cargo ships, he recently reached the rank of chief engineer; for years he has seen of the land that strip over there, the long, distant rim wich emerged even after two weeks of sailing on open sea on the same route (not many knots so as to save oil more expensive than time): Persian Gulf, South Africa, etc., etc. In Trieste he rebelled against the diagnosis – six

21

months ago – he made a couple of trips to some other places and then came here. Diagnosis reconfirmed. The first two months a nightmare. Then the nightmare becomes a habit and finally something which is neither one nor the other, but dances and leaps about in his head like a grasshopper which bites even in flight. He is fully informed about everything at his own express wish – even about the months he has left . . . How he had been poisoned by all his toil for all these years far from his wife and little son. As if he did not have them – two little strips of your flesh but more and more distant. On boats, always among men, it's well known etc. but not on his – he starts the subject not me. In prison, on the other hand, they put the pretty boys up for auction. So he had heard, had read, naturally. What about you? Me? What about me?

I got up off the little wall, I was really sleepy. He caught the ball on the rebound and between his teeth cursed the moral he draws from his tale into the night, which is misty in the open window, and with long elegant strides went back to the room determined to have a word or two with the little old man, if he was still there, pretending to read and always other people's papers into the bargain. He turned towards me and threw me a single look of agony. I fell asleep right away, doped by my lethal clairvoyant powers: one reality chases away not another reality but the same illusion.

At 10 o'clock someone comes running down the stairs, a watchman with a cartridge belt and a pistol in its holster, he's doing the rounds – at night the door to the entrance hall is shut – and those ladies who are still up smoking and chatting (the sad pyrotechnics of throats being cleared: the syringed lungs, the 'bipopsies', the arthritis in the bones, the grappa to be hidden from the nuns) have all looked towards this apparition from a Western.

'Did you see someone of my height – white Dolce Vita sweater – blue windcheater, black leather trousers, dark hair, long and curly, green eyes? Someone like that who is going round the women's wards and behaving oddly?'

'No' was the woman's chorus.

'Watch out, he's up to something.'

'Oh,' said the chorus. The watchman saluted and having

discharged his duty ran down the stairs. The ladies withdrew immediately with measured steps and not furtively, with flushed cheeks – some on to the landing to look up and down the stair-well, each for herself, suddenly enemies and strangers. Somewhere there was the phantasm of life lying in wait once more – something one could not share with anyone. A rape is better than nothing.

From the expression 'to eat the air promise-crammed' I must derive some euphonious hints to send me to sleep. Another good title for a novel would be 'All the Geese in the Pond'. I counted the snorers – three out of five. A horrid lowing, reconciled to its source, caring nothing for the delicate ear drums of the night. In my view, complicit and indifferent. Oh to punish them with a uvulopalatopharyngo plastic operation in their sleep! The sick here are all heterosexual.

Homosexuality is the empirical sublimation of nothingness for its own sake; heterosexuality is the abstract sublimation of no case to answer.

Patients who tell their life-stories at all hours and think, poor things, that their life would really be a bestseller.

Most people's lives are so worthless – all reflected in what they think is their individual story 'different from all the others' but actually full of animal social behaviour between similarly human beings with common interests. Sooner or later they all use a paraphrase of the *imagination* which – as is well known – is the spirituality granted to the poor in spirit with an opinion of themselves. Incurably linked to their *humanity* 'they would do it all over again in exactly the same way' – it is enough to be alive.

There is no reason to consider life an absolute value – and everyone abuses his position against whomever he can in an absolute way, to the point of institutionalizing the extermination of one ethnic group rather than his own, of a group which does not fit his own Hitlerian idea of the perfect complexion.

And at the end of every decade there we are again with the same sun-tans from the crematoria in some racial kindergarten of this world.

Now I am dreaming about a bacon roll, hot, the fat a *tutu* on the browned crust of the bread. I did not know that fasting and enemas evoked such beautiful images. People have the Anglo-saxon habit of associating enemas with banal, *erotic* practices when instead the enema has a concrete power – not a figurative one – to evoke things in a chromatic-alimentary way, which ought to sweep away any sado-masochistic thoughts. With an empty stomach there is no need to reason, to sublimate culturally or erotically the intestines, bombarded as they are by tepid soapy water and Vaseline, given that one can see things through rose-coloured spectacles without any conceptual effort. Hunger fixes the outlines of edible things, it goes into detail, causes gastronomic novels (not simply Victorian or Japanese pastiches) to be written – for example hams evoke a delicatessen, the watermelon a woman selling fruit (have them make private appointments at dawn in the inn in the Municipal Market with the least lonely and most distinguished clients), bread, the young bakers of Venice (in the dark story of the doges you insert the first case of agitation by the nobles against gondoliers who are too ugly to row). The difference between a writer and a literary figure is that a writer with an empty stomach writes a novel: a literary figure gabbles sophistries till he bursts. That is why the most authoritative literary persons are good trenchermen and can never find themselves in a state of indigence; philosophy and the writing of books about books follows the gargantuan diet of power: refined foods to satiety and continual laments about growing fat, but liverish melancholy with which to redeem anthropologically the image of the paunch which rolls about under the little thinking head.

Thinking does not justify the act of writing about it. There is nothing necessary about the direct act of thinking and of transcribing by means of concepts what has been thought. The memory of the literary figure is made up of concepts; the memory of the writer which incorporates all others, is the memory of *styles* and of techniques applied to concepts which are taken for granted. A writer is not an emanation of power (of a political trend, a party, a social class) but only of himself and, if he is a genius, not even that – not that he must renounce his precious individuality and personal history: if he manages to understand that nothing can be substituted for it, the next step will be to understand that one writer is as good as the next. If things go well for them literary men become von Platens,

Anatole Frances, Marcuses, and for a while act as poets to some court or regime, embark, that is to say, on a so-called intellectual career which has very little to do with art (and even with the straightforward epistemology of *liberty*). Now I am falling into the same error as the literary person because, dreaming and dreaming, I have really eaten that bacon roll, and more than one of them, without noticing and I am *philosophizing* – that is am justifying at a *high* level the elementary nature of my needs or of my weaknesses – those of greed. With a full stomach I manage only to make myself *think* – which is depressing – everybody does it who can do nothing else. When they invite me to supper, isn't it because, being inclined to have a blow-out once in a while like all sober persons, after the second course I begin to hold forth on 'where is all this going to get us' and thanks to the magic of a full stomach espouse the ideology of the hostess? It is inevitable that a good, plentiful stew makes one very well disposed towards good manners and to the compliments – to the rhetoric of high society: one begins with an obeisance and finds oneself enlisted. From here to making propaganda is just a step. That is why I almost always take my revenge the next day (an insulting letter or phone call to the host for having tried to poison me), when one's indigestion has passed, when the moment has returned to bring the intellectualizing voracity of one's stomach under control once more. The stomach is like the arsehole – it runs the risk of becoming the motive force of the brain. The day before – as an invited guest – I had too many *ideas* – I was like a leading article, something from other times which in the nature of things I do not know thoroughly, and all that is needed is a fiat to suck one in. I leave myself with an empty stomach for a while – I don't want to end up badly, *thinking ideas*, wrapping them up in cultural/political intelligence, so as to spread them around in the hope of a pay-off or even something more. One might as well set up a hotel that lets rooms by the hour to *éminences grises*.

A writer eats at home or in a snackbar or in a restaurant. Or skips it.

～

'Have you a relative here?' I have seen her twice coming from the women's ward.

'Yes, my grandmother,' she says, perhaps sending me up, raising from her book a fine, artfully dishevelled head. Her head was already more than raised towards me, to one side, to my imminent curiosity.

'Is it serious?' I ask (I couldn't care less).

'A woman – I mean a grandmother is always a serious matter' and she lowers her head again. But not much – it is more up than down.

Perhaps she wants to tell me that the clumsy conversation about her grandmother is finished. She starts reading again. But I quickly say:

'At that age it can go on for years. And then the State goes off with everything' – this because in my view this woman doesn't love her grandmother and is only waiting for a legacy.

'Oh it has done quite a bit of that already.'

I don't know which has precedence – the State, the state of her grandmother or the grandmother herself.

'Has she just been admitted?'

'Today,' she sighs a little impatiently. 'It's the first time this year.'

Today is the 23rd and it is January. I very much wish she too would ask me questions – one at least – it can't always be me that asks stupid things – maybe she thinks I am trying to pick her up. And then she is obviously not concentrating on her reading. There are notes at the bottom of the page – it must be a demanding text – so many glosses by the translator or editor, the shuttlecock of low-level creativity getting its own back (*shuttlecock* I found four times today in three different newspapers and haven't yet understood what it means – clearly this is its moment).

'Bedpan for orchidectomy 26! Analgesic for orchidectomy 41!' shouts a nurse outside the ward. That is what they call the patients who have been on their tits for a good while – *bloody nuisances* to be exact.

The old orchidectomy (the despair of the man from Trieste) arrives holding the bottle of Lambrusco hidden in the leaves of a tropical plant because it is forbidden. He begins to chat to people off his own bat, point-blank, as if everyone had to pay attention to him and he had known everyone all his life, including the stuck-up woman beside me. This way of socializing regardless is too easy. Standing there he tells me and the reading woman – who is distracted but not actually very annoyed by this intrusion (she really doesn't like me – well, never mind) – about shrapnel extracted forty years ago from a shoulder-blade, about previous useless admittances: this is the twelfth and at least eleven times they all thought he was a nut-case who had an itchy back – as different as *brandy* and cognac.

Come on, let us breathe the sophisticated sleep of communal living.

\-\-

The nth little old man admitted. He arrives on a stretcher on wheels and he is hardly in bed before he lets go of his 'business' but refuses the bedpan and oughtn't to get up. So they take him in their arms to the throne because he is ashamed. The throne is a wooden WC on castors and while he is doing his job the trolley skidded to and fro about twenty centimetres. The nurses – to get their revenge – had not put the brake on. He farted his very soul away, poor old thing.

Today above his pillow there is a piece of paper with 'almost total immobility' written on it – and he has already been up thrice, a prey to an impelling need to restore his mask of respectability. The first time to wash his face which already has a high shine, to comb his hair, to cut his moustaches with unspeakable vanity, to look at himself in the mirror from every angle; the second time to freshen up his hands, put a little lavender water under his armpits and on the little fur of his chest and to retouch his moustache; finally he went up his nostrils with his little scissors with the deference of someone crossing the threshold of a temple. Between the second and third times he sent for the barber who lathered and shaved him, combed him haughtily, and seeing a pair of scissors being proffered, gave a little start and then removed the eyebrows from the bridge of his nose. I nearly shouted out loud.

The third time he got up to take a critical look at the barber's work in the mirror, made a very slow grimace, took his little comb from a velvet case and re-did the parting on his head and under his nose. The precise little strokes of the comb, his eye enchanted by his own image which projected a vast array of hedonistic possibilities. He unscrewed the little flask of some sort of eau-de-cologne – it must be bitter-sweet by now, a treat for those other filthy old men who are obstinately opulent and proud in their own little smell of death by magic.

. . . one of these men who, had they been born women, would not have noticed the difference and the only thing different in their lives would have been their spectacle-frames rather than the wife-husband or the husband-wife and the three daughters who come to adore and fear him even here. In the end his wife brought him an oval mirror from home – she was a bit embarrassed and gave a glance round before taking it from her bag as if excusing him.

Now he readjusts his (dyed) hair, blinks, pulls down an eyelid with his first finger, inspects the straw-coloured white. He puts the mirror back on the bedside table, keeping the palm of his hand on it. I wouldn't be surprised if he were here for breast cancer.

~~

The doctor on duty, who is also the head of the team which has me under observation, calls me at 10 in the evening and we shut ourselves up in the consulting-room. It is a conversation at once intimate and exhilarating ('What does life mean to you?' – answer: 'A waste only for the rich in spirit, whereas the poor in spirit must give it a *meaning* and hold on to it tightly'; 'With all these things wrong with your urinary apparatus you must have loved a lot – deeply' – answer: 'Love cannot be deep – depth is a miserable measure for it', 'I must make a note of that.'). He has always done the asking and now it is I who know about him. I classify him as obsessed with sex and tell him so. Having had a lot to do with doctors in general, mostly with surgeons and gynaecologists, there is one sure good mark you can give them to attract their sympathy: tell them what would fit the wildest characters – that is, that they are obsessed with sex – and it will be accepted as a high academic honour: a peerage of gnoseological refinement in the League table.

The somersaults their psyche has to make – accustomed as it is

28

to deal with *flesh* in cuts and in single organs to be examined – in order to keep alive a global carnal desire which is not that of the butcher's shop, to justify their curiosity which is morbidly over the top. They are so nibbled away by professional conditioning that their wild imaginings have something painful and infantile about them – they make one feel protective. Woman, seen by the male doctor, is a monster that carries around at one and the same time a rose-bud vagina and a purple-ulcerated prolapsed womb. They lay themselves open to all kinds of indelicate suggestions and then – if, like mine, they are high-class doctors – to interrogating you in order to speak about themselves. In my case, no one has ever been quick enough to know about me – I have always been several lengths ahead grasping (while myself making confession) their *quiddity*. He asks me, for example, what I would do to a woman if I had a sub-machine gun aimed at my back and I got an erection and I was forced to penetrate her (I practically plunge into a story by Asimov): Would I *take her* from the front or from behind? I give him the answer he anticipated, blocking that karate move of his which sends science fiction head-over-heels . . . He is delighted with the verisimilitude with which (without his noticing it) I sketch *his* desire with women – to bugger them all, slowly but thoroughly. The second is to reveal to him that he must be largely Jewish; he is amazed – how did I deduce that? No one here knows and even his surname is not revealing. But because his questions are Jewish questions! The shaping of the dialogue like a spoilt cat, his big buddy jaws, the hetero-orthodox malice on the topic of feminine orifices redeemed by a vein of sly humour that is close to sensibility, and then (come on!) that nose, I lie, which invites onanistic reflections to outlast a Flood and then some. And then the way he comes to the *therefore* as a pragmatic reflex of nothing. And that the Jews are too chosen to waste intellectual energy on the *being* which does not *have* something. They are not consumers of transference nor do they ever identify themselves outside of themselves, just like me. They are too busy hawking mirrors for all the others, the less chosen. 'I shall cure you for *ever*, you will *never* die,' he tells me, profoundly enamoured of himself. Then he asks me my opinion as a homosexual about the size of the *member* (I who am not very well acquainted with this term,

29

instinctively think of some local association). I think it right to quote *The Golden Ass* and that 'graffito of the year' found in the women's toilets in the Faculty of Jurisprudence in Bologna: 'Wanted – minimally endowed husband. Maximum 25 cm.' And then we pan over travels, dreams, ambitions, politics, literature and then – once more – sex: Brazil, panoramic shot of the beauty and *glamour* of Brazilian women – tits, bottoms, cunts with reference to the *favelas*, big, small, enormous lips on fire with metropolitan sunsets rendered languorous by a *fado*. A pity about AIDS.

My plans for the future? Well, it depends on them. Oh, an operation but no panic, there's no hurry. In other words a kind of papal imprimatur – a propedeutic to certain beatification: cancer of the prostate. Oh, prostatitis is the other side of the coin to virginity. No consistory would ever undertake the examination of any candidate who, one way or another, did not furnish proofs of some excess. One does not become a saint simply by putting forward simple headaches. The prostate as a relic full of powdered mystical milk.

'But to change the subject – excuse me – what were you doing in the women's toilets in the Faculty of Law at Bologna?'

~

The Palatine anthology, literature of Byzantium: tinned peas but all organolectically fresh and full of nutrients. And instead what a sorry lot are the little Italian literary tins of today with the 'use by' date falsified in a Byzantine manner. They should point to a present future and are all a rather nasty fifty years old.

~

During the temporary leave of the weekend there have been no arrivals to awaken my interests – nor any departures. The invalids are the same, all as before, even the ones who weren't there yet. No desire to track down their histories on the diagrams at the foot of their beds the moment they go out to urinate.

One of the ward doctors was saying to another one something out of *The Magic Mountain*:

'My view is that many of these tumours have their origin because people's bodies are unhappy, unsatisfied, ill-used –

without knowing it – sexually, I mean. Love flushes out the glands . . .'

I have told my acquaintances that I shall consider it a particular mark of respect not to come and visit me, seeing that there is no one I particularly want to see, people who come and sit there for two or three hours and tell me about their ailments and then you have to say to them: 'Come – I'll see you to the door.' I don't like to talk about mine, to make them personal as if they concerned me as *ailments*, I keep them to myself. If possible I make them better, if there is nothing to be done about them never mind, and let them come to an end or start all over again. I have thought of everything – for another week I am all right for underpants, handkerchiefs, T-shirts, socks, I am even elegant, I have a change of pyjamas and have bought a dressing-gown at a bargain price. I look like an astronaut in the sales. If one has the chance to choose a costume even illness becomes a masked ball. And then I do not believe in *illness* – I have had so many of them – nothing with which one cannot live. I don't go to carnivals – all that walking about, elbowing one's way, to have some fun. Now patients' funerals are beginning to leave. The thought that one of the many pricks in my life might be the work of one of these *mater dolorosas* desexualizes me for long enough to stay shut up here. But even outside the situation is one of exile – or rather of a frontier. I live having planned an escape route through the tents that surround this one. What I am sorry about is not having decipherable desires, to have no aims and to be short of means. The desires I allow myself – if seriously pursued – would cost me violent exhaustion to which I would abandon myself, confusing it with the attainment of total happiness.

There are several women with bright red dressing-gowns – they take the lift together, go down to the shop like supple tongues of fire devouring the white space of the corridors. With no thought of doing it on purpose, a canary-yellow dressing gown has joined them, the most restless of them all, which accelerates and slows down the fire by flickering among the others. It is a very vulgar and very beautiful girl who will pay for this quarter of an hour of running about with twenty-four hours of pre-coma. Not one dressing-gown that is green or black.

Generally they are sepia-coloured. This life (and any other) oppresses me and each one of us is here to fight for a horrible existence to take away with us. It is horrible and could not be more dear to us.

Two nuns arrive looking like excited walruses – they are visiting a fellow nun leaning on her pillow, with a little face like a peevish hawk, all hooked and squeezed inside a little linen coif which half-covers her cheeks. She looks like the racing cyclist, Fausto Coppi, on the last stretch of a steep hill. What a lot of little kisses they gave and the hands with their thin fingers which, when they took their leave, frenetically touched the black stuff of the gowns standing there, at the arms, the shoulders, hardly an embrace, an unrestrained hunger for affection between little girls who have never grown up, never again turned back, without memories. Nuns' memories are the memory of God whom they call the Bridegroom. Their lips continually whisper the litanies of oblivion, of the imperfect divorce from themselves because of their vocation to Him. They monogamous; God a great whore-master. Five minutes after her sisters lifted their moccasins, the nun opened her eyes wide, raised her shoulders imperceptibly and passed over to the other side. I had never before seen how a dead sparrow-hawk smiles.

The woman from Naples goes up and down, arms crossed under her rancid breasts which give off a stink of garlic – or of capers in brine. The point is that since she came here she has not yet changed top or bottom. After thirty-six days of confinement to bed she still does not know what is wrong with her. Naturally not – the first thing she asked on admittance of the doctor in charge of the ward was, that if that was what it was, she didn't want to know. So in her uncertainty she complains, she can't go on like this, anything is preferable to this doubt whether one is well without being able to resign oneself because maybe they lied to you. They who cry wolf . . . She finishes her march by flopping on to the black mock-leather armchair, saying: 'The last earthquake at Pozzuoli, it threw me right on to the ground . . .'

Now the blondish *chanteuse* begins her progress – enormous sun-glasses, plastic violet frames with tinsel, little china teeth and fringes of swan – or ostrich – on her dressing-gown of fiery-red velvet. She parades up and down like this, as if in a fashion house, with capricious twirls, always at the head of two others, voluntary subjects who flank her with dressing-gowns which are infinitely more modest and who conform to her wisdom as an invalid from high society. Today again *he* hasn't come – he is an important man, he has lots of things to do. Is he married? The blonde sighs and carries on. The two are peasants or house-wives, with nothing to talk about except her man, grateful to be able to count on someone socially superior who is satisfied by their gestures of assent with head or shoulders. They say 'Yes' with their whole bodies – could do nothing else – and all their poor dressing-gowns quiver like an exclamation mark rising up from a dunghill. Theirs are bodies mute by definition and dressed of necessity, covered up. At the shop she instructed the two about the names of the French perfumes and the breed of animal of her furs. *Him* oh, he's a real gentleman. At the till she ordered a liqueur – orange-flavoured – and the two wistful handmaids said 'No! No!' with their bodies – even with a slipper on the floor – and blushed with joy and scandal. An orange-flavoured liqueur! One felt they would have given their lives for her because, inciting them to a kind of breaking of the rules, she made them feel important. What about him in the future . . . Oh, we'll get married right away – *afterwards*. The one on her right, before leaving the shop, blew on the ostrich or swan feather (whichever it is) and then put it right with a touch of her fingertips which were conscious of the great honour – not to say liberty. As if on an undulating keyboard the notes of which must reach only celestial spheres to which the peasant woman wished to send her message: that she had been at her own *Requiem* to the very end, even if all the others had sung it for her. In the lift, turning their backs out of discretion, they stand huddled together as if in a nest, and whisper about bridesmaids' bouquets until the end of the trip.

➤➤

A woman friend of mine who works in this hospital but in another department – Neurology, not to be confused with Neuro-psychiatry, since they are as like as two peas – comes to visit me: 'How woman end up there – old at forty, at fifty, at twenty – scrap-iron, them and their special *feminine* weapons! With no sense – husband, children, house – they have lived by saying "if you please" which has nothing to do with pleasure. And into the bargain they have continually asked if they could please do this or that, even the toughest of them, the independent ones, especially the matrons, the matriarchs with the key to the cupboard in their pocket. All those who had resigned themselves to *getting away with things* . . . because a woman's brain, the less she uses it the better she manages . . . Fortunately these mammoths, the big mammas, at least they are dying out. They have lived as if clad in armour – and it was stripped off them the moment they said they weren't feeling very well any more and people saw that inside the power of woman there is only a woman who has been scooped out, emptied, stripped of her flesh hour after hour, a kick up the arse and allez! It serves them right. Another ten, twenty years of life before them and they're already completely empty, broken down, junk of Mummies, aunties, grannies, cunts, stupidities of the womb. They gaze into space – not that they are mad, oh no, I mean it's not as if they were doing a turn *now* – they have always been mad, only now that they see that as women they are *finished*, that they no longer please, all one can say is that the realization – a moment of lucidity in decades of behaving like stupid geese – smashes it for ever, blows up the armour built round them by husbands, fiancés, lovers, sons and their very mothers-in-law. They did the same earlier on but earlier on ah! they were young, beautiful, or in any case someone, now that they are old or think they are, it's one thing after the other – and they finish up with me. A nasty way to end up being a woman – but then when it all begins like this . . . And then take the alcoholics! The richer they are and have had *everything* the more they come here got up as if they were going to the theatre and the worse dressed they are, past all hope. You know the kind of beautiful woman the industrialist marries to be seen with, to get her to produce the children for the business, to show her off for a few years in society while he is setting an even younger, *unconventional* one up in a flat? There they are, all alcoholics, hysterical, two packs of Silk Cut a day, a litre of grappa, with their eyes coming out of their heads and when they begin the second sentence say Where was I! Euthanasia is what they should sell down there in the shop. Not a nice

34

way to end up for women! There isn't one that rebels, when it comes to it, not one that wants to define her own unhappiness and madness, they all have to turn to the man . . . Maybe if they said 'No' a little oftener and for valid reasons, not like stupid little cunts, they would manage better – even with the men . . . Women don't deserve pity – they are too happy to be stupid and ignorant, to leave it to men to think for them too – or to other women, beginning with their mothers. All chronically patched up with what these idiots call 'being feminine'. And all this for a clumsy fuck when nine times out of time the men fuck so badly that if they had taken a trip on a cable-car with the wind blowing through their thighs they would have enjoyed it more . . . *Pleasure* makes much of their *femininity* so long as it lasts. I am in the place where it doesn't last any longer and will never last any longer . . . OK for men a hole's a hole even when it's one of these gaping cunts stinking of wine.'

'It's a pity about them, just the same', I say merely to say something.

'Pity? People who are their own worst enemies disgust me. Women are worse than arseholes. And don't tell me that we're talking about yesterday's women, who had no work outside of the house and were dependent! The young women of today with their salaries or pay-packets are making exactly the same mistakes, they live *in and through others*, damn them. They have been lost, bit by bit, for years, never mind centuries. Every case is a desperate case. Fortunately with chemotherapy – with that at least – they get a bit of personality which has nothing to do with penisitis; for a while they think they are some great hero, tomorrow it will be some phoney holy woman, then a dwarf magnolia, then the Virgin Mary in flight, one thought she was that mad scientist on the telly. They make me mad!'

Ah Women!

⁓

Evening. Television news fanfares. A son who has come to visit his father (a white sheet of parchment trembling in his chair) with the day's accounts; he asks how he is a moment before going off, shutting his briefcase, the father shrugs as if no notice should be taken of this and exhorts him to adopt a certain kind of accountancy for the new cash registers. This word turns up in every sentence. The father has lymphogranulomas which are dissolving his inside. He grows more skeleton-like from day to day, the sheet of parchment becomes rumpled but does not let go of the *till*; clearly the real pang in his sieve of a heart is an attack of inland revenueitis. With VAT like that one might as well die.

The trill of the lift stopping at our floor. Faces that light up at the echo. No one. The lift has come up empty. If envy is the daughter of ignorance and jealousy the betrothed of guaranteed adultery, then greed is undoubtedly the aunt of avarice and tolerance stepmother of bad faith.

The ashtrays on brass steles are overflowing with fag-ends, sticking-plasters, silver paper, chewing gum. I am here alone, it is very late, perhaps 1 in the morning. Through the window the misty landscape with the street lamps on a few black fir branches. Another planet must be like that, like this one.

A woman in a fur jacket – both middle-aged – has arrived in casualty accompanied by a tribe of relatives. A lot of epitheliomas on hands, face, neck, cheeks, forehead – they won't have come up all at once! Ash-grey the whole seen from the back – their backs. I no longer want to leave here – it is the Disneyland I needed. Even as a boy my great dream was to be kept for ever in a mountain hospital, to have a coarse cotton night-shirt gently tied at the back and round the wrists, with me there all the time looking at myself from a point in the room, neither seen nor noticed by me who am sitting on the bed, with ivory complexion, almost musical, it goes without saying, a pale light from the big window, fine snow falling. Motionless like a transparent idol which lets everything filter through and holds back nothing. I realize that I have enjoyed the most intense emotions, which can no longer be perfected by a ritual communication, which have sprung up from the human possibilities of man's neurological system. I threw myself into the world, one might say, in order to deny it and to create my models *from nothing*, annihilating myself sufficiently 'to hide the dagger in the crown of myrtle' (Heine) and to cut one's throat. Then, how does one go on living if one has not at least once been heedless enough to stake one's life for nothing but *one's own*? No longer – de Sade is not a psychoanalytical prototype but a linguistic one and psychoanalysis one of the many existing poetics. Marx gets the better of Freud and de Saussure of both. One might as well take a trip to Morocco.

※

At the airport of Agadir a swift is fluttering under the corrugated iron roof – and at night in my room in the *Résidence* Karan I shall hear the crickets whinnying. The noises here are dilated or perhaps are only unusual for an ear from the Lombardy countryside.

In less than twenty-four hours I have achieved my touristic end – to escape from the clutches of the hotel-owning organization (more strict than ever in this city – contacts with natives in the street are forbidden) and to go to a family outside the city in a hut of cement blocks with a roof of beams and corrugated iron. The Moroccan mother looks a hundred and is forty-two – with her son and his friend I went to the market and, for what it would cost for a day in an average hotel, bought supplies to satisfy the hunger of five people for a week. It is not that I am simply generous – I have a good business head and then I do not like comforts, I get bored at once, I am not used to them. I shall always have time to try out those soft bedclothes, but it will be more difficult to return to this pallet of beaten earth and matting and two boys, one on each side, who fuck me in turns and modestly turn the other way when it is the other one's turn. I don't know whether it is lust on my part or good manners but they have to discharge their debt, and it feels to me that I am merely adapting to the rules between guest and host in an Arab country when the guest is a European. Well! be that as it may, by dint of butter, milk, bread, mutton, sugar, coffee, peppers and salad, soup-cubes, oil, vinegar, Coca-Cola, orangeade and long-lasting chewing-gum, I am loved. They constantly bring me mint tea – the women of the house who keep laughing with their hands over their mouths and running off. Poor things, they don't know that we are here talking about the Koran and Paris – and now, one after another, the men of the house arrive, brothers, cousins, nephews, and friends of the above, a string of hard pricks in Indian file.

They make me laugh, the single men who say they go to Africa for the folklore! Today for the sixth time I am going along with the local tradition – the hospital doctor, worried about my predisposition to bugger six-footers just out of prison who have sphincters like a sewer of the most exotic and difficult to deal with bacteria, when my discharge has stopped says to me as he gives me my discharge: 'For reasons of hygiene I advise you, for a little, only to be on the receiving end.' And here I am, obediently, the white man who, while he fills the bellies of three generations of mixed blood, lets himself be stuffed, comfortably served and revered. Colonial shudders! There is a continual bringing of *lukum* with almonds and every so often a male child appears in the door – women, given the influx there is, are no longer allowed – and I keep on producing dirhams so that he will put his little weapon in again . . . I profit from the situation rapidly because I know that I shall quickly get bored with all this, I am not in training for linking sex and money, to try out what pleasure there is, if there is – there is, there is . . . Besides here, away from the big hotels, to play the miser could be more expensive than throwing one's money about – so long as there are dirhams one can hope not to be ill-treated. A little kindness amuses me – I am certain I am not doing anything bad, and then it is always I who beg them that it is really not on again, that it is hurting me, that I also want to go out and take a mouthful of air – and for them to stop warning me about other quarters and camps with the excuse that it is cooler here. If they manage to be alone and to get rid of the others, many of them say words of love to me and that I have a very beautiful body and a skin they like to caress – they are mad about kissing and their saliva is sweet like frozen fountains of mint and nothing.

In fact after two days like this, Kleenex in hand, I place a fortune in the mother's lap and, to acclaim, am accompanied to a spot where they have already called a taxi – and return to the hotel. Too much of a good thing all at once is harmful and depresses one – I was like the prisoner of their zealous covering. They even came from far away on mule-back to see the Italian who sleeps on matting – never able to shut an eye, unknown faces suddenly behind the blinding crack of the door, and at night one had to smoke, the merry whip-crack of the women laughing in the dark, a real procession, one had to smoke *khif* with all the men – and I paid for the *khif* as for the *lukum* – and then, if you said you were sleepy, on came more mint tea and off again to go round all the bottoms. In the taxi I begin to laugh, waving to the crowd, fifteen or so boys of all ages who bid me farewell (the ten-year-old: 'Monsieur, next year when I am big you come back here?'). I have to sit sideways on one cheek only, it is like a third degree burn. It is incredible the sense of fraternity which stems from the down-to-earth use of a hole.

~~

Dear Bertolli,

I would advise you to take the first plane and fly here – there are rooms for two with waiters for four. It costs less than the ticket for a discothèque where you don't get anywhere or a box of chocolates when you go to one of your nice old millionaire ladies. All the boys ask for here is to lock the door – because no one must suspect – and to ask you questions about Maradonna while they ask you if it is all in. You who, unlike me, know so much about football could forget for a little the editorial splendours in which you have been caught up for twenty years and be a reporter to the joy of all the Moroccans who think – not mistakenly – that Italy is merely a great stadium with the Pope blowing the whistle. You would derive great satisfactions from it, but you would have to stop using the line 'I have never done it.' Three years ago, however, near Tangier, a place full of surprises and uniqueness, just over from England, I did truly bugger a Moroccan with lots of beach, full of shells and thickets of low and dusty eucalyptus trees, seeing that for you the setting is everything. I gave him a T-shirt – they even make you walk on the water and touch the sky with more than one finger. Yours with salaams . . .

~~

Here in Morocco, sexually, if you are a foreigner and white there is nothing to deny, nothing to affirm, everything is according to one's purse and one leaves one's psychologizing at home in the West. For me who adores gymnastic coupling, this *nothing* is well worth a holiday – I like to exhaust the possibilities of the loins and the lot, to no longer have the energy to get up (I ask myself – what is the use of getting dressed again?), to mime a human sympathy which is not there and it is impossible to have paying

39

or not paying, not for me, for my head swimming. Nice to use human bodies with one's own and to cancel out the most global desires of the unilluminated part of the brain. But one must always be quick to cut the painter and to go to the bank before tying up once more. Certainly sometimes one has to pay out for circumcisions done with an axe and with the eyes shut, which if one had known before . . .

Next door there is a couple of Italian women and I will just be back from one of my philanthropic-*colon*ial missions. One was standing in the corridor with a Moroccan dressed in European style in brand-new clothes, who was showing her some karate moves. A little blonde with very fair skin, who was admiring or patiently taking part in the game while her friend, her skin more tanned, slipped on her bathing costume with the door half-open and revealed a small, firm breast with a little nipple. Two women with deep-sunk eyes – two of the liberated kind who come here to screw in freedom and in whom the corners of the mouth are typical of the woman who has split sentimentality off from sex, losing thereby. Some revolutions have to be programmed – to have many pedals available, not just one to stand on till it is worn out. Losing thereby, because in my view a pig looks good naked, a sow dressed up. A stark naked sow does not give off beauty and desire (one needs a certain unthinkable intellectual refinement not available to the first couple who mistakenly think they are squandering capital they never had) but a funereal sadness, a certain disgust at a world made up always and only of naked pigs – from which a woman seldom is able to collect the kind of beauty-that-can't-help-it.

This morning I saw them on the beach, they were accompanied by the Moroccan and two friends of his. Then in the afternoon I caught sight of them in the agency next door where they hire cars – and in the evening the negro driver had already taken on another colour. They go about getting screwed in the dunes of the interior – but they do not come back with a little gratitude that might lighten the obscene gravity of their faces. They carry around eyes which are more and more black; the fold of their mouths says a lot about their procrastinated gratification of a further orgasm – not as if it was what the doctor ordered, as he did for me. You'd think they were nauseated – but they haven't gone far enough to admit it and leave. They keep on, crazily, what a disaster women are when they join the sexual vanguard without any rearguard behind them! They behave exactly like sour, unsatisfied and impotent queers – practically insatiable. Well, the one with the reddish or black hair and the dark skin I greeted in the corridor and she didn't even respond – perhaps I smiled in a certain rude way, permissively allusive – but I don't think so – I'm not so vulgar nor such a troublemaker – and then here the sexual mechanisms are infinite, there is nothing to take away from anyone, abundance for all, male and female. Perhaps she read in my thoughts what I read in hers, and the truth here is hard to admit for anyone, far less someone from Piedmont; for here, whether men or women, they all pay their miserable tuppence-worth, putting their hands *straight on their wallets* – which, maybe for a woman used to spending a salary to buy a man a trinket, is humiliating. Women are incapable of going through with things when it is a case of merely being superficial.

There is a little Nordic brunette on the beach who has in tow a Moroccan got up – because of the continual police checks on their compatriots – like a European (Bermuda shorts, sun-glasses that aren't shoddy, a copy of the *Times* which she puts in his hands the moment they have lain down). Simply found, paid, loved. He carries her purse, takes the sand off her back, has a deferential attitude – and his prick is always stiff under his shorts. He goes a kilometre to fetch her a bottle of mineral water or an ice – he keeps the change but not before he has brought it back. He is nice to her – and he is a very handsome man, a macho all muscles and white teeth. And he laughs. He certainly costs her ten times less than a Dane or a toy-boy from Calabria who cheat you, deceive you and then ill-treat you because, at least in this way, they let you see who wears the trousers. What come the way of my two Italians, alas, even here are only show-offs. As far as class goes, they haven't got beyond training school.

A travelling show arrives on the beach: a Berber lady of easy virtue – or an artist from the folk group 'Ocean Dance'. She comes alone and unleashes excitement for a radius of half a kilometre – she has a profusion of soft flesh around her black-indigo glance behind her raffia picture hat; face and body flaccid,

41

opulent, and her skin violet. She knows she is considered very beautiful by the men of her part of the world because, being fat, she doesn't feel hunger and has herself a power to nourish. Every so often someone comes up to her, from the student whiling away the time to the policeman in civilian clothes, to the toothless beggar whom you might have taken for a piece of flotsam spewed up by the colourless sea. She does not deny anyone a word, is polite to all, but smiles only to me, sends me messages in the shape of Islamic-educational jokes with the tip of her tongue passing and repassing over her somewhat yellow teeth. She is a woman of noble character, a big privileged girl – I try to imagine the blueish colours of her vagina, the maroon mother-of-pearlish hues of her Phoenician clitoris. Her bikini is too tight for her and down below the loin-cloth is slipping down one thigh, some Titian-red hairs stretch out their claws on the inside of the buttocks – she must dye them, she will have a hennaed cunt.

I go up to her:

'One should come to Morocco with two arse-holes,' I say to her to see how she takes it.

'If you like it, even a threesome with a man is no trouble. Offer me a cigarette, darling.'

'Dancer?'

'Yes, You too?'

We burst out laughing, she rolls half-over on the sand like a ninepin.

'That's just what I needed – to be buggered so much that I can't sit any longer and so am obliged to stand or to lie leaning on one side – the only two positions in which I can't write and so perforce have to do something else.'

'Leave me, duckie, because I am busy. Au revoir, agreed?'

In a little garden full of students there is also a toilet – completely open – with lots of bowls for washing oneself. Up comes a boy with a prick with a huge knob. Not that size matters – it's enough if it never fails. The truth is that whether they have a big one or a little one they don't know how to use it in any case, so it might as well be big. With a haemorrhage there is always the possibility that the memory will become a souvenir – (10 dirhams).

Today the two boys from yesterday did not come to the appointment. I'm sorry – I was counting a little on their company, all the more since I have been in their village and there too I made 50 dirhams' worth of purchases so that they would invite me to supper at their house – here an employee in a hotel, a most sought-after post, earns 700 dirhams a month, required to be there for thirty days and fourteen hours of work a day. I had been advised to cook myself some couscous and I gave 30 dirhams extra to the M'ui for the inconvenience (she hasn't seen 30 dirhams all together not even on the day she got married and for a so much greater inconvenience). I'm sorry too because I wanted to start to get rid of all this clothing I have brought in my suitcases – jumpers, trousers, bodices, my niece's skirts, my sister's blouses. I don't find it at all ridiculous that there is still in me some of this boy scout (never been one) resipiscence and I accept the unpleasant consequences of being good or, if nothing else, of showing good will (and yet to drag all these suitcases here from home is a sign of positive obstinacy . . . after all why should I be ashamed? – I do what I feel like with my stuff even if it doesn't please me!). It follows that those who manage to get something go off without thanking you, indifferent and almost contemptuous (because I have asked for nothing in return . . .) and those who are left without anything, because they came late, spit gobs close to your shoes because *you* left them out – and then you could at least take off your shoes and give them to them. Patience – the sound of Arab curses is so musical. Next time – three suitcases, not two.

In a house of wattle and corrugated iron, sweltering rooms packed with young mothers, old women, children, few adults, the official head of the house – a fatherless youth and so head of the family – since he is studying theatre presented me with some Arab tongue-looseners. With organized tours these delicious touches cannot be enjoyed and the dangers you run in the swimming-pool are exactly the same as going at dead of night into a thieves' brothel. Mohammed makes the salads at the Sahara Hotel – he has a Nigerian father and a mother from Mali, the result is a negro as beautiful as the light; we make love in a frankly passionate way – he clasps me to him saying incomprehensible little words to me which enchant me. I gratify him by inventing a belly-dance seated on him (he is inside me) while I, being outside of him, am beside myself.

✌

Never refuse any invitation from Moroccans from the most ragged to the most distinguished: they are on average more intelligent, more civil and upright, than Italians who are forced into prostitution, promised but never kept, not even after payment in advance. All you need is to make some rules for yourself and then you can go anywhere with them alone or in a group: at home (huts, caves, roofed boats), in gardens, in woods, on the shingle of river-beds, by day or by night. If you are sensitive enough to do the sums, five timid men who look at you with the drop of prostatic milk already in their irises cost less than a triple-X film or a translation of Garcia Lorca by some poet laureate. If the rules are respected no one is in a hurry afterwards and no one is doing it out of spite: they participate. Thus under that two-metre-wide building a sort of young lycanthrope – considered to be the village devil because of his rage – spends everything he has for me and buys a big bottle of Coca-Cola and then asks me if I know Gorky and Brecht, putting their baptismal names in front of them.

I know where I am unbeatable – in acquiring in five minutes what is essential in the ethical codes of any people or social class – including the Papuans. The important thing is not to hit the nail on the head right away but not commit howlers right away. The sibylline pleasure of going along with their hypocrisy, knowing that beneath it all there lurks something spicy; obviously they are proud of this hypocritical moral process – it forms part of their spirit of adaptation and of survival, which aims at dignity at all costs, as well as the pleasure of performing psychic feats on the lines of what the eye doesn't see the heart doesn't grieve over if you are *in the midst of it all*. Sex is had secretly but, very curiously, by preference in the open air. They deceive each other, they throw challenges to each other across the street – my tourist is better dressed than yours, my German woman is blonder than yours, my second-hand shorts are less wide than yours . . . You are a luxury animal which they momentarily have bridled – for the animal it is always amusing, it gives local colour, and then it

44

is repetitive therefore reassuring. But I am also here to know things – this is not an alibi seeing that I would never dream of unlinking knowledge from applications – parsimonious ones – of *Anusol*. I hate the condescension of the man who remains seated in one place – an intellectualistic expedient behind which an obscure desire for power lies concealed. True knowledge is not accumulated – it is consumed.

Cautious visit – let them go round the corner first, walk by oneself, changing one's side of the street every kilometre – to two students who live in a hut on the outskirts. 15 dirhams for a bottle of Coca-Cola family size (real price – D.2.5) and then another 20 for bread and little portions of *La vache qui rit* cheese. The extremely beautiful sixteen-year-old was apologizing for having a little one, and the other for having a squat and bent one, and I was encouraging them, paying them compliments etc. They make love with tourists as a second out-of-school activity and kept on talking in Arabic, never in French, perhaps to decide who had to be the one underneath and who would spread the cheese on the bread. I kept protesting that it didn't matter – no use – professionals to the bone. Then, both of them having calmed down, out of a little heap of rags from past tourists appears a plastic saxophone. Do I know Louis Armstrong? Neither of them knows how to play but they take turns at blowing into it. They lavished on me everything they had by way of luxury – basic knowledge of a musical scale. Basic knowledge: 25 dirhams.

⤞

Yesterday evening I decide to go to a hammam. I get a message from an old man who works over my tendons with both feet and stretches and twists my limbs arranging them in positions of terror. And, voilà monsieur, colds, headaches, backache gone. What a life! I go out into the night with the one happiness that seizes me from time to time – to be myself, only myself, no other than me, a variation in the universe, an incommensurable being: a man.

Here he is again: the old fox recorded on cassette – readings from the Koran on television. Then His Majesty Hassan II and family – the reporters repeat hundreds of times how many illustrious unknown diplomats His Majesty has received today and what His Majesty inaugurated for the progress and well-being of those few score privileged persons known as 'the people' – and in French says loud and clear, lest any tourist should not know it or should dare to have his own politics, that Everything flows from Him, His Majesty Hassan II. Monarchies must be extremely boring for those who are part of them – never mind those who are not part – between a piece of chat and a dirham I talk politics with these boys: many students would like to found a communist party or at least begin with a trade union to look after the interests of employees in the hotel trade, but mere suspicion brings with it immediate imprisonment. But in the souks all of them quote Lenin and Marx, of whom there seems to be an edition in Arabic, cleaned up and dressed in velvet and lace gloves out of respect for the king. Here, as in Naples, one breathes in the marasma of burnt souls. It is the usual smell of blood in every reactionary society where the need for fresh intelligence is reduced to a minimum because it damages the system-as-it-is. It is sacrificed not as a votive offering like the lamb in Jewish culture but as a useless weed, harmful, evil.

At the University of Verona the Moroccan students were the most gifted of the foreigners – much more than the Palestinians, who were too religious and insufferably *prude*. It is a splendid undertaking for anyone to yoke together revolution and Islam, communism and religious fanaticism. The Moroccan students were, in this sense, the most free and realistic. The Palestinian students then were also Arabs, but they were boxed in by the same inconclusive anti-Zionist ideology, a genuine external outlet for anger in order to forget the irreconcilability of their *internal* political assumptions. I always told them that it would have been much more profitable to exploit Israel rather than fight it *uselessly*, that there should be maximum time for defending an indefensible opinion and that when an ideal *does not work* and (after a score years – since 1948 to be exact) does not change reality, one should pass on to another ideal which takes into account, alas for it, the technological revolution undergone by the temporal concept we have today of past ages. The Moroccans in Italy – I also shared a flat with Moroccan students – have only one burning desire, which is a very just one; to ignore their origins or at least to redefine them if they don't come in handy for their future careers; they were not very inclined to be enmeshed in *outdated* ideological romanticisms, exactly like young Germans in the case of the historical pasts of their fathers of not so long ago. The young Moroccans staying in Europe and the young Germans have, unlike their Palestinian contemporaries, a more *immediate* idea of time and history – they affirm above all the need to be individuals rather than the ideological expression of a *people*; the Moroccans, because by educating themselves, studying and organizing their ambitions, they immediately recognize the outdatedness of a present; the Germans because they recognize the unlivability of a recent past; and both sets of youths attempt to free themselves with all their might from any national mortgage on the future for which they are not responsible. There would be a revolution – a positive one – in the Arab world if this consciously ahistorical concept of the relationship between Time and their own time took root among the Palestinian youth and, beyond that, among Middle Eastern youth in general.

That said, and having established the anachronism of the ideals of the *liberation* of Palestine by the Palestinians, I consider Israel and the foundation of the State of Israel an immense patrimonial loss for the Jews, a pure failure – don't they say that when the Gods want to punish us they make our dreams come true? The *wandering* Jews and I, on the other hand, integrate in a flash wherever we happen to find ourselves and we never go *home* because we have understood that *every home* is a different place in the same emptiness we have within us. Certainly there will always be those who are *nostalgic* for a fatherland, but there is nothing like, *hélas*, the possibility of going to Paradise to make one realize that one was better off where one was before. This conscious act of uprooting (with no more dreams) seems amazing to me on the plane of how the wise man is able with extreme subtlety to do violence to himself with methodical lightness of touch, if he can derive some definite benefit from it. One transplants one's roots within oneself and, like the snail, carries one's own house with one. It is like laying up an ideal land in the ventricles of the brain and abandoning the land where we were born and grew up because the bold and spiritual man grows only *elsewhere*. To found a nation in a desert, by comparison, seems to me a surrender on the part of the character and collective memory of a culture – but a very *special* one each time it halts its caravan somewhere – which is nomadic by tradition. First the Jews were persecuted piecemeal and extemporaneously, now in groups and with computers – and they have come to the point of turning their historically expiatory nature upside down to such a degree that they have become persecutors – they who as persecuted had attained the perfection of perfections. To leave the Talmud for Reagan is not a great step forward not even for victims already marked down.

～

In such a state of sensual bliss, a thought pops up which I don't wish to describe as atrocious but which would become so if it turned out to be justified: from one of my suitcases which had been lost and was delivered to me in the hotel only today the folder with the drafts of Chapter 3 of the *Dolphin* is missing. Perhaps at the last moment I decided not to bring them with me, perhaps it has been zealously confiscated – at the Customs books and papers are more carefully leafed through than anything else. It would be grotesque to have to give up my notes because of a literary Moroccan policeman who values unpublished texts in Italian.

Over there the two choosy Italian women with their expression of unsatisfied bitches ready for a challenge (of what?) have found company again; they are being stuffed by the kitchen staff without thought of the cost. I hope they have realized that this is not considered *a tip*, which in any case is given separately and never in kind.

This morning I make the acquaintance of two guys in the shower on the front. Immediate understanding: you let yourself be seen lowering your trunks from behind and you see that their magic wand rises up from amid memories of ancient drawers. If, after having made an abundant lather in the groove between the buttocks, they are still there it means that with all possible patience they are waiting for you to rinse yourself off and follow them. Good luck wills it that the more beautiful of the two – and he speaks English – travels for a bakery (of stale stuff, obviously) and out here under the eucalyptus trees he has the firm's van. He makes me climb in, lays out a blanket, and amid the nice perfume of coconut oil and honey biscuits works away untiringly at various holes. While his friend – a Berber mountain shepherd who has never been in town before – munches at a biscuit shaped like a gosling, the bakery rep gives me a sign to press my prick against his and bash them both together. It is an unusual concession – usually they don't know if you have one or not. Too much! Then it is the Berber's turn; he is timidly shy – the new city ways too much all at once, gets up behind in the place of the other but does not get excited. He explains in Arabic and the rep translates; it is because the Europeans, about whom he had heard stories, he had not imagined them like this, that is, not even the men, and that I am not a woman – you can see that a mile off – and that he is very disappointed. Moreover I was there in front of him, resting my calves on his shoulders and jiggling the difference under his nose, and that too was not very feminine, according to him. Oh a translation of a dialogue which was not only extremely long but pedantic and full of nice distinctions! I do not go down on my belly – if you do you've had it – they give you no room for pleasure and press you as flat as a pancake. Then Abrahim, the rep, says to me that his friend being a Berber it would be better if I played the lamb. OK? And the young shepherd's prick at once gets up between my buttocks and in an instant is swinging, like a pendulum in a well. Abrahim, since I felt the need to sneeze or cry out, says to me please could I keep my mouth shut because there's already quite a lot of people pricking up their ears and that nothing escapes Arabs when there is a smell of sex in the air and would I not like to munch a few biscuits – the broken ones in the little bag. I raise my head, look out at the chink in the side door – at least twenty eyes staring at me fixedly from all sides – staring at the sheeting on to which their imagination is projecting the most detailed scenes of group sex. The Berber makes my back undulate, pressing down all the time on his hands and lifting them when I recoil. Fortunately the Arabs are very jealous of their property and no one would ever lend a wheelbarrow to a neighbour, far less a little van to strangers, and I can get down. Odd, however, that they didn't ask me for money but only what I was doing this evening at eight. It is a quarter past six.

The trade in bodies on the grand scale continues and at one in the morning I got dressed again and walked to a discothèque in the open where there was a brawl going on between natives – who are not allowed entry – and the employees as well as the Jewish owner who is, I think, one of the men most hated by the population of Agadir and the one most honoured by the local authorities. A little man on a home-made racing bike – the pride and joy of his life, his only possession – has braked suddenly and has cleared a way to calm the brawl. Probably he seized the opportunity to have an excuse to set foot in a place forbidden to him, a kind of step up the social ladder in the estimation of the hated Jewish proprietor whom the current legend calls a guzzling, currency-dealing drug-trafficker and pimp etc. The Jew – linen trousers, Rudolf Valentino hair-style, flowered silk shirt and shoes with lifts – had already called the police who made the brawlers, badly dressed people from round about, who had been repulsed at the entrance (which can be crossed only be Moroccans of high lineage), climb into the police van. I saw that the poor had been beaten till they bled. The little racing cyclist, who had contributed to the restoration of order before the arrival of the police has had a plate of chips, certain – dripping with blood as he was – of having risen in the world and of having deserved them and, indeed, thanks to his *mise* (green and red – the colour of coagulated blood), to be able to sit and eat them tranquilly among the privileged. Since there was still some confusion (the same confusion as had allowed the rash cook to give him a plate of chips like that) he asked me for a cigarette; I gave him one and, like a true social climber lying in wait for his chance, he did the daring trick of moving himself, cigarette and chips, to a vacant place at my table. Immediate arrival of the proprietor who tells him to be off and leave me in peace, and I who tell the proprietor to mind his own business and that the gentleman cyclist is my guest, and the Jew who insists that the *gentleman* could not stay there. At that moment two sumptuously elegant Arab women arrive – the wife and mother-in-law of the Jew – laden with jewels and escorted by two soldiers in uniform. The Jew called over the two military men who lifted the little cyclist from his chair and threw him out of the garden. He ended on top of the bicycle. I got up and railed against the soldiers and the Jew – proprietor of the hotel where I am staying – saying that I was ashamed to have been in his discothèque and that I wouldn't come a second time. I went and picked the little busybody out from among the spokes of the wheels, removed a little blood from his knees and one ear but did not feel myself humiliated nor a prey to the sacred fury of indignation. I could do no more except leave the place with the intention of changing hotel next day. Which I did not do – every other hotel in this street belongs to closely related Jews. To bloodsucking racist Jews (of all people!) and to American queers who in the doorways keep soldiers who bend their knees and touch their cocks by way of a military salute even when someone short-sighted passes.

☛

Night night night. I see a policeman in a special uniform. Very showy, flashy, of the usual dark-green tattered material. He looks at me, looks round – no one but him and me. He goes further into the park. Me after him. I catch up with him determined to humiliate him, to refuse him because I know what is expected. Now we are facing each other, he touches his cock, shows me that it is hard under his trousers. I say 'Good evening' and start talking about politics, offering him a cigarette with the most cordial air in the world. A tourist is never refused anything and he, disappointed though he is, is forced to pay attention to me and to *speak*. I express all my disappointment at how here in Agadir – and elsewhere as I have discovered – the hotel-keepers and the police are in cahoots to keep ordinary people away from the wealth which is arriving in rivers from abroad. He explains, disconcertedly, that it is done for the good of the tourists, to discourage the beggars from running after them asking for alms instead of learning to do something. I keep on saying that the police treat his fellow countrymen, his unhappy, ragged people, very badly. Take him for example – for him to occupy the post he occupies – he is an officer – is it really necessary that people should forget that he will have been born in some shanty? The officer swallows, livid with anger. He changes the subject – he asks how come I am taking a walk at this time, don't I know it could be dangerous? If I meet Jewish hotel-proprietors and policemen, yes, I answer, but not if I meet drunks who at most are a pain in the neck with their umpteenth request for charity – it's clear where the danger comes from. He does not answer and walking as if he wanted to shake me off, we arrive at a truck at the end of an avenue; a simple guard stands by the door smoking. I start the conversation up again as a threesome – still with great formal elegance, I come out with all the atrocious things I think about them and their system (taking the precaution every so often, however, of stressing with hints that I come here very often and am a very, very rich man – ah what eccentricities are permitted to the insolent with foreign currency! for the half of the half of what I have said an Arab hero would already be in irons). And so on with more *populist* claptrap – the lack of freedom in this country without television or papers or a free press (everything filtered by His Majesty's *commis* including the short obituaries of illustrious dead) which would be unimportant did not large strata of the young population feel the necessity and importance of it. I put forward the thesis that Moroccan youth, in spite of the lack of freedom of speech in the schools (the teachers do not have it – far less the pupils), is much more advanced than it is comfortable for the monarchy to think. The two soldiers on patrol are a bit taken aback, perplexed. I step things up – a sea-breeze and intoxicating perfumes from the park – choosing the least aggressive but conceptually deadly expressions. In fact I salute them and they come to attention, as polite as ever – clasping my hand the captain tells me that tourists he has met in their hundreds but no one as odd as me – his colleague confirms this. Tourists spend money only for the sun and *le plaisir* – it would never occur to anyone as it did to me to go into the shanty towns and listen to the hot-heads. I say goodbye telling them that normal tourists need to be understood – they are pure fascists under whatever flag. And whatever party they belong to.

I know the left-wing intellectuals on holiday: it is a continual struggle to have the maximum amount of privileges and servants with the minimum involvement. Then, to show they are communists, they do the same as Pasolini who at all the receptions asked the best-looking waiter how much he earned a month. But what do you expect a waiter – however sexy – to earn a month? Just for once ask the decrepit proprietor.

~~

I would like my biography to be made up of my sexual encounters logged by date, name of partners, place, duration, position, smoothly written; it would be immensely more interesting and enjoyable than the thoughts in my life, the greatness of which lies in their neurovegetative nature.

Here in Morocco the ritual of human misery is the same as in Berlin – drugs, sex and money. Here the most refined poverty-stricken people plant shots of Coca-Cola and aspirin in their heels; it makes them feel more European, more on the same level as all the others.

I foresee trouble tomorrow – I did not keep two appointments – I fell asleep. If I meet them and it is impossible not to meet them – I will give them their money; it will be the same as being punctual.

Today I was at the house – doorless, windowless – of the volleyball giant; twenty-five years old, two storeys high, well proportioned. Arrive with my little plastic bag – a pair of trousers, a shirt, two vests, a jumper – and get rid of 13 dirhams right away for the wine and the cigarettes (they must all run and buy something that is considered a prime necessity). I was also expected by his brother. They smoked unhurriedly, punctuating each mouthful with limitless dreams. I said I wanted to leave – they became alarmed. Sometimes I try the expedient of giving them the sum agreed – tacitly – right away to see if they will thaw a little on the human level, if they will say something to me they really think (they think the usual wicked thoughts and they are not wrong to do so). But it is a tactic doomed to failure because once they have pocketed the money they lose all interest. They have such an unsatisfied desire for *right away* that they end up thinking even something they have just got is finished, burnt-up, non-existent. I try to revive their morale by promising them a pair of shoes that fit and it is quickly a party, and the longer you put off giving them the longer the party lasts. How depressing it is to corrupt people, and if you are not cut out for it the pleasure becomes a headache.

Meanwhile new voices rise up from the (beaten earth) ground floor. It is Assad, their friend who is like a brother. Mustafa – or Mohammed – precedes him upstairs, comes into the little room and says to me before Assad appears:

'Shut your eyes, Monsieur. When you open them you will be dumbfounded by his male beauty.'

Assad arrives and I am petrified. It is always unnecessary to describe a man when he is not a literary figure – I shall say only that his brown eyes are sunk into the cheekbones like two meteors planted there to recall that somewhere there is an infinity patiently waiting for you. Assad fought in the war in the Sahara and the spilling of blood – always of brothers – has given fluidity to the sculptured veins of the arms and neck. The mouth is the equal of mine when I still had one – have you never heard of the most tumid lips in Europe? they were mine. As far as definitions go I had nothing else very beautiful except this mouth which, when closed, hid a mass of carious teeth. It seemed then that to have lips like that meant great, undisclosed destinies. A great writer has the duty to be able to kiss because he breathes *the word* into every man who will become a character – there is always a page sooner or later where two characters kiss because there is great trust between them. Assad leaves the room because, having entered the lists as well, he will be the last of the three. The giant has the first turn; he demands expressions of appreciation of his physique. I obey – with the rest as well – and so too with his brother. It is Assad I want. And when it is Assad's turn and the brothers go out on to the reed matting of the landing I follow with astonishment my imminent happiness, who is removing his T-shirt and white pants in front of me. It is all true and mine. He leaps on me and at once takes my tongue between his teeth, draws it into his throat, clasps me and kisses me, makes me kiss his nipples and goes wild with me and says what a lovely surprise, thank you, thank you, how nice, how nice, he cries. How to set down the sound that he makes crackle from his amber skin against mine, the mouths which bleed like two fighting wild animals and says you're mine, you're mine, I couldn't wait, I love you, Italy, I love you, and my whole body clings to his words and has become hunger. I am so overcome that I end up abandoning myself to him. It is uninhibited sex,

54

violent, refined – of cunning violence, in which each detail of the use of the lips, the hands, the pricks, the nostrils, the orifices, hairs, skins, nails, armpits, tits, reveals the last and deeply sad reality of man – that he is never the source of his own light but owes it to another. If it is a great light that transubstantiates every single electron of his being until he feels *a whole*, it does not belong to him, is not his. For this reason one must forget it immediately after it goes out.

~

I am reading an interview by Dürrenmatt; he does not read many novels because, according to him, the true spiritual adventure is enclosed within philosophical research *per se*.

This seems to me the greatest piece of nonsense that a senile writer – and one not even of the first order – has ever spat out. It seems to me that Kant and Fichte and Hegel come several lengths after Lenz, Goethe and Hofmannsthal, and that the *true* writer precedes or sets off every philosophical speculation, including the philosophy of science, and never plods along – quite apart from the fundamental question of the regeneration of the language. I don't know whether Heidegger or Husserl or Wittgenstein ever read Proust to learn that they had all been lumped together in *La Recherche* twenty years earlier.

~

There is only one reason why a spider goes on repairing webs which are at once destroyed – it cannot help it and has no memory. Its life depends on the physiological stubbornness of its survival.

~

Illuminated palms gleam in the night and this oriental panorama seems all plastic. Those who go on a journey to find themselves again would do better to stay at home.

Now I am looking at a European sitting at a little table not far from mine. Love is possible only between men in whom it is not 'an aid to nature' but a speculation of the mind on a certain type of human prototype – I don't like the word *archetype* – *prototype* is already very close to a stereotype ready for the press.

One cannot love anyone who is not already oneself sitting to one side and looking towards you thinking exactly the same thing contemporaneously on two diametrically opposite seats.

Each look an offer of sex. Here I am always on heat – food and sun, the mind with nothing to take in hand, the future a zero – and I am no longer able to feel like skimming myself twice or even three times a day just because I am sentimentally fried.

We call *mechanisms* extremely elaborate states of mind; when the mechanism reveals itself for what it is – mechanical – I no longer accept it. It is not out of fear of reaching the bottom; it is because there are constantly very beautiful phosphorescent worms which wander from tunnel to tunnel and attack other flying worms. One would have to put the mind in the incubator of some traditional 'sentiment', let it warm up. I feel bitter and acid, like an adolescent of thirty-seven in a jungle, and tomorrow I have to make my début in the old world and know nothing of its customs. If my mind is isolated it is no one's merit; I have developed an instrumental reaction to a code of laws which does not exist outside of myself. With others (even in sex) I live on appearances which are their substances – not mine. That is why I am so *understanding* and good with their values: because I have other ones and feel a little guilty about the privilege of *feeling* in the ambit of an intellectual refinement *which does not exist*. To make up for this, none of their 100 per cent alienation seeps out of me.

◆◆

The animal which causes the greatest sensation does not present its lineaments to you in order to contract its tail. A fascinating man is a man who makes no concessions and gives everything because it is already in itself so little. Sexual dignity is to get down to hard tacks as quickly as possible after circling round each other once. There is no *hard tack* which does not conceal unthinkable hardening. The human adventure lies all in this: to lose time beforehand, not to gain time during it and to put the alarm-clock to afterwards. (It is no coincidence that I have begun to use an aphoristic model after having invested the first 30 million lire in investment funds. Wisdom is a direct consequence of the vanity of everything once it has taken refuge from the void's inflation rate.)

~~

I arrive back in my room at midnight. The door is ajar. Strange, I was sure I had shut it – I am always anxious not to lead anyone into temptation. I hear a noise of a falling scent bottle. An aftershave thief, I imagine. *Two* thieves! Absolutely terrified although one of them threatens me with a knife. I shut the door behind me and say 'Shhh' to them with a finger on my lips. Suitcases turned out on the floor and more than a watch and sunburn oil they will not have found. I comfort them, tell them not to be upset, and although they are not hot, they are all sweating. They undress. Needless to say they are both so beautiful that it seems to me like a naïve thought on the part of the Tourist Office to make my stay more exciting. When they come out of the shower I ring the porter's desk and tell him to bring up the usual bottle of wine – they are mad about this watery stuff. I advise the two to pick up their vests and to slip into the bathroom again while the porter is coming up. I put my clothes back in the suitcase and in my bag. Without my collaboration they would never have managed to rob me; impossible to carry off the loot – it is in the *safe*. They drink, smoke, say thank you – stories about large families – like in Milan in the Piazza Duomo. In exchange for a watch of no value I give them 50 dirhams, profuse bows and benedictions, and I programme another hundred. We make love more than anything else because I don't want to make them feel outside the law. Neither of the two of them allows me to lick his arsehole in the other's presence – a pity – this nation is so clean and healthy that a gramme of their excrement can only be good for hepatic functioning – a new kind of regenerating protein. They'd like to do it all over again the moment I handed over the 100 dirhams. Please, let's make ourselves comfortable again. In the end the knife appears again: 'Out with the rest.' I give them the other 50 I had put under the frame of the mirror. Both salute me in the French fashion with three little kisses on the cheeks. All calculated. I help the second to clamber over the balcony. I warn them to be careful about the railing with the lance-like spikes. Once on the other side – the first (a Berber, tall, thin, who fucked me, licking my back as if I were what was left on a dish) asks me in a whisper what I am doing tomorrow. I shall hide the 50 dirhams in the same place, I answer. But please come past the reception and don't be so stupid and open the door of the room to see if anyone is coming. Here tourism is mass tourism and they still employ a kind of romanticism that belongs to raiding desert robbers. I recall both of them with a whistle – the knife – they have forgotten it – and throw it over to them in the street. They make me laugh those people who say I am asocial and can't even sit still at table.

For me there is no escape when faced by those who are offended. Since I am not a bottomless well, as the offended beneficiaries believe, sometimes I force myself to be firm and say *No*. Then I feel bad and go and look for him to make up for things with a *Yes*. If on the other hand I continue to say *No*, I get cross with myself, call myself a coward, but that's the end of it. When I am firm with the offended, my conscience does not stop torturing me, as if it were I who had been offended. But when I am weak – a gift out of weakness in exchange for nothing – conscience continues for a good while to insult me for the opposite reasons, but then stops and, on the whole, in the second case I feel better (but not always: once a man who had done me an injury came to ask me for money into the bargain saying I was the only person he could turn to, as if it were a favour to me, said that without the money he would end up in prison etc. and I did not have the courage to take my revenge – he gave me the chance on a silver platter – by telling him to get lost and that prison was the right experience for a coward like him: I gave him the money, I continued to hate him more than before because my hate for him piled up on the hate for myself). To offend the offended cannot be defended – I must not have scruples about giving them a little false relief – the only kind they are able to experience. The humiliated are full of defects and of vices proper to their social condition and their humanity is thereby crushed in an irreparable way at least as much as that of the *elect* is for the opposite reasons. One must not rail against the fact that the humiliated person, who has never had enough and who has lost everything, is unable to be content. The elect too is humiliated – but my God – while I want to limit myself to those humiliated/humiliated – by men.

Here there are people who go out at night to rob fertile earth from the subsoil of the fields (or from their neighbour) so as to establish a garden, people who literally rob from private sand, digging deep down like moles and leaving someone on top as lookout. There was a man who popped up from a hole which went down diagonally and was passing buckets of mud to a child with the terrified look of someone who has been caught in the act but who can only continue the crime. To steal earth . . . I prefer to be weak with the weak and to be what I can with the strong – that's definite. But one must not feel sorry for those who prosper from the humiliations inflicted on those – victims of earthquakes, floods, hunger, unemployment, the sick, the conscripted, neg-roes, pariahs, drug-addicts, prostitutes, abandoned children – humiliated by the modern slave-dealers who offend with full legality and think *this is the way of the world*: you are either top dog or bottom dog.

My desire for justice doesn't exist only in air, in words – it is sensible and credible in my own eyes because I am prepared to put a great deal into it – and to do so over again – for that reason. Oscar Wilde says: a map of the world without the country of Utopia is not worth considering.

(Take now, for example – why can't you sleep? Because today you ordered a steak and four kittens came and from a respectful distance stared at you. A long and narrow, sharp spine, a hunger uncontainable but disciplined by the habit of hunger. I gave a little meat to only two of them, after a struggle, because I wanted to see if I was *strong* enough not to give anything to any of the four. In fact before giving it to them I chewed it a little – tried to find a way out. And now instead of falling asleep I keep thinking about the other two which had none and I am slightly disgusted with myself, because I feel as if I had the worries of a young Werther, who feels like a murderer because when he walks he knows he is trampling on hundreds of insects . . . And all for two cats . . . In Muslim countries an existence is denied to no one – it is survival which is a privilege and life an unheard-of luxury.)

Dialogue in the usual circumstances after having used the sea as a bidet and fearing to drown, as peasants believe horses drown, through the arsehole, because it is no longer any use as a valve.

'We are like flies,' says the educated Moroccan stallion, 'we are considered insects by the king and his political class. They do nothing for the people, because at the centre of the hegemonic culture of this country the concept of the *people* does not exist even now as if . . . And the king moves about with a court of six hundred dignitaries who have to applaud him at every public appearance. He comes out of the loo and at once – applause. The tourists don't grant us a glance that is not *sentimental* – that is to say erotic. Studs. The public organizations and the Jewish shop- and hotel-owners tell them we are all thieves – thieves and rapists and murderers, and the tourists give us a wide berth or come up to us only sufficiently to take our measurements . . .'

'In Italy,' I say, 'its fame as a tourist attraction began like that many centuries ago. What do you think the Huns and Ostrogoths descended on Italy to do? Today the Italians not only no longer rape – the end of any extravagant romanticism and that's that – but they rob and the treasury benefits. With us, tourism is falling off every year. In fact, here in your country, you are better off – a few rapes and robberies in the old style. Your king ought to understand what the Moroccan *charme* consists of for European housewives and employees – of being accosted by you in the streets, while in Agadir it is forbidden. What do you imagine they think about for eleven months of the year, hanging up the washing and going round the shops on Saturday? To be finally robbed and raped by someone with his hand on his heart. I don't say one should carry out a blitz of rape and robbery, but an occasional coup helps tourism, and then the tide of wealth would pass through you, the people, and not the Moroccan airlines. Western routes to happiness are not infinite, only a little distorted; it is easy to smooth them out and reach the goal. But you people who have a political conscience and strong class feelings are too isolated. You must come together, form secret societies, arm, as in any country which aspires to an overthrow of the system or to civilizing the majority. Gadaffi, for example, who hates Hassan, denies no one a long-term loan – in any case Russia pays. A prick, quick reactions and sub-machine guns. That is what gives birth to technological civilization. You do your masters – even the masters of the prick – a favour in terms of mental hygiene by robbing them of the mark of God: wealth and power – and by fucking them brutally remind them that they are men, that they have something between their legs and that the farce with God – *their superior gifts, their merits, and their eternal human values* – is over and they could actually relax. This would guarantee, into the bargain, only a tourist class of a certain level – if you only knew how many rich men and women are sick to death of their *superiority* and those who believe in it. What is needed is a good trauma, they would pay you for a nice fright, an unforgettable souvenir. And one fine moment you would over-throw the king.'

'And what if the three of us' – meantime two others have arrived – 'were now to rob you and bugger you two at a time?' We are on a terrace in a remote spot along the coast, night, a lashing wind, myself naked and trembling, the three of them under the blankets and they haven't even given me a towel.

'I'd very much like to say *please*! But it doesn't make sense. I sought your glance, I did not disdain it, I fell into your arms. It is the glance of one rejected being to another. I was there before you. So long as there is one, long live the king. I am your king now. You will get much less from Hassan than from me – there is no need for you to content yourselves with robbing me – in any case you will be a little tired. I am one who rapes himself on his own – I am not a typical tourist, I am grateful to you for being the victims of my spontaneous generosity. As for the fits of terror, oh, how many I have experienced! But my drawers, at least these, you must give me back to get back to the hotel.'

I leave my room – at 3 in the morning. Outside there is me, the cats and the usual policemen. A scooter far away. Certainly whoever planned the gardens of Agadir thought of everything, the damned sexophobe. The only one a bit overgrown is shut at night. Mine is a hunger for emotions. I would need a less ordinary fright to reconnect me to the daily round but here they are so servile at any hour. Anyone who looked in my store of medicines – from those idiotic ones to make water drinkable to antibiotics – would think I did not need to cling to life. Health has a value of its own – it is nothing to do with life. An idiot has been following me for a good while; now he gestures to me to go into a gateway. At this time of night I don't take risks with those who are too ugly and too dirty like this one – it is difficult enough to endanger writing about it when it is a case of big hefty fellows. I am obsessed by the conservation of the species – mine and myself – only when I am writing about it. In order to safeguard the physicality of life – that at least – I write all the time or so it seems to me . . . Between one novel and another, between one project and another, I become dangerous to myself: I live, merely live, and therefore go in search of physical destruction. It seems to me that self-destruction is part of the wish to live. But I am much more pathological about self-conservation in order to write about it than about self-destruction in order to live.

~

Who knows what sort of a day today is and what I have in store for it. I wouldn't mind being born again as a cat – in Egypt though – although I believe that 'I' am synchronously all the 'selves' that have an animal existence at this instant. I am sure I am divided into a unity which draws its life from the separate creature identities that die from second to second. What I detest in the novels of the twentieth century is the cunning lack of religiosity. Creative mysticism, even given its inevitable rhetorics and superstitions, avoids the stupidity of any fideism or laicism of consumerism. Religiosity means to find the breathing mechanism astounding, allowing oneself to be overwhelmed by this beauty of mortal clay which no one lacks. 'Everyone and everything breathes like you' is a political formulation for big lungs. 'It's enough that they breathe' and we are on the threshold of the divine. It doesn't take much to renounce religiosity – listen to the click of shoes on the road, find it necessary in its irrelevance to you, concentrate on the unique marvellousness of those feet moving in their chosen direction. Mobility is sacred like the lock of hair ruffled by the wind, which then resumes its shape by itself. This is the ultimate sense of religiosity, a fine poetics of living: to know that in each present gesture and function there are millennia of genetic collective toil

62

to turn a pain in the limbs into *form*, into *nature*, an immense effort of memory which it preferred to cancel out. Perhaps at the beginning men did not even manage to lower their eyelids and their eyes were always wounded by the light, and the darkness in which they used to be able to sleep was the external one of the night and the caves. They went down into the grottoes and dreamt with open eyes that they had a nervous interior nature so refined that it created its own darkness, thanks to a supplementary function, which is not only that of seeing but also that of not seeing, and man invented the eyelids for himself by himself, *within*. And so it was with all the rest. I feel in myself a great predisposition to religiosity when I notice that the person who is making eyes at me is winking from an altar and that is what God is all about.

I so much like the ocean and the planes of the waves, I spend hours far from Agadir – I move about by bus – but then I can't wait for the moment when evening comes to go back and write about it. The waves seem more like waves to me on paper than in the ocean. And they are the only ones whose noise I notice once I am home . . .

What does a solitary shepherd do in Asia?* What the son of the shepherd at Tamrah does – he waits for the solitary tourist in order to show him the sheep and animality. Between the dunes and the cactus and sardine tins and plastic bottles there is a herd of black goats and two caftans sitting under the eucalyptus tree: one metallic green and the other bright turquoise. Hands that flutter, mine replying, a lowed welcome – oh Arab good manners! They express themselves very well in Arabic while both give off a luminous fragrance; beautiful clothes, beautiful faces, beautiful hands, beautiful muscular legs which issue from under their clothes – they don't wear pants, both with their sex coiled like a cobra – beautiful teeth, beautiful black hair. The father of my age, the son seventeen, and both immediately with the stiff homage which pierces their caftans and lifts them up. They make me choose who is first. I prefer to go from the smaller to the larger but with them it is not possible – they are both equally big. Mentally I draw the shortest straw, I begin with the father. The

*A reference to a famous poem by the Italian poet Leopardi. (Tr.)

son controls the movements of his thighs and meantime learns. I have found everything I did not know I was looking for on this trip; I have entirely recovered my prostatic sensitivity. I feel it tremble and gossip – I have no need to handle my cock; it bursts out on its own, oh! I imagine this is how a woman's cunt works – it minds its own business ignorantly. Previously I had only had clitoral orgasms.

A German has come into the pâtisserie with a pockmarked face and a glorious bottom; the bottom remains the most beautiful part of the human male, what most distinguishes him from the other animals. It would be terrible if he had a tail, perhaps he had to leave it behind when he was chased from the earthly paradise (as a punishment or a prize?); perhaps the fashion of tight-fitting clothes is born from the need to pretend to protect what formerly – thanks to the tail – indicated that the way was clear . . .

＊

At least once an hour I think of Adele. When I wake she is the first image evoked by me. Adele is two, is my niece. My loves are unhappy; I think I dirty her by the mere act of thinking of her. I write about it, doing violence to myself and overcoming my disgust. I also think of this child before falling asleep. It is not nice when at last you could have an excuse to give life – physically – and you are not asked. To give life to someone is no small thing, and to give it for Adele does not seem sufficient to me, because it would cost me nothing, as if I were throwing away a damp match.

＊

Today I went to Tarazut to fix up a room – in a fishermen's hut. Through the room two of those Italians had passed of whom there is no more news until their photos are published in *Christian Family*, under missing persons. Delirious phrases – with spelling errors – under murals with skulls floating on the waves. A mattress dirty with spurts of blood. One of these Moroccans who have grown up with the first tourists arrives and immediately invites me to smoke a joint. I – a non-smoker unless forced to – had to pass up the trip. Going back to the beach I counted up the extremely beautiful health experts who said to me 'ça va?'

Five. It is a village of about 500 well-fleshed souls. I have calculated that, to save on the hotel, I would have to give out ten times more for a quiet life than if I stay where I am. The poor don't let go of you for an instant, they look after your well-being, they all feel themselves unique and are a multitude, while I, the rich one, am alone against them all. I saw a tourist who started kicking one who was too insistent – a second later he was receiving bows in the street. I continue to shell out – not to mention when the children arrive and I am eating – and when they see me they smile treacherously to each other, as if to say 'Come and see the village idiot.' They don't know that I think ingratitude and contempt to be the only capital virtues of the indigent. If someone is grateful, he no longer has any reason to be poor and probably is so no longer; he has already started on a profession.

~

I am immensely fond of being alone. The hours pass in contemplation and I do not wish to be distracted by anything. Here there are residues of hippies with rotten teeth and filthy hands who look at you as if you are usurping their Sixties paradises of which I didn't have the right to 'discover' the holy of holies. I detest *travel journals* and travel literature. People who discover nothing usually discover geography.

The unreadability of literature taken from literature – travel and sex – when it is long-drawn-out. Unreadability also of Italian writers who emulate Henry James: 'I don't go to Crete otherwise I wouldn't be able to set a story there.' How many detestable little works *du regard italien*. An industry for the aesthetics of ways of asphyxiating nicely. The soul of the *self* who writes does not permit stylistic compromises between within and without: in order to have need of them, one must forget about them and not take their name in vain as if they really existed. For the sublime to take off you have to attach ballast. Anyone who does not venture into the vanity of large undertakings should abstain from putting his hand to the vanity of writing.

Here there is a little hollow smoothed out by the wind across the millennia which now blows a little less strongly. Little shepherd girls with a sheep, old men walking along the hill-tracks, shameless voyeurs, a French designer. He has been coming to the same place for sixteen years and is fifty-three. For sixteen years he has lived through the same approaches and consequent disenchantment but the enchantment never ends – it is like being at a needlework school run by the nuns. It is not by chance that *high* literature has not dealt much with everyday sodomy; there is no story to tell because there is no *development*. A prick in the arse is legible in its direct contingent dynamism – transposed on to the page and the inside of a novel it loses any aesthetic friction. The characters become 'all those poor things' (a weary dandy on the subject of gays in *The Standard Life*). The same goes for pricks in cunts: either it is pornography or it is Mills and Boon. In Proust, there is neither sex nor love, only images of the erotic bestiary in order to narrate the words demanded by the representation of what cannot be represented. Swann's passion for Odette is seen as a sarabande of the mediocrity of the desired object faced by the desire of the words set in motion by this banal pre-text (there is nothing to give between them – it is the same legal-linguistic shorthand as is adopted for scenes of homosexual love including lesbian ones). Truly *high* literature as an end in itself with all the consequences that flow from it – see Walter Benjamin* – does not deal with the common sexual desires whether satisfied or denied, but with the unleashing of frustration in the character and how it reverberates in its customs and social surroundings. The great passions in the novel are always a metaphor for political sickness – there is no intimacy in the adultery of *Anna Karenina* or in that of *Madame Bovary* – they are therefore either examples like a monument (to the fallen, to those who will fall) or they are not *interesting*, they do not add to what is specifically literary.

Translating is a skill and one learns it; it therefore improves with each book translated; writing is not (otherwise there would be no explaining why the first work usually remains the best of a writer who continues to give us works). One day (after you have been writing, let's say, for twenty years without any appreciable results – and you know it) you get out of bed and write and find

*No poem addresses the reader, no picture the spectator, no symphony the listeners.

yourself thinking once again: THIS IS LITERATURE. That is what it is all about. But one does not ever learn to write *better* once this passage from dilettantism to professionalism in obsession has taken place: writing changes the writer (as reading does the reader), but the contrary does not happen. Therefore, I repeat, it is not by chance that the best works of minor writers are their youthful ones; for the others, myself included, aware that maturity is a positive sign where writing is concerned, they are all synchronous, all *first and last works*, works per se, *without parentage*, unable to be related to each other, evading any hierarchy of quality. We cannot teach ourselves something which cannot even be learned from any one else.

I have burned masses of papers in which I had celebrated every haemorrhoid because, believing I was doing good by giving an epic quality to the arse, I had ended up by confusing my little sultana-raisins with the literary *theme* par excellence, since they were the two princessly topics of sentimental gay literature: *sin* and *pain* – that is to say good excuses which would have enabled me to make reassuring *serials* for well-bred ladies but never works of art as I aspired to do decade after decade – and not for *any reader*.

Only continual practice with words gives you the measure of all the words you discard because they do not fit into your favourite *theme-tune from Dr Zhivago*. By observing this accumulation of words which have never made themselves heard, one succeeds finally in discovering in filigree a consciousness – *through the looking-glass* – of what we have not yet understood we are and what we want to be in order *to write*. The miracle of literature happens when you understand that the totality of language is *the theme* of the writer and nothing else, while everything else may or may not be part of it, but without prejudice or particular predilection. I knew only one thing confusedly about myself as a writer – I did not want – no and again no! – to become a *homosexual writer* but as it were a real writer, that is a writer. It is possible, in retrospect, to hazard the guess that I resolved my homosexuality in great style and with great beating of drums precisely to avoid the error of making it *the* theme, the *souhaitable* theme of my literature, which was also homage to my real homosexuality. One cannot delegate one's arsehole to anyone other than oneself: by liberating it in life and freeing it from the word, so that it might enjoy itself in pure adventures of its own, I have not condensed it within a linguistic grid to compensate for the *impossibility of living with it*, which never was there. As a reward, I finally found myself face to face with *the* subject *par excellence* of language: language.

~

A character in a narrative who is poor in political and metaphorical dimensions is the exact equal of a social person rich in dimension of feeling and deprived of life. Both lack everything.

~

Each minimum movement of the epidermis unleashes coals of fire. I have peeled everywhere. Now I know by heart what pretends to happen under this burning sun; places, approaches, both suitable, and pragmatic charity. Today I learned that just as the Europeans come here for the men, the most deserving Libyans and Croats come here for the Moroccan women. There are many Nigerians too who are rewarded by their government. A great brothel is the basis of the kingdom of Hassan II. Moroccan women are not fucked from in front but buggered, because this is the speciality which fills the African and Jugoslav charter flights. Whatever way you look at it, there is an obscure link between Africa and the arsehole, which is very clear to the travel agencies. Here something begins which ends in glorifying organized sterility – buggery deters demographic growth. The fascination for the arcane symbologies that link pleasure and shit, black and pink, sex and money, Africa and Europe, is locked in this posterior rhythm, the oldest rain dance of man who, born by chance, finds himself in a desert which must be manured before it is peopled. The vagina will be considered a bane in these parts, whereas the behind is a mother's heaven-sent gift. I imagine the Moroccan sisters who, as teachers, after anal intercourse run home to discharge the fertilizer in the arid little garden and among the ungrateful cabbages under the eyes of their little sisters – still in swaddling clothes, alas! – Nigerian and Libyan sperm are good for the date saplings, the Serbo-Croat for the savoys and turnips, and moreover the women can a) get married as virgins, b) have a good dowry, c) make a soup right away of home-grown vegetables. The earth is always the best big breast.

⁜

Usually at 9 at night I am in bed or on the balcony. In front of me on the little table, a small bunch of flowers – wild barley, ears of wheat, daisies, blue and azure flowers – gathered yesterday when waiting for the bus. How does the majority of humanity manage to be almost always with other people? I am not talking about prisoners, evacuees, peoples in hutments, but of married couples, who have to be with other people by day for work and at night have to divide themselves between bed and cradles. No one who has a moment to themselves. I am sure that, for some reason or none, almost all humanity is side by side twenty-four hours out of twenty-four, and that there are few hours when an individual can be or manages to be by himself. Man's company wearies man, it saps his energy, the desire to do things and the enthusiasm to live, which consists in not needing anyone else to breathe. Solitude is not an exact word – it evokes unjust melancholies and languors with hints of tragedy, like a guilt or a punishment. No, that is not it. What I mean by *solitude* is to develop a capacity, a sensory function of synthesis *vis-à-vis* life, which is a happy event for anyone, a process of learning to go along with the functioning of one's own life to the point of socializing one's own deepest peculiarities like *the worm* or *the gnawing woodworm, the secret of a whole life* and other puritanical *etcs*, which impel us to a false mediation or an equally false isolation from the world. To promote one's own *breakdowns* means to learn not to need a mechanic in the short run – unlike mechanical things the motor of life goes on thanks to that particular *breakdown* – repair it and it stops or changes into another unthinkable and often more flashy machine – I am speaking of my own case . . .

Naturally I also enormously admire those who decide to conceal what they consider a *breakdown*, and succeed in doing so thoroughly, and give a perfect dynamic to their apparent movement. But it is a road which, once you take it, is, and must remain, a road of no return. Bad luck for them, is all I can say, because I have not yet known one of them who did not turn back – also because all the others, if they exist, exist but one knows nothing about them. Those who change course are the most contemptible – those who are half-masked, with delayed bursts of *truth* and *sincerity*, which in them can be nothing other than the umpteenth attempt to camouflage hypocrisy. I am not saying that a *face* is qualitatively preferable to a *mask*, I am only saying that it is more comfortable because more mobile, more plastic, less self-conscious. A face is, after all, within the reach of all, a mask not: the first brings with it the comforts of democracy, the second the iron law of a dictatorship.

With your *breakdown* well displayed in your face, you can, from time to time, choose your own road according to your purse; with a mask you may get as far as God and then, however, it is a failure if, while succeeding in deceiving yourself, you have not succeeded in deceiving Him. If you are not certain of a natural grandeur that leaves no traces, opt for mental hygiene, which is a grandeur within the reach of humanity. If you are not a writer at least be yourself.

D.P. asked in Milan how I live my homosexuality. I thought I had a friend and that to have a friend was an aspiration common to all mortals, and more realizable for certain exceedingly lucky ones than for others – a colossal mistake: handicapped people, deaf-mutes, paralytics, have lovers with curls.

According to him I am a) a handsome man, b) a great writer, c) a nice person, vital and much more innocent and feeling than I would like people to think. In short he would have sworn to my amorous *happiness* and by *happiness* he meant an on-going relationship. After a lightning examination of my personal (?) situation I replied that homosexuality is a gift from heaven if one lives it without mistakes and if one invests one's capacity for passion in one's *solitude*. To be a homosexual and then to depend on the sexes of one's own sex seems to be a contradiction, like being born in a monastery and taking advantage of this to rush and become a monk. He asked me if I fall in love (he has before his eyes the example of a Catholic artist, a friend of his, and the mad things he does to go to bed with one boy after another, the heart-art-sacrum tragedies of his homosexuality, his *ups and downs*, more downs than anything else . . . until, to be precise, he sees the Madonna) but of course I fall in love with fools and knaves with olive colouring, but I don't see what connection there is between me and this other person. Do you keep everything to yourself? says he. Not at all, I express everything down to the micron, which is the best way to exclude from my love the interference of the loved one – a cretin incapable of dribbling the ball from me, a victim who has all my solidarity. I give a form to the hysteria of love which cannot be mediated – there! Obviously I express this too. My hysterical *form* remains suspended in the air I breathe – does not pass over into the breath of the other; I contemplate this new psychic form for some time, then it fades away, I go back home and shut the door on the other's air – nothing very original. In *Seminar on Youth* I wrote that when I love I cannot work, that I have not sufficient energies for both ties, and received many letters of support. Now, on the other hand, I would say either you love or are written, and writing excludes loving. The crudest prejudice vis-à-vis homosexuality is that one must be *someone who desires incessantly*, because that is what they all do. First of all, I do not make love because *I like it*, but because I do not know what else to do; it is more a matter of accountancy than of the heart – understood? To love, to love! but what on earth is this packaging? As Signorina Scontrino (*The Byzantine Dolphin*) would say one can do better and more: inspire-expiate-aspire. There's always time to expire. And then I don't go to bed with anyone; I go on foot.

To buy sex with money is like buying a kilo of rind in the shape of an apple; the kilo is always a kilo but the flesh is not included in the transaction. Abulia from fraudulent foreskins (Golden Delicious variety). Fortunately the vitamins are contained *only* in the skin.

~

For years I have no longer been faced with the circumstance of having to make myself known personally, and therefore even I don't quite know what I have become. I know that everyone who knows me is sure of knowing me. But I am certain that I have no longer given myself to anyone in my historicity because what exists is the reception of information rather than the information itself – it is not so much a question of saying or not saying, doing or not doing, but of being two of us who do it. There will be no more time for anyone either to be known or to know, I and me first and foremost. Essentially I am too distracted, too concentrated on the heedless solipsism of my wild days, and on the linguistic whirlwind of my fingertips, to deign to take anything away from my *works* to invest it in *life* wherever some sort of global knowledge of another person is possible. In truth I am interested only in those persons on whom I depend as writer – printers, editors, critics, photographers, journalists, cameramen, presenters – that is to say, people like me who have very little time to be historical, to be human. We are useful to each other and we have to put almost all our energies into our professional interactions. So I also have to write to allow them to keep the wheel oiled which also makes my books *circulate* – indeed which makes them exist (it is more likely that when I write I am thinking of them rather than of a hypothetical reader or market). One ends *loving* whoever is useful to you, who furthers your project and uses you without half-measures. Disinterested people, from a certain point of view, horrify me; why are they all popping up now? where were they before, when I was underneath the arches, unemployed, ill, hungry?

I owe more to my publishers since I have become a successful writer than to any other eating-house when I was a miserable scullion. Therefore, having been rendered incapable of having nostalgias and joyful memories, I ended up nourishing an almost adolescent affection for the various cogs of the wheel, I understand them, respect them, try to make life easier for them, to honour their work for me; yet one does not form alliances with cogs but only momentary agreements, everyone has the right then to forget you if you are no longer useful, one has to be strong *at once* to accept such a law – it is not a great life to be part of the gears, very little indeed if the wheel is big and pitiless and always wants to grind something out of you, demands constantly new sacrifices. So long as I am a writer and *take part*, I prefer to sit beside a woman correcting proofs and to follow her work on my manuscripts rather than to run off with someone who offers me the earth *now*, when all I need to know is if some spellings can be left as they are, as I wish, so as to be able to restore them to their pristine form on the first occasion. Ah, how many phoney romantics are popping up now, stressing that in me they love the man first and foremost, no less than the writer! The *hidden* man, naturally. Who is already given way, or the bearer of happiness to take away. My libido, which has been unleashed for years, without either slaves or masters, friends or dogs – I now lavish on the commissionaires at my publishers, on the ladies of the Press Office and the technician who does the covers. Abandon hope ye who want to know me personally – content yourselves with the works because the man is *written off* but is not in the catalogue – for all and for ever.

~~

Taroudannt.

I arrive here from Houara on a lorry packed with sacks of cement and another eleven people thrown about like me. Yesterday, having arrived in Houara at Mustafa's, a student met at Agadir in the showers, I left the moment I woke without making any excuses. The family with whom I had supper and spent the night was nice and the children amorous. They all live in the centre of a farm, an ex-colonial set-up, where plants and flowers for the market at Gadi are grown (bougainvilleas, rubber-plants, palms, every kind of flowering creeper etc.). The buildings are of red earth, the water from the well is good, there are hens, a pig, and a citrus orchard laden with lemons and oranges. There are other huts round about while the house of the French couple, who died without heirs in the Fifties, is abandoned in a tangle of falling walls and briars. Outside this unkempt little paradise there are huts made of bamboo canes, goat dung and cardboard, where certain mountaineers – not from hereabouts, survivors of an earthquake – have lived for years. Hamid, the most beautiful son of Amita – forty, eight children, gold teeth, a proud woman and mother – is scarcely three and if you put a coin in his one hand he shows you the other, which has been left empty. A son like this would be the dream of any banker or shop-assistant. Students like Mustafa are *petits cons*, slyboots who show you it and after you have given them enough to live on for a month say to you 'Combien tu me donnes pour ça?' as if they had two pricks to show you. They wanted me to 'eat' it and that was all, they wouldn't stick it up me because it is better that way, so that 'si ton cul est malade ma bite se sauve', that is to say 'if your arse is ill my prick is safe.' I left him with a stiff prick in the middle of the lemon grove and went to bed. He explained to me that a German left him a little souvenir, even if he was so nice, so blonde! He longed for him, perhaps he will come back to find him. Ah well! Sentiments are only a Western elaboration of long-winded blennorrhagias, which then give you a discharge just the same. I took the first truck at dawn and here I am in Taroudannt (I don't know where that is), in a hotel with a hundred men intent on watching a film on television about Al Capone. Every so often a break and a commercial: the Koran.

➤➤

Adventure. I see someone deep in the souk. I keep on following him among baskets of saffron and mint and little green peppers – now he is coming towards me, his eyes cross mine, they stir up in the sweltering heat a possible madness, I follow him again and what does he end up slipping into? The Hotel Mentaga where I am staying. I run. The man has a nonchalant gait, loose-limbed, someone who undoubtedly inserts the key in the lock with due lack of haste.

I catch hold of him discreetly on the first flight of stairs. Dark-skinned, he stares at me without revealing an emotion, a message. He has gone in, leaves his door ajar through heedless-ness or in haste.

From within a voice says to me 'Bonsoir, Monsieur'. I throw open the door, enter, shut it behind me and lean on it. When I open my eyes I might see anything – stars or the stars caused by a punch and a rebound. I smile. Inviting but innocent, he rolls a cigarette as he speaks – a joint. His voice is hoarse, thick, the kind that makes the backbone of invertebrates vibrate and the legs of caterpillars tremble. He is twenty-eight and is an engineer with a mining company with its headquarters in a citadel on the outskirts; on Sundays he comes to this hotel far from his colleagues, buys hashish and sits in his room smoking and eating. Always alone because he doesn't want to see anyone – no Arabs. He does not communicate with any Moroccan; he despises them. Because they are all beggars without dignity, from the poorest to the richest. Do I know Camus? I could weep

74

as he takes off his shirt after removing his jacket – his chest strong, slim and hairy, his lips which murmur calmly, spell out the rite of an understanding which must be deep or let's forget it. Some mouthfuls of smoke. God, the way he has of opening his mouth and making a smile glide over the rim of an abyss. He invites me to take off my shirt and, why not, my trousers, says to me '*Tu la veux*' and takes my hand and puts it on his fly. It is always as if the prick were an extractable or portable appendix which has nothing to do with them. He is very excited and his prick juts out from his trousers like a head of maize at the point of full ripeness. I am in raptures too, I feel a kind of unusual tremor in my balls, as if they had started to revolve on themselves. I want to kiss him, he lets me. I think – he doesn't like kissing. And not offering his mouth for the second time, he takes me by the nape of the neck and draws me to him so slowly, without stopping looking at me. We stay motionless for whole minutes sucking each other's tongues – I know all this will cost me a fortune specially because of the talk about *dignity*. Usually those Arabs who criticize their fellow countrymen for begging are preparing for an incalculable piece of blackmail; they put out their hands as if to say – I won't be satisfied with as little as that . . .

The skill with which he rolls my body on to his, directing it as if there were only one of us and we were rolling off the earth in a star of rough sheets, which get less and less dry, in a silence of flies beating against the window-panes, our pupils dilated out beyond us. Again and again we arch our backs and we shoot out darkness after darkness, ready once more to profane an unhappiness which semed fixed and eternal and unrenounceable, and which instead, now I look back at it from a distance, was a chipped ornament thrown away amid the rubbish of general pains. He seemed to suffer in every nerve, the intensity of his need to discharge love petrifies him in an ineffable state, which fills him with joy from his pale Calvary feet to his eyelids half-shut in ecstasy.

Confronted by his arms, which detach themselves exhausted and fall back open on the bed, I do not know what to do. Take out my wallet? Go away? Say goodbye or say nothing? Shut the door without saying anything? How many hours we had been together. I ask him, greatly embarrassed, if he allows me to make a contribution for my share of the hashish – I took one draw out of five. Looking elsewhere, at the wall, he says with clenched teeth '*Ça vaut pas la peine.*' I swallow, understanding the grave error, the insult to him. I blush crimson, this is the most powerful emotion of all – it was all free of charge. I feel a worm, I invite him to dine at least, wherever he wants, even in the thousand-and-one-nights hotel in the nearby oasis. He says no. I leave, I join my lips to his once more, he remains passive, accepting my excuses, which are full of gratitude, respect, love, whoredom. But the damage is done. And I am out in the corridor, humiliated by myself, by my lack of faith in myself, in others, by my total unpreparedness to be loved for *myself*, which this time has screwed me thoroughly. Reaching my floor I see someone who makes a gesture to me to come in, I go along with it at once, to forget speedily the uniqueness of the earlier feeling and to re-enter as soon as possible into the repetitiveness of the *commedia dell'arte* of offering one's body piece by piece, each with its name and function, until one forgets the very notion of *spirit*. Great loves can be seen from the very few traces they leave behind them. And from door to door, as evening falls, a company of young teachers has formed in the rooms next to mine. There are eight of them, they teach in the mountains, in the villages scattered across a radius of a hundred kilometres.

On the first floor the handsome man's door is shut; light filters from under it. A desire to knock, to be with him, to present him with my watch, to ask for pardon. He cannot make me guilty of the vulgarity of a whole world. I go up to my room again. Of the eight I line up the best-looking four, I make a present of the other four to a Frenchman with a hearty appetite and, while the second is fucking me, we talk about the political situation in Italy and I calmly answer him with the little I try not to know. Between the third and fourth, my melancholy for the engineer alone in his room, wounded, thinking who knows what, naked and thin and intense, like a dethroned pithecanthropus, passes and I stick it in. I am so excited, hot, juicy. I have reached such a pitch of *sensitivity* that I feel floods of sperm one after another press against the anal walls and the pulsation of the urethra deep in the interior – and I too explode crying out automatically. Since, when they come, Moroccans remain impassive, not making cries or other signals, this sensitivity of mine is a great convenience – but they all complain that when I ejaculate I spill the seed on the ground, they say Europeans don't usually do this, that it isn't allowed etc. At this point I tell them to fuck and stop thinking about it, Europe's a funny place.

(When I have to pinpoint absolute emotions on the map I feel a great cervical pain – I lack words, they evade me because, whatever way you take it, the absolute emotional values of poetry are absolute rhetoric; the great pains and great joys find their ideal place on the Altar of the Fatherland, not in the *relative* intelligence of the alphabet.)

        ••

Tomorrow I am going up into the mountains of the High Atlas, to a little Berber village where no tourist has ever set foot. I shall go there with a robust and merry elementary schoolteacher who spurts right away. I'm not sure but it seems he is here with two friends who have come to visit him from Marrakesh and that they will join us (or rather I shall join them), two boys of different race, shy, mad about gangster films and football. In the middle of the night I pass the door again, the only door of this disorderly hotel; the voice from inside tells me, '*Je t'attendais.*' I go in. At quarter past seven in the morning I tell him I must go, I manage to speak with great effort. What our lives have sweated out in these seven hours, the chair, and the walls know, they, too, damp with our humours and warm breath. He doesn't bat an eye. He asks when I will come back. I could even give up leaving while I gaze at him, incapable of transmitting a thought. He cannot keep his eyes properly open, it is as if he had to carry me on the back of his eyelids and I am heavy. I feel we shall miss each other and that probably he will miss me. He says to me, '*Tu ne veux pas venir avec moi dans un désert?*'

Running for several kilometres along with Said and his two friends to get to the place for the trucks and public lorries, I feel the immense beauty which sets up an electromagnetic charge around dawns that insist on emerging in full light among the whiteish landscapes on the horizon and that I am so alive because I dare not to think about it any more instant by instant.

We set off jolted about by the potholes in the tracks from which boulders and palm-tree trunks emerge. The three friends form a gang in the opposite corner of the truck, as if I were not with them and they did not know me. It is odd how the Arabs, when forced to be too close together, don't open their mouths because of their fellow countrymen. A hundred kilometres or so like this, standing up, squashed, towards a goal I do not know, and along with three friends (among themselves) by whom, I suddenly understand, I am not considered a friend. A vaguely boring sensation of stupid danger. It is still too late even to go on, far less to turn back. I might have a chance at a stop where the three of them get down to take refreshments at a *buvette* and tell me, please not to leave the truck. Which sets off again, each one in their established corners.

❧

And here I am in Halouan among the orange mountains of the High Atlas, crossing delicious precipices and slopes full of pink oleanders and *arganiers*, special trees from whose fruit a most precious and choice oil is extracted, the Berbers' only source of income which goes along with the rearing of goats, which have the task of feeding on the pulp of the nuts of these trees and of defecating the kernels, which are collected by the population for a radius of tens of kilometres and pressed by a stone mill and a donkey. We arrive down at Said's hut in a cloud of flies with green-golden wings, crossing streams starred by the diving of the frogs as we pass. The hut is of earth and dry dung, with two rooms one on top of the other, in the room on the ground floor is the cow as in all the dwellings – the byres are underneath so that they give natural heating during the night, because the heat from the sweating of the beast and its dung filters through the porous walls and rises up to *the rooms*.

As we descend, the first Berber children, his scholars, come to meet us, tall and sparkling, their lineaments delicate, taut with a natural austerity, with a calm and sincere smile. Simply to see them I, who am not really naïve, cannot but think of the arrogance of our civilization: I am among primitive and analphabetic peasants before whom the only right thing would be to kneel and kiss the hem of their robe. The most regal thing in man is to have created God in his own image and likeness *then*, taking the people as a model; today it would no longer be possible for any man to imagine God to be as ugly and useless as he himself is *now*.

There are many peoples more and more threatened and gaunt (and look at them – instead of considering me as a natural enemy they come and shake my hand one by one, lowering their chins a little, as no prince or admiral would know how) whose citizens are like the ears of wheat of this miserly earth; if they exist they are proud, richer than ours, which flourish as far as the eye can see.

An old woman, bent under a bundle of brushwood, bids me welcome, and she has never before in her life seen anyone dressed like me nor has been down to the city; she does not even wonder what I am doing here in her parts, hidden among the mountains first accessible only a few years ago by truck; she greets me with deference because I am a man, therefore am a God, like her and all the others here, an *ambassador of the good spirit*. Said translates for me, yesterday on the subject of my argument about the ears of wheat and religion and ideology he said to me, drying his fingers on my sheet, 'For Roland Barthes no discourse is innocent,' trying to tell me to beware, because there are a lot of big proud ears softened by blight, although they have avoided the law of natural selection . . .

I am a little put out by the presence of the other two, one of whom, the thick-set negro, maintains an attitude of hostility, almost of aggressiveness towards me and passes from Arabic to French, sipping the mint tea, to discuss how good human flesh is, which has gone on being eaten in this village. The matter does not impress me much: mine isn't good, I say. But here, alone, because I feel strangely lonely and exposed among most beautiful people with unfamiliar customs, a tiny doubt crosses my mind: that they aren't quick enough, that they are making me suffer too much before serving me up. A mouse streaks across the floor; the three dislodge it and Said kills it with blows from a stick, cursing these animals that carry off half the crops. From far in the Oued three women arrive bowed under loads of straw which perhaps only a mule would be able to lift. Behind them a very tame *lebon*, dog, which lies down at the foot of the hut and

79

falls asleep. I go and drink water at the fountain although I have some in my bottle. The water is good and I drink a lot – I ask Said if they eat the frogs; no, he replies, and that, if I like them, tomorrow he will send the boys to hunt frogs and we will grill them in the open, spitted on bamboo-canes. I have forgotten the desert engineer and am falling in love with Said and his solitary life here where he is not very well received, like everyone sent by the central government – which isn't recognized by the Berbers – and where the Koran does not form part of the religious heritage, all the inhabitants here being wisely animist and impeccably oral. In Said I like the strength of character, his ability to pass the greater part of the year (of his youth) in complete solitude – no private relationship is possible with the inhabitants, who are respectful but distant. Yes, every so often they bring an egg, a piece of chicken, he says he sits in his room and thinks, meditates . . . and that sometimes he feels he is going mad and oh! thank you for coming and that . . . But here his two friends come in, the light which had shown in his eyes previously is extinguished, they begin to speak in Arabic, excluding me for minutes which seem hours, while the light in the room gets worse as do the lips of the three of them when they look at me, shifting about with a hint of something bad which I feel slowly mounting towards evening, the dark, although not yet imminent . . . there is a vague wave of evil which gathers, second by second, to form a crest made up of every moment, I have the distinct sensation that the three together form a . . . *pack*. Yet when Said is alone you should see the gleam of his glance at me, the desire which emanates that I should stay here a long time, to speak to him, to allow myself to be embraced by his quiet desperation – that of a hermit – to teach him to make love. I don't know, I don't understand. I feel it is not easy to hold off this terror which he does nothing to calm – and darkness is already at the door . . . there is not even the possibility here of forgetting that I am a *pédé*, someone to bugger and despise, serenity does not exist even in the remote paradises and now I feel my presence here to be *artificial*, not fitting in with anything, disliked – and what are the voices which *inside me* cry out to be on my guard? But it is Teodora, it is Anastasia, and Signorina Scontrino, whose incomplete lives depend on my survival. This is the definite alarm-bell.

The bell has scarcely stopped ringing when the squat negro tells me to move over on the matting, giving me a kick in the side, and not to touch him. Then the three of them begin to snigger. I pretend nothing has happened and there was no kick. Suddenly they turn nice again, say we're going to bathe in the Oued, perhaps it wasn't really a kick – it was a comradely way of getting some room. Certainly it was more than a year since I suffered so concretely a sign of contempt, I tell Said, who makes no comment but goes ahead and joins his two mates outside in the dusk.

I am writing by candlelight. So we have been at the stream to wash ourselves and it is as if the old harmony had returned between us. Maybe I exaggerated a bit with my persecution mania, but it's because I have had several unexpected attacks and obviously the wounds are more open than ever.

Here the ethical problem is excreta. People go kilometres for a piss and I don't dare think what I shall have to do when I have to have a shit. The most moral man here will be the most con-stipated, or the one who goes furthest away. I do not attempt to go further into the social code of defecation.

Because one of the two friends, Samir the negro, had thrown a stone into the water, an ancient peasant got off his mule and began to rebuke him because the water is full of spirits and devils and who knows whom he injured with that stone. The two of them, being of another religion, did not say a word. Then their pupils appeared in a procession that moved along with a solemn and plastic pace, the long robes the same for all, little princes with bare feet; it is only beauty in them that is a tyrant, dazzling even at twilight and something that compels obedience.

We go back, they cook something, we eat and it is suddenly dark. The cow underneath lows, gives notice that the central heating is on, I think it must be the bell in the theatre and that behind me there must be a curtain going up. Here it is again at full flood, dripping with damp: terror. The characters from my novel scream *in there* – they do; I do not scream at all. I have never done more than try to live with all my power – if it is one's destiny, that's that. Signorina Scontrino is the one who is least resigned and she prods me to think up a tactic to get home safe and sound; Signorina Scontrino does not permit herself to be

interrupted at the finest moment of her ascent to the papal throne . . . I look at my luminous watch – ten minutes to midnight. Still huddled in my corner. And at midnight the cruel carousel begins, the Berber idyll plunges into a horror film at the ritual hour. A large stone has been placed in front of the opening in the wall, the door has been barred, the candle put out ('What are you going on writing, stop, idiot!'). I lie there huddled up with my throat choked, and a feeling of vomit at all that darkness laden with bad omens. The flash of a torch! and then from another point another torch and a third, all converge on me, the three begin to curse in Arabic in my direction, chasing each other round the room, trampling on me in their mad race, throwing themselves on me and falling on me, a din like cats and rats. And once more, suddenly, silence and total darkness. I say something witty in French but no one responds. What are they preparing, where are they, how far from me? Little laughs, a neigh, a cock-crow. A hand on me – whose I don't know, the voice says 'Je veux tirer un coup, pousse-toi là.' It is the tall skinny one who is not very well and stinks of garlic and wine. Signorina Scontrino says to me: 'No fuss! mine is infinitely more important being a spiritual violence.' I let it happen, while the other two play a game, keeping an eye with their torches on their friend's prick, which is going in and out of my thighs. He comes between my legs, the idiot who has not even noticed that I was pretending to have it up my arse; the other two take me by the legs and lay me out more towards the centre and I hear that they are doing a kind of dance macabre round me, round my face lit by the on-and-off torches. I am struck by a punch in the ribs, by a kick in the ribs – but no cry comes from my mouth, it might incite them more. Tomorrow – to reach tomorrow, to flee immediately afterwards, if I manage, as if nothing had happened, the end of holidays in the mountains . . .
Then it is Said's turn, Said the sweet criminal, whom I attempt to repulse in his hasty brutality perhaps in order to rediscover – hidden from the other two – the same complicity as impelled me to follow him here. Nothing doing – he does not accept intimacy, he is brutal and resolved, he traps me with his arms from behind while the tall skinny one holds my head down on the little pillow. I manage to twist a corner of my mouth outwards to breathe. Now it ought to be the turn of the squinting sturdy

negro who threw the stone into the water . . . Instead they started to run about in the room again, I can breathe with full lungs, hiding my panting and fatigue without making a noise . . . perhaps they have taken some drug or other . . . The dawn, the dawn . . . or at least to see the natural darkness of the night, to breathe something of the day that is drawing near . . . Someone seizes me by the arms, then another by the feet, I am dragged round the room, I bang my head against objects and walls, I cut my wrist. Their sarcastic laughter . . . and I by an instinct of preservation allow mine to join in: which is felt to be an intrusion, an attempt to join the game which instead is theirs and excludes me . . . In front of the cone of a torch a knife appears . . . shouts like charging marines . . . they are imitating the onomatopoeic sound-tracks of American films.

It is 2.40 in the morning, I have managed to take the clock out of the plastic bag I carry about with me and to press the button that turns on the little light on the dial . . . the other two push the negro towards me, he doesn't want to, he repeats a single sentence in French '*Je ne veux pas attraper une maladie*' . . . A sentence like that is dangerous, it can have a devastating effect on the other two who have already raped me . . . Now a hand takes me by the hair and pulls, I go round the floor once more. I say with a laugh that I'm a bit tired and want to sleep . . . I am suffocating, I know that, if I utter a cry of fear, it is all over with me, that is what they are waiting for – to hear me, to see me a prey to panic. They light something in the dark, a little flame that comes close to my eyes and passes rapidly over eyelashes and eyebrows which frizzle away in an instant . . . Shouts in Arabic, of incitement it seems to me . . . the skinny one is back again, he comes again between my legs. After which silence, I hear them lie down, exhausted, I hope, not far from me. Oh, if they would fall asleep . . . Instead I know that the modest and hypocritical negro, moralist and squint-eyed, is lying in wait there like a hyena – they are the most dangerous ones, these educated negroes, those sexophobes, who criticize and stir up the rest of the herd, which cannot accept that it had suddenly behaved in a *different* manner . . . In the dark Said starts talking loudly again in Arabic, the negro replies, the torch lights up again; Said, as if to give a good example for the last time, comes on top of me and sticks it up my arse once more while the negro throws a light on his friend's balls which are pressed against me. When he finishes Said begins to roll on top of me with the skinny one once more, trying to draw in the negro. 3.26. Finally the negro wavers, his friends leave the torch on and take off his drawers, laughing, shouting, and take me and make me open my mouth on their friend's turgid and enormous member, which I suck off unrewardingly because it is stuck between my lips, while he gives me hefty slaps on the cheeks and punches in the neck to adjust things so as to get it well in and all of it all the way. I know I have to make him come publicly if I want to have any further hope of saving myself, I must make him the equal of the other two, thus robbing his hatred for me of its drama. And, when he comes in my mouth, I let the spunk slip out on to his prick so that they all may see that he came, that he too is an animal.

I got up and drew back the bolt on the door. I went out to clean myself up, I thought of getting to the nearby fountain. At the bottom of the dirt steps there yawned the jaws of the dog, which seemed to have stayed there to wait for me as the final bone of a banquet. Scant moonlight – but the calm and threatening silhouette is there, upright on its paws, on guard. I examined it well with the torch, seeing how it looked at me contemptuously, too eager for meat, ready to leap on to me if I came down another step. Then I pointed the cone of light on to the palms and the spring – there was in effect neither stars or moon. Behind me I heard the bar being put into place and shutting me out all of a sudden. Bursts of laughter and then nothing.

➤

I prepare myself to spend the chill night outside in pants and T-shirt. Their contempt inevitable after having abused me like a novice whore. I don't mean with this to play the goodie-goodie, seeing that I go looking for it even if this is not exactly what I expected. One ought never to expect anything. It is not nice to be badly raped.

The dog goes off after having made it clear to me what the limits of my space are – where I am; if I moved away I would have it on top of me. Then, seeing that I neither implored nor knocked, the voices inside died down, I remained outside a good long time then someone – Said? – came to the door and I heard the bar being removed. My teeth were chattering, I went in there with the most natural air in the world, said 'merci' and huddled down in my corner without a blanket because they had taken mine away. I dried my snot on my T-shirt and thought 'The dawn'. But I didn't have time to recover through the natural warmth of the room where the dark now was comforting: they jumped on me, all three, and two of them laid me out and, while one buggered me and I shouted at the nasty blow (from the weight of it it must surely have been the negro), the other two banged their pricks on my face where they ejaculated. Sperm in the eyes hurts very badly, it burns like bleach.

A bit after 5. All three are snoring, more done in than I am: still anxious, I keep my eyes open in the dark, but I sweat and shake. To be able to kill all three of them! But I don't know where the knife is and I wouldn't have time – I'd need ether to make them unconscious one by one and then to slit their throats in my own time and go off down the mountain. My attempt to move the stone from the opening in the wall lasted an eternity, but I succeeded millimetre by millimetre, and I stayed there for precious moments imploring the sun to rise, because at 7 the same truck passes that goes down to the post and from there to Taroudannt. How I shall contrive to get away without being disturbed has still to be discovered. And I don't even know where my shoes are. From the little opening fresh air came in, once again I stuck my nose between the stone that closed the opening and the wall, I breathed with my mouth in a heartshape; I felt like a fish out of water. If one of the three has noticed that I have moved the stone I don't know what might happen to me, because to keep out the light of night – which is believed to be malignant – is linked to the most delicate superstitions.

The skinny one turns over and asks me in a low voice and nicely if I feel like having another go. I say no thank you and this time he does not insist. He starts snoring again like the other two. I must not fall asleep or I shall lose the truck and I do not want to spend another day here. But there is a mad feeling in my head – the overpowering desire to wake them, provoke them, strike them, insult them, threaten to make them go to prison – if the police know that a tourist has undergone half of what I have suffered this lot would not see the light of day again. If I threaten them, thus determining their sentence, the loss of their jobs and honour and liberty, I also determine my certain end. Anastasia has no doubts on the subject, she says to me: 'Dear writer, sort things out with your cankers yourself but don't disturb our trinity' because she and the other two are triune. I masturbate to discharge the anger and energy of hatred, so as to continue on the straight and narrow path of passive diplomacy, and then alas! I fall into a short but deep sleep. Short but irreparably long. I look at the clock – Said is already up, he is cooking barley, he has to go up to the school – it is half-past seven. Goodbye truck! I say nothing to him, while he has his back turned to me I get my things together and put on my shoes. Said turns towards me and asks if I slept well and says make yourself a cup of barley. I reply, rising to my feet, that I want to go, that I am leaving at once without coffee. He wants to know why but without paying too much attention. A sore stomach, I reply. But it's not possible, the truck has gone past already, there's not another till tomorrow. I shall go on foot, I insist. He tells me I am mad, it is tens of kilometres in the sun. He talks in a low voice to the other two, who are half-asleep, and says goodbye. He tells me he will come back early from school and then we will talk again about tomorrow. I say all right. I let him go off, I say goodbye, after which I waken the long skinny one, I tell him to put me on the path, he tries to dissuade me, says the consequences could be unpleasant for me, I say to him what sort of unpleasantnesses now over and above those I have received? . . . The negro turns on one side, says 'What's up!' and falls asleep again. Fortunately they are all a bit worn out, I go out, go down the steps, pat the dog's back and at that point the skinny one says he is coming with me to the casemate where Said teaches, that we must speak to him first. As we climb from sloping to precipitous land I see one thing; that I must walk alongside, never go in front of him – by instinct. When our eyes meet I feel fear in him, a spirit of vengeance and . . . the desire for another trick. My left foot is still very sore, the wound from the operation on the recurring verruca opened again yesterday evening when they seized me to drag me along the floor. I am losing blood but say nothing, nothing must affect him, I must continue to pretend nothing is

86

wrong, clutching casually at the official reason – dysentery. We arrive; Said is called out by another teacher who is not part of the gang. And the moment Said sees me and smiles to me as if nothing had happened my anger explodes, thunderous, sudden, as if it did not belong to me sufficiently to be kept under control. (Signorina Scontrino turns her little head away and curses, 'Jesus Christ.') Said makes me come into his classroom, hoping to calm me and make me change my mind, all the students leap to their feet, Said says, 'Give me your address' – here everyone wants your address, it is a tic. He was explaining a passage from the Koran to the children, he talks and talks and talks in a silence of the tomb. In Arab countries the pupils, from the smallest to the biggest, do not have the right to interrupt or to ask a question, if at all only to reply to a precise question by raising their hand – they are vessels and all receive the same stuff in the same way, without any chance of criticism or personal intervention. Now I am really fed up – I get up and formally say goodbye to master and pupils, Said turns pale, he accompanies me outside, I shake his hand and set off up the mountain. Then suddenly Said says to the lanky one to accompany me 'for a bit'. Catching up with me he asks what my intentions are once I am down below. To leave, I say, to go to a chemist's. No, he says, about what happened last night. So you know that what happened last night is not normal? No, it is normal – on the contrary – isn't it what you wanted? To my face! What more could we do!

We set off. Teodora is fairly indifferent about whether I am on the side next to the ravine or to the mountain above us and to the fact that the lanky half-caste is coming with me to throw me down the moment he manages to take me by surprise and that it may look like an ill-fated walk. But Signorina Scontrino takes Anastasia to one side and both escort me to the ridge on my left. The half-caste walks slowly, slouching along, I have a much quicker pace. In any case, if they have decided on something, the other two will come up the slope sooner or later. Perhaps they are tracking me from bush to boulder. But now I am well under way, I tell the boy to turn back and many thanks, straight on I can't go wrong. He shakes my hand, I am ready to ward off a punch or a stab or a tug towards the precipice three metres away, I keep my body tense at a distance, ready. The lanky boy turns back. For every hundred metres until I reach the lower Oued I live with the certainty that any moment now they will descend on me. At last after ten or so kilometres I meet a cheerful toothless old man, the only living thing in this space of fear, sun-drenched at its zenith. The old man is walking along at a brisk pace, he doesn't speak a word of French and his incisor wobbles cheekily in his whiteish gum. Every so often we stop and with a dry branch he makes marks in the sand and so do I, thus we can carry on a bit of conversation. And from far off I see the truck station, I bid him farewell and run limping, as if I had wings to my loose-fitting sandals with my big toe covered with blood and sand, an excellent bandage.

﹌

You would think the education department had posted a sentry because there was a big school here too, and outside the wretched inn stood all the teachers taking their break who invite me to go up to their rooms. The usual Islamic behaviour like a wolf-pack which is like the way they moralize over football in a bar in our parts. I shall stay the night because until tomorrow morning there is no truck for Taroudannt. They are nice – but it is still day – they offer me an egg. I hope not to suffer from other nightmares. Not even a banger going about that might take me right away – I have no other choice.

By candlelight I am writing the usual notes, I would never put into print anything as coarse as carnal violence – because frankly the flesh of my male being doesn't give a damn. How ridiculous these little schoolmasters are who are now talking *freely*, certain that I am not a government spy – with a foot in such a terrible state . . . They are all anti-monarchist, they maintain that political and religious power are profoundly separate, that the police indeed persecute their Muslim brothers, shaving off their beards if they push forward to the point of threatening the monarch's authority with their *integrality of the Text*.

Yet the most exciting thought in my present life is Adele. Thinking of her I almost feel like living *my life*, not that of these three criminals of *The Dolphin* – here is Signorina Scontrino a little while ago: Don't you think you have already exposed yourself sufficiently and uselessly? Isn't it maybe time to go back to

Montichiari where you come from? We are fed up all three of us with sleeping on the ground! We are from Romagna, we are, proper ladies of ample means, we would never travel in such a disorganized way.

Yesterday Giulio Andreotti, the Italian prime minister, arrived in Rabat for an official visit. Who knows whether he too spent an *Arab* night like mine. A *close look* would do him no harm.

We sleep. Without a pillow, three of us under the blankets – myself, a boy of eleven and the extremely nice but rather fanatical teacher who has put me up, Salah by name, who has no intention of fucking me or of allowing me to fuck this young bull here beside me, because he wants to stay a virgin till he is married.

'Oh, the heterosexual! now that is a good idea,' sighs Signorina Scontrino blowing out the candle.

~

This morning's truck having been lost too, Salah has sent me his pupil-nephew with a note: 'If you are rested after the fatigue of the mountain can you come to visit our beloved school?' Samir, the nephew who did not move a centimetre last night receives me on the threshold of the school with a sweet in his hand.

I stayed an hour and a half in the classroom with twenty-five pupils from seven to fifteen, none of whom uttered a word or a whisper. With them the so-called dialogue does not exist – the teacher is an authority and only gives orders. That is why there are no women teachers because here the woman does not exist. Yesterday little Samir did not once open his mouth in the presence of the adults: in a corner on a mat he did his homework by candlelight, perhaps he kept his ears open, but nothing else, while we five chatted about politics, the economy and agricultural machinery. That is why they made me lose the truck – I am really an overflowing source of information for them; they aren't likely to have someone like me turn up again out of the blue. Samir's allotted task was to receive orders, the little servant kept by the little community of adults and teachers – they made him get up to do this and that – everything in short – and he was always ready, without batting an eyelid, at their disposal. I asked at what age a man can express an opinion, let's say a *No*. And why should he say *No*, it doesn't exist in our parts! they replied in astonishment. He can express a *Yes* – only a *Yes* between sixteen and seventeen, they all confirmed with a smile of progressive smugness. In the sense that up to sixteen *Yes* is taken for granted – after that it expresses a precise will: *Yes* and one that can be articulated. The difference between these two *Yeses* would, in other words, be fundamental, like that for us between *Yes* and *No*, there you have it. To women not even this is granted. And no sooner had these profoundly religious *intellectuals* taken me into their confidence than they really relaxed and begin to sing the praises of revolution or, better still, of having it carried out by someone else. I say to them: Why don't you begin to let the boys in the classrooms speak too or give a different pattern to the reading of the Koran – two hours each day! Answer: No teacher can introduce his own ideas – if he has any – and if he does he must keep them well hidden, otherwise he doesn't become a teacher – into his place of work, the penalty being immediate transferral to prison. Moreover, it is obvious that individuals don't have either a power of association (it is a very egocentric civilization the Arab one; the Arab thinks only of himself and his own family) or a pedagogical tactic in the long term to overcome this social-political-cultural impasse. The problem is not *what to do* (the ferments are in the right direction) but who will begin – to go to prison, to let themselves be killed for a revolution which they will never manage to see. No one, but really no one, is prepared to be the first martyr and to give up the ridiculous privileges, which cost him so many tribulations to attain a diploma in education. I tell them that since time immemorial blood has been the international passport for overthrowing any de facto State. The spectre of Khomeini was called up, and Salah, who like all of them is for Islam but isn't religious (?), who is against Hassan II but is not communist, who is pedagogically easygoing but woe betide if Samir takes a long time with the bowls of tea, has said that Iran is not Islam. If we put it like this, people would say we were getting the best of both worlds. It is the same with the countries with a socialist system for the communists of the Western countries, where communism is built into the capitalist system and is not so much something abstract, or that is yet to come, as a perverse expression of capitalism itself; communism is never what it *is* where it *is* but always *something else*, something that *doesn't exist*. To spell it out: what is most *real* is what is yet to come. Up yours!

~

For Salah it is not good to bugger another man because his member would end up 'in a rubbish dump'. And here am I explaining to him that shit is the true Allah, the gold of life, the prime motor. That we who are our contemporaries are no more than the shit of future contemporaries, the indispensable manure which gives the starting signal to every placenta. No use – the Koran does not contemplate such a thing, shit is shit – discharge – according to religious convention. It may be God in the Catholic one but not here with us . . . patience – Salah is one of those brothers with a tolerant smile, understanding, far-sighted who, sooner or later, end up by taking the reins of something and make the others carry out a revolution – and first and foremost will have all those who are not as sweet and tolerant as himself exterminated. I was telling him that it is so *thrilling* to give up a system of thought and habits, to feel one's own *genetic* tradition in all its spiritual partiality, and that tourism also has this effect – of taking things up by the roots, whether one wants it or not. After an hour's silence over what we have been discussing, one of the teachers jumped up and said that if I stayed with them another fortnight they would lose their *morality* (but not in a nasty way – in fact they tried to make me miss the third truck as well). They were mistaken, I told them, I don't want to corrupt individuals but a people. And then good humour doesn't corrupt, it strengthens the intestines. Where it passes nothing of the same species grows any more. The roots become shoots and one must wait till the seed for the new roots is scattered by them. They were completely fascinated by the fact that someone could then detest and say he detested *his fathers* and that the individual cannot subject his own destiny entirely to the destiny of a people, of a system, a condition, but must always discover the arbitrary element in himself and turn it into law out there.

Seeing that these Moroccans dream of Europe like so many American young ladies at the end of the nineteenth century they

91

ought to know from now on what they might come up against once disembarked at Genoa or Marseilles.

～

Here I am back again at the Hotel Mentaga – which takes its name from this region. I was booked in by the kitchen boy, by the member of staff in the porter's lodge (an office of bits and pieces of wood) and by the host. They said Ah, Monsieur! there is no life without you! Would I be able to stay over Saturday and Sunday as well because this time all forty teachers from all the mountains of the region are coming down. And who would I be on Monday! A very rum Baba?

I feel elastic, intimately flexible, delicately available. I have lost ten kilos in ten days. My neighbour in the next room is lamenting at having to leave – he ejaculated so well here, he tells me. A pity about that little maid who never leaves the corridor for a moment and makes the toing-and-froing between the rooms more difficult – for the others who don't want people to know. I have such a desire to make love today. My body is completely animated and receptive. Everything is going well for me: the food, the smells, the lack of comfort, the dust, the heat, the unexpected coolness of a doorway near the hotel while a youth insists on shining my shoes. In the souk, two boys followed me showing their hard pricks under their ragged shorts. How relaxing it is to wake up and not to hear the village band about to open yet another cattle show.

～

How to express to Berber children the concept *missile* or *atom bomb*? Such is the analogical swindle borrowed from the natural phenomena – the only ones of which we are conscious so that each head of lettuce is supremely sacred – that I wonder whether it is worth while staying here to satisfy their curiosity (they have heard talk about things like this on television, probably in some Argentinian *telenovela*). They will understand what a missile with a nuclear warhead is, exactly like ourselves, who think we know what it is: when it falls on their heads.

The same goes for *writing* – I can explain it by having recourse to a vocabulary which derives from criticism or engineering and will still not have said anything about its essence – at the very most a great deal about its inessentials – by saying as in so many fields of knowledge what it *is not*. Anyone who is not a writer doesn't know what to make of theories on writing, any one who is has no need of them. A true writer is at the same time the most qualified theoretician in his field, he does not need to articulate the problems inherent in his own art – he identifies them by cultivating them and that is that. To write a novel is the only possible theory of writing. All the rest has to do with reading or is an attendance fee.

A thing of beauty can cost immense toil to man and the meticulous arrangement of extraordinary cases, but once brought to the light it has its own origins all before it and nowhere else. A thunderbolt from a clear sky leaves at the same moment as it arrives. The same may be said of writing.

～

The emotions are not even half of themselves if they are not played out and I hate repressed or unspoken emotions, because the great truth about man passes through the *mis-en-scène* he contrives to make of them – sad but true, in fact sad and agonizing. I am moved by anyone who makes an effort to give mediated form to his own emotions, and not by the person who remains in a cynical and often utilitarian purity of silence and gnostic withdrawal. Emotions humiliated by their own representation may seem stunted and ridiculous but they never betray themselves. These emotions which do not succeed always hit the bull's-eye just the same.

～

Those people who pursue great wealth in order to have the most beautiful women and the most exclusive pleasures (?) distress me – big houses and a yacht and strong-arm men have never guaranteed in themselves great adventures for someone who would not have constructed them in any case from a mud hut and a floating tyre. A great lover does not allow himself to be conquered by anything in the nature of a *bodywork* or *superstructure*, one attains the heights of reciprocal sensations between consenting beings by arriving in a wheelbarrow and the subtle gradations of reciprocal feelings by arriving on foot. Sex has often uncrossable frontiers and is a most delicate and fugitive substance: what drips is not all libido, often they are only leaking taps.

One has only to move about a little among people's *love* relations to realize that, by writing banalities full of common-sense and nothing else, one runs the risk of being paradoxical. *Men* who meet *women* or other *men* or other *women* are very rare. They are almost always engineers who get together with female captains of industry who meet life-guards who get off with female decorators who go mad about designers with a weakness for the unemployed who secretly have it off with their hair-dresser friends who *en passant* satisfy the curiosity of a *commendatore* who would expose himself only to a leading male dancer permanently resident in a city which is preferably a port. Adam and Eve were chased out of the earthly paradise because they insisted on not putting on their fig-leaf and on not making a profession of virility and femininity. I find that great goals are pursued because there is always the same basic desire: to conceal one's own insignificance.

➤➤

Blessed are those who show consideration for their lover only if he starts kicking them. In this sense I am not sufficiently witty. If my lover exploited me, despised me, beat me or amused himself by shaming me publicly out of love, after a while I would become annoyed.

I went to the house of the *brothers* of the guide who is a permanent lodger in the hotel. He is a young half-breed, destroyed by everything caught here from European civilization; drugs, alcohol, twanging guitars and brawls. His room is like an Indian reservation and I have given him the nickname of Cochise. He earns more than two hundred dirhams a day by acting as mediator between tourists and sellers of bracelets and passes the rest of his time smoking hard stuff and getting drunk and banging his head when he falls. He has a lot of visitors because he spends and distributes largesse to everyone, but they must go along with him because he turns nasty when he is drunk and needs someone to be violent to.

There were two of these *brothers* of his: a government employee – the grease-spots on his clothes are different from the citizen's ordinary ones – and a soldier on leave. Both were eating boiled marrow on a tin plate in the middle of the room which was littered with the ends of joints. Their movements were slow, laborious, their smiles stupid, the air unbreathable. A young boy had come along with us, a tall gangling sixteen-year-old with the most beautiful eyes magnified by smoke and alcohol, an adolescent enthusiast for wine, the natural little slave for Cochise, who provides for him and is bringing him up and giving a helping hand to the boy's family. Since the boy is almost always stretched out on his back, one might think that he is being flattened on the ground rather than being brought up. Once they have arrived, after a trek of several kilometres, there is no dialogue between the four of them after the greetings, but they organize another drink and another joint to be taken in the hotel at a certain time. Happy and content, they barely raise a hand to say goodbye and set out on their way back. They stagger as they walk and the boy stumbles every so often and collapses on the ground and laughs grandiosely but without uttering a sound. End of external worldly opportunities. I go back to my room and the two of them to theirs. Every so often someone arrives, knocks and books me in the sense that if I say no they put me down on their own accord for *tomorrow*, since no one can believe in a refusal. Cochise sent the little slave to ask if I want to join him in his room to drink and have a suck at his pipe. I say No. Before leaving the boy comes close to me, hugs me, and keeps kissing me for an incalculable time, I let him do it out of compassion, he gooses me a little. Arabs too need affection.

Now in Cochise's room there is an alcoholic, undulating, chattering coming and going of extremely skinny people who are sent to and fro to buy more bottles of wine – they buy one at a time – and Cochise, who never lays down the guitar and sings Arab songs that would be the equivalent of *O sole mio*. The little slave he has adopted comes back and implores me this time to take off my drawers for a little and to turn round because he's got one too; poor thing, I let him, he can't stay on his feet, I feel as if I were crossing a ford with all the household goods on my back. He brings it off, I was chiefly watching where I put my feet – it is like being a removal firm, the transports are all theirs. I feel as if I had used only one colour and that always the same with aestheticizing monotony. I have never put on extraordinary or deplorable numbers, such as getting myself up as *celeste Aida* or Madonna or Sarah Bernhardt and going and spending a week-end relaxing in the Tangier cinema called Rainbow Road, for example, because I do not like the half-measures of people who do it in glorious Technicolor.

Evening meal in the hotel – one course of nothing but giblets. I did not know that I have always shared Berber customs; my mother makes them once a week to save money. With a chicken she makes horrible dishes (but admittedly succulent ones), ten chicken wings in the frying pan – a monstrous animal without breast or drumsticks. At home I often refuse to eat the cultural shit of poverty which underpins it even now when times are different and people could allow themselves a chicken in its totality. My mother said to me once: 'You take two wings from the plate and pretend you chose them from the *whole* chicken on the table.' As if to say that there is never a choice – real or illusory – in the face of the real possibilities of the moment but only the capacity to give wings to fancy when you 'bloody well either eat this soup or jump out of the window'.

Poverty is the creator of all the aesthetic peaks – it imagines the finished article in the incomplete, satisfaction in privation; it adds the existing detail to the absent organic structure, it furnishes a text for the context and makes it into a bonus; it gets along in a grand way with little, the indispensable minimum on which every proud sensibility for things sprouts and a princely sense flowers in the humiliation of surviving as best one can. The ancestral habit of poverty contrives to take in with a single glance the shapeless and ugly matter from which the perfection of the rich whole has been forced, it welds the inadequate reality to the ideal dimension of being, without suffering any frustration. My mother with her ten chicken wings doesn't wish to deprive anyone of the breasts and drumsticks but to provide a whole chicken for five people eating together so as to habituate them to the peremptory nature of free will. The obtuse discipline of poverty often allows itself the whimsical idea of disregarding the *perfection* and integrity of the model as if to say 'I am very well aware where you come from – from nowhere – you are perfect because you *don't exist*' and to this ideal form (the whole chicken always and only seen in childhood scratching around and never had on the table) it prefers – with bellicose snobbery – to brandish its unshakeable ethic of half-measures and of poverty: the memory of hunger camouflaged by choice. It has the incomparable aesthetic quality of humbling the *perfect* form and of denying it the form of forms: a hunk of bread.

The mothers who went gleaning – forget about des Esseintes.

~

The little slave with the teeny-weeny prick has returned to the attack and once again I said yes without hesitation – at least he is performing some other youthful function than taking drugs and getting drunk, maybe he'll lose some of these tendencies . . . Here in Taroudannt it seems to be against nature to make love during the day, to give vent to the humours of the spirit crystallized in the flesh. A little prick is in any case the only thing that dares to unpeel itself at this time of day and over and above that is maybe a way to sober up. People with fine pricks know they look good even in the dark. *El ojo* – which in Spanish indicates many kinds of eye, including holes – no longer plays its part in the dark when one has one's hand on something a little more tactile. I ended up by telling him off and, just as a start, told him that at 9 o'clock I stop the merry-go-round and put out the light.

~

Good sex enriches the aesthetic sensibility, bad sex enriches the speculative intelligence and therefore changes in one's career. But either way it is worthwhile.

One can only expect ruin and civil disaster from anyone – a demagogic playboy – who would forbid sexual liberty – unless it were with the aim of buttressing its disruptive and revolutionary character. To humiliate sex with the aim of *really* humiliating it is typical of any system, capitalist or socialist, in order to canalize energies which would otherwise be dangerous if they were used to check the effective ideological gaps between intentions and results, between promises and the keeping of them, between programmes and factual reality. The *overall system* rewards the chaste and makes castes of them – witness the number of repressed homosexuals in places of power. Anyone who becomes excessively preoccupied with sex (and chastity is one example) goes – in the eyes of those who have power – far enough to be stopped at any moment and sent back to where he came from. Political organization, having nothing to fear from those who are sexually frustrated, has everything to gain by using them. A frustrated lesbian or a repressed gay can make thousands and become prime minister or *grand commis* some-where – or on the other hand go on suffering hunger replete – but they will never challenge the system which has integrated them not – as they think – *in spite of*, but because of, their circular vice and, being necessarily neurasthenic, they must waste all their energies to conquer as privilege what they have been unable to impose as a natural right: to be themselves – in other words, serenity as an authentic political passion. They are the classical homocrats, members of the fucked oligarchy that is still in its cupboards.

(The seventeen-year-old came for the fourth time, I think, his lips dry, cracked by joints. Talking a deep breath, I did not say no to him. But on one condition. At this point, if he respects it, since my shoulders are sore from having him on my back, he makes me lighter by a thought.)

Man was chased out of paradise for another reason as well (in short, he was becoming too much like what he is): he had noticed that, since there was such a thing as mineral water, if he stayed there he could not bottle it, he realized that the simplest things are the most precious, he discovered commerce, in other words, and he laid on all that stuff about *sin* to get his splendid licence to trade.

Today hell on earth is general: air, water, vegetation, sex have to be paid for and if you can't then you must breathe, eat, get by as best you can. Life has been polluted by the cunning of Adam and Eve, not by the harmless serpent which plays the part of scapegoat under the Madonna's feet – perhaps life itself *exists* because there is a concentration of pollutions, not of purities. Man, flesh by a process of adaptation, has infected the Earth by peopling it, thanks to his capacity to become acclimatized to the poisons which he has been busy creating in order to so corrupt things as to render them commercially competitive on the market. No point in thinking of an ecological renewal on the lines of 'when things were better'. In various ways it has always been *like this*. If it were true that man is an eternal child, he would already have been struck off the face of the Earth; if he persists in existing, it is because he is born an adult and adulterated and takes every precaution genetically against *purity*, because it would be fatal. If there is no beginning, there cannot have been a time before this. Only the poisons we shall discover and put on sale tomorrow bear a date.

～

The seventeen-year-old came back and begged me to let him in 'for the second time'. I told him to do his sums better. There must be something intrinsically didactic about the way I speedily assume a posture, ready to give a hand and to indicate the lost passageway with a little piece of chalk on the blackboard of sex – otherwise there would be no way to explain why an Arab – they have mathematics in their blood – should get his tables wrong just to score better.

～

My legs are finished, and that dead weight of a boy must have a discharge as well. What comings and goings (that's what life is all about!). Fortunately I have finished all the liquids . . . I am so generous – to cover myself with ridicule gives me a frisson with which no dignity can compete; and that makes sense, because I am certainly not a masochist but someone who imitates God. Now I feel a bit like going home. The correspondence, the first proofs of *Standard Life* are ready, the anonymous telephone calls, the provincial papers which interview me by telephone and then call it 'How the VIPs will spend their holidays', the worry about not lasting to the end of the month in a few months' time, and the conclusion of the third and penultimate chapter of the *Dolphin*. Decent and possible pleasures await me. The lullaby of someone who has nothing better to do than to bask in his own undoubted boring fame in a field which is cratered by the obvious. To stay here flat broke tempts me – God knows it tempts me! There is no one among the Italian writers with whom to compete – here I would have at my disposal goats that have become possessed through hunger and the rare blades of grass. Rimbaud too was not far from an extremity – he was in Somalia, over on the other side. I do not believe that I have ever heard or read anything negative about Rimbaud and his work. He is the ultimate taboo who has not fallen under fire of the critics' blank pistols – critics who dream of knives and scimitars and, from their slippered ease, follow the adventures of God, the Author, in Africa. Who knows who will be the first to dare to bring Rimbaud down from his liana – someone able to fly at least as high as him or the usual paralytic who begins his sentences with: 'If . . . '? Rimbaud's Western flying trapeze routines are conceivable in the cultural mythology of the pen-pushers only because, since Rimbaud had a gangrened leg (later amputated) and the landscape being exotic, the pen-pusher has transferred to him both his own, which he doesn't use.

But among the great Great Ones they commonly limp along talking about the weather and nothing more.

. . . Hashish makes the calves of the leg shake and makes one sleepy. Fine discoveries. It ought to be time to draw the shutter on this day – but it doesn't fit well, it remains more open at the top than at the bottom (just think: all American modern poetry is made up of this sort of boring stuff!), it wants to let the late pricks in – ah, the poetry of the last-minute pricks!

. . . an Arab voice in the cold dark – someone is calling out making a prayer fade away on the last vowels. It will be trying to sell a Bic lighter to the night.

∞

I go with the pimply ones to get antibodies (or to kick the bucket . . .), I am not really so unendowed as a member.

At Tiznit the wind is the only touristic invention which is doing well. Changed hotel because the first was too nice and had plastic carnations and a tea-service with a festooned Nativity on it. I am beginning not to be able to stand any more of these 'psss' at the street corners. Tomorrow I shall go to Trafaut and then to Gulimin. Oof! one would need thousands here. I might as well stay in my Lombardy plain and there develop the lust for sex/

money I lack. My big toe is losing pus – a damned verruca which won't be excised! It is well ventilated here – 'How much?' is all the wind carries away.

It may be due to a bad habit that every approach, whether on my part or on theirs, finishes up with a con; but is it possible that no one here can ever conceive of a disinterested gesture or phrase? One goes to Morocco, apart from anything else, to understand – since one is there – southernness (just to spell it out). In the south to accept something gratis or as a *favour* means putting one's life at stake. So how can one enjoy sex, then? By buying it? Gide and Wilde, unlike me, brought this lust from home all ready-made. The bourgeoisie, however petty, does not even discuss certain facts: money is money, above all if it's used for getting humped. The only way to get on equal terms with a beggar is to kick him. Real gentlemen take no account of expense when it is a question of wearing out one's shoes in that way and the miser in this case would be myself because, while continually putting my hand in my purse, in the long run I would save on leather. The temptation to stay broke and to compete with those wretched creatures who beg for a kick of attention from every raised foot. But it would merely be the first step towards the abyss of kicks taken by a beggar who is himself kicked.

. . . And in Tiznit I end up in a smoke-producing bar near the Post Office where I went to post some postcards. Frequented by soldiers coarsened by hashish and boredom. Ten of them come to my table (I should make it clear that I am not at all the kind of person who goes about with stiletto heels and am not a blond) together with three sellers of smoke.

American music at full blast – 'Tea for Two' in rock tempo and with mint, naturally. I get a headache right away – I'm suddenly assailed by all the American music one hears even at night because they do not turn their transistors off even to sleep – they have to show they have one and that, if it is playing, it has not yet been stolen. The whole squad want to offer me a coffee, which would be decaffeinated and made from barley; I refuse. I get away only after having paid for drinks for everybody – which was what they wanted, threateningly keen and full of propositions. Their form of intimidation (made up of smiles and invitations which become orders) is powerful. I have my own way of sending them to the devil – not too clear a position about the future: this evening, tomorrow, one day. The mirage of the prospect tames them. As with all weak people, the future is stronger than they, stronger than their present anger – it threatens the hope they have seized on. They have been accustomed for thousands of years to being fooled – they consider *tomorrow* and its instrumentalization a form of investment respectful of traditions. Try talking to a professional criminal, failed or unsuccessful – after a little up pops the hope of opening a restaurant *one day*. Playing on this fixation of becoming a good little pizza-maker, you can serve them up anything you like, if you are a real *maître*. I wonder if a heterosexual would ever make a trip like mine alone, and what sort of countermeasures he would adopt, because those one *thinks* of adopting are no use. But I have never met such a man nor have I ever heard one spoken of. A heterosexual does not travel – he moves forward.

~~

Hassan II appears on the TV screen in Pharaonic pomp. The pomp, the majestic pomp of the ceremony, only to place the sacred behind on the throne; the band and the procession to go and entertain yet another delegation from the Arab States; behind him he is flanked by his two offspring, splendid wax statues; journalists dressed in the European manner who ask him little protocol questions, hunching their necks as deep as possible into their shoulders; the infinitely calculated opening up of the scissors to cut a ribbon, and I think of the goatherds and smelly wretches of Fez, Marrakesh, Tiznit, Layume, who watch the recorded transmission and get a basis for their highly developed penchant for science fiction. Hassan II is the moon, and the sun besides, a remote planet which emits cathode rays to a people/country of scattered groups with whom he maintains astrophysical relations. What will the mind of these millions of customers receive? An ideal? The paterfamilias? A Sarajevo presented on a silver platter to the first volunteer? E.T?

Tourists should be grateful to Hassan II for the diligent effort he has put into not moving a single straw during his reign, which is inspired by a painstakingly realistic Middle Ages, so as not to disturb the precarious equilibrium of the migrations of holiday-makers. In the name of the people, the Despot always leaves between himself and the people five or six centuries, which form a little historical-touristical cushion. The people exalt him and exult, and the monarch at the end of the day gives a sigh and moans to his favourite lady in the usual way as he unties his sword: 'What a tiring day, *ma chère*.' It is an exhausting business for both of them – king and people – never to forget a line in their own immemorial part. Commercials follow: Danone, Philips, Renault and Nivea. Lying on palm mats and surrounded by tens of brats, eaten by flies, the mothers dream of detergent-like milk, powdered milk and milk. The fathers in the next room how to fix a passport, how to start a new life in France without telling anyone, to marry a nice piece in Ventimiglia, blonde if possible, with a driving licence, virgin if possible, with dishwasher . . . If reality outstrips fantasy the Third World outstrips reality. Just like at home in Italy.

Met the busybody student who in the bar had put me on my guard against the dissoluteness of the military and the sellers of drowsiness – and here was I already moving to a somewhat out-of-the-way barracks. This morning he went on and on about the *moral* devastation of smoking – this evening he asks me for 10 dirhams to buy a special pipe. Because, being brilliant but unreliable, there is no coordination between their ethics and actions, between idea and practice, and they do not even know the Renaissance art of dissimulation – which is so European. They lie shamelessly, certain that the intimate harmony of lies (by the logic of which they are inspired) will not escape anyone. I made an appointment with him tomorrow between midday and 1 in the bar in front of the inn with the bath – there was an oldish soldier with a newly shaved prick who gave me a couple of bangs and the rest in small change and bye-bye. I shall leave three hours before the appointment. In Italy I wasn't aware of the stupid snags of joints: they cause diarrhoea and headaches and there's only heroin, they tell me, that can cure it. It is also true, maybe, that heroin has never given anyone a bad complexion, but in the long run it is no great beauty cure. Fortunately one is still free not to use it. The use of drugs depends on the psychic presuppositions which are the bain-marie in which each person's brain is steaming. There are very modest brains which have only one intrinsic aim – to evaporate. Cocaine, on the other hand, if regularly alternated with hashish brings back a little of the lost histological solidity. One drug drives out the other and together they dislodge the weight of the brain. The rents are too high if one wishes to keep one.

~

I never talk about Moroccan women because they lead a very withdrawn life. I do not believe they even weep. Water is something very precious. The eyes are exuberant oases in the wrinkled desert of what is left under the veil: if they could see their own charm it would not be so burnt, turquoise, blinding. I shall come back to Morocco again. Anyone who does not like discomforts but cannot renounce enlightenment should go on pilgrimage to Naples at least once a year to be robbed and to restore vigour to the ancient consciousness – of their class.

Those Moroccans who speak French do not call the prick *bite* or *queue* but *noeud*, knot. Probably a running knot.

~

One can talk of *natural right* if every generation and every individual in a society affirms its *naturalness* from time to time and so corroborates in no small way this *natural* right with an up-to-date definition of political will. There is nothing natural, or given, per se, the earth and its territories less than less. Populations have been coming and going since time began, they camp, they set up perimeters, they are once more decimated and chased away. Thousands of years ago, just like this morning, everywhere in the world. Peoples are dispersed, reform, and even the human violence of a tribe is considered a natural calamity, no less than earthquakes or tidal waves. The right Israel claims to re-appropriate Palestine has been as absurd as the duty the Palestinians have laid on themselves not to relinquish it totally. But the land never belongs to the most just who live there but to the most strong who take it. The strongest is always the one who invents motives *in the flesh* and goes straight for his illegitimate goal, putting everything to rout by force of arms, after having created an ideology that fits this end, which one could extrapolate from the Bible no less than from *Lady Windermere's Fan*.

What I hold against the Palestinian students with Israeli study grants is that they do not understand that the Israelis' interests coincide with those of the leaders of Arab terrorism who, *in words*, want to raze it to the ground, and also coincide with those of the Arab satraps who wage war against Israel in the name of the people but have the gold baths with jewelled taps made in their own names – the ones who will have invested of all the petro-dollars (apart from arms) .0001 per thousand for the well-being of their people. I also hold it against the Palestinian students with the study grants from Tel Aviv that they do not know about good manners: when I ask them how many study grants their historical leaders granted for the education on an international level of the sons of the people (of the proletariat), they do not know how to answer me. Perhaps to spit in the plate you eat from (but I am against it because there is an ideal solution – to pass up the meals) is still admissible (it is typical of servants with no destiny of liberation) but to spit in the purse with which one studies is sacrilege, because then there is nothing better than to remain ignorant and faithful to one's own cause. Besides we see so many young people politicized in a critical manner who have seen that they must first and foremost rebel against their internal heads and this is now on the order of the day even among the youth of Israel, which is wrongly labelled *pacifist*. It is simply politically acute and has made very precise economic calculations on the pockets of the warmongering State. I wish this attitude would gain ground also among the Palestinian youth against their leaders who send them to the slaughter in the name of the ancient right to build themselves oases and fountains with a hundred jets in peace and quiet, while outside their subjects are busy dying either in war or from thirst and dust.

There is no difference between one enemy and another if both are external, but no enemy is such an enemy as the one we carry inside ourselves.

Hassan II, who when he pulls the plug, each time does away with the water of an oasis, doesn't say to the Moroccans that he is their enemy: he directs the rage of his nation of beggars against

105

the neighbouring nations and the President of Algeria does the same with his nation of beggars, pointing at Morocco every time he gets up belching from table, rolling his eyes with satiety.

Welcome to the renegades – those who at once identify the other enemy and go over to the enemy who doesn't exist. But even here, the existing conventions are few and confused and the known collaborators in the various professions are no great images and models to emulate: avid, cowardly, petty *traitors*. They would have to be retaught manners first of all. Above all to establish that the lack of nationalist ideals is the highest ideal of the patriot and not abject servility personified. What does the effigy on the stamp matter to me so long as the letter arrives? What do I care about a Minister of Posts if he can't compete with a carrier-pigeon? What is the difference between a refugee camp with powdered milk and the boundless powdered sand of the desert without a little milk? *Freedom?* What is the difference between the political liberty not to live and the political liberty to die? Ah, the great internal slaughters of the French and the Russians! I would never go off to a war outside the frontiers of *my country*; imagine leaving for Lugano to kill Swiss with whom I have never eaten even a dish of gnocchi! Such an abstract waste of time and of blood. But to stay here and fight a civil war in the province of Brescia would come more spontaneously to me – no one would refrain from a strictly fratricidal struggle. I would find bloodthirsty motivations in the course of a curfew. But Sinai, Vietnam, the Falklands, Afghanistan, Lebanon, Kuwait, no way! You go and kill a lot of people whom you don't know and whom therefore you can't hate and then if you're lucky come home and find the same pain-in-the-arse neighbours alive and well whom all your life you would willingly have killed and instead the Government has said No because they are Italians *like yourself* and sends you by decree to kill Somalis as if they were less Somali than you and if I insist in preferring the killing of Piccinelli, the accountant, who annoys me by existing, I have to put up with the state of illegality.

The Moroccans form a nation of beggars which instead of having a revolution loses time – centuries – asking for alms, ringing the rare and only benefactor with a palisade of human arms which threaten as they implore. Instead of claiming charity from the tourist, it would be better if they asked for explanations from their government – instead of vampirizing an anaemic subject like me, they would do better to spill a little of their give-some-alms-blood over their century-old vampires – their venerated leaders.

The sceptics, the wise men, the philosophers, the princes, the biographers of rulers, the reformist historians ask what use a revolution is. And what use should it be, if you please? None. But this is the ground for its irrenounceable necessity – to have one does not help to change the world but to show a certain world that it is possible to have one.

➤➤

Two in the morning: have been with an old soldier who arrived half an hour ago at the Albergo Bon Repos . . . Ten dirhams to give him what he wanted and he was in such a hurry that he came on the trousers I was taking off. They arrive from the desert, their palates are pickled (because they all, including the non-commissioned officers, want to kiss you and suck your tongue), they are finished, for months they have fucked neither a woman nor a dromedary nor a tourist, but first and foremost comes the negotiation. To lay a finger on me (because he didn't touch me that much – only what was strictly necessary to keep my balance) a type like this in Italy would have as a minimum to make me win the Strega Literary Prize and into the bargain do me the favour of mugging Maria Bellonci, the *grande dame* of Italian literature, or what is left of her.

. . . I write, I write, I write. A letter as well. I am fed up with writing. But what sort of a fucking holiday is this? Fortunately the reasons for things we don't understand are the least interesting. I am not at all curious to know what the universe or writing came from – they seem synonymous to me. They will have done their best like everything else.

➤➤

Up at an ungodly hour. I fell asleep at 3 in the morning after a very laborious masturbation which visited all the stations (they are in a bad state by now) of my sexual history. I am writing in the shed of the ticket office and am waiting for the bus for Gulimin where I should finally find the desert, so I strip and change landscape as well.

Giulio Andreotti is the bad conscience of every Italian – that is why he cannot be extirpated: he is all they have.

⚬

I got to Gulimin by a hair's-breadth, seeing that on a bend the bus skidded into the guard-rail to avoid a collision with a TIR, which happened to be there and not, for example, on tens of other curves with ravines a hundred metres below.

In the Albergo Hollywood full of unemployed mercenaries and soldiers in transit I give 10 dirhams to a hairy plump youth for hashish; he insists on getting 30. I think now he will disappear. Instead here he is back burning the little piece of shredded tobacco and rolling it in the paper. A man of his word, you have to admit. I didn't mind but he didn't have even the flicker of a thought of letting me have a draw. One of the usual people who reappear only to disappear all the better with the excuse that they are there. In his own way he knows good manners: to smile at you so as to in fact ignore you through and through. I am more and more amazed by their code of behaviour.

Have washed my pants, socks and T-shirt – the only ones I have and I wash them daily. This is a frontier zone – the soldiers ask me if I would be kind enough to send them pornographic magazines and little figurines of Maradonna. Why not – a single number of the *Osservatore Romano* ought to be enough for a whole battalion of lusting men. Without too many efforts of the imagination.

Here it is raining. The Sahara is cold. All the guests in the hotel have a cough. Lots of venereal disease here – outside the town there are brothels accessible only to soldiers – they notice syphilis only in the tertiary stage when the glans is perforated. Blessed pastoral youth. The whores very dear; the soldiers stress that here the women do it as a job (as if elsewhere it was because of something stronger than themselves). I make up little packets with ointments against thrush, against gleet (antibiotics in any case no longer work with me and so I sort out the five little boxes with a big syringe for everyone on my floor), skin funguses, cockroaches, anti-sunburn cream, compresses for diarrhoea, a syrup against coughs and catarrh, an anti-wrinkle cream which I recommend as a female aftershave if they want to give it to their fiancées . . . Once my portable first-aid kit has been pocketed, when they meet me on the stairs they can barely manage to greet me – and obviously here there is no chance of even talking about treating them for premature ejaculation for when they will queue up in the brothels, sacrificing me.

Today a splendid specimen of a beggar came creeping up when I was eating mackerel and tomato somewhere and I saw a hunk of open bread thrust under my nose and I put my meal into it. He went off and walked about the terrace gnawing hungrily at the dressed bread. Fine, I took a big piece of bread and filled it to overflowing with mutton steak and carrots and went and brought it to him, almost pursuing him. He seized it without changing expression and turned his back to me. Hereabouts they would chase him away from any place where he went to sit. When I left I had three cups of sugar with me and wanted to give them to him. He looked at me as if I were transparent with the neutral disdain of a hornet, already flying off with its dragonfly victim, for a solitary worm. If I come across him again this evening I'll make him pay dearly for it: I shall make him sit at table, eat till he bursts and then I'll go off without saying goodbye. I want to see. A poor person like this I like – he asks for something but keeps his distance; if you then take the liberty of giving him something without his asking for it he does not accept the compromise of gratitude, whether it be true or false. He knows that it is he who is doing you a favour.

The heart . . .

By now this journey is a pretext for staying where I was. A state of immobility as expensive as it is necessary.

The sense of space in Africa: where do they sell cigarettes? I ask after going all round the square and the side-streets. There, says a little black boy, raising his arm and pointing towards the square opposite up the hill. I make my way towards that distant tobacconist. There they sell not tobacco but wools and skeins for embroidery. What colour do I want? No really – I wanted cigarettes – with filter – I thought . . . But no, M'ssié, where are you off to, you'll see we'll agree on a price, how many skeins do you want? I . . .

I leave with five hanks – perhaps my niece some time . . . The little black boy catches up with me: Not here – *there*, he says pointing to the place where we met before. I get it wrong again – no cigarettes there – I don't even like these honey sweets and they stick to me everywhere . . . the little black boy comes back, frees me from the paper bag and raises his arm to the zenith. In theory I should go back to the market. I begin to swear, he says to me calmly 'M'ssié, why cross?' and I beg his pardon but what about the cigarettes? He accompanies me himself *there* – to the only stall not more than eight metres away. We both shook our heads, commiserating with each other.

Like my mother who was born and lived as a peasant – doesn't she talk to me from the other side of the table as if she were calling to someone from the other end of a field? It is confirmation that what gives her an edge is the theory of the internal absolute. It is better that way for a writer. With a single space available to all, the characters would end up going about with the same pompadour as Signorina Scontrino (who asks me when am I coming back? What would I say to a foetal infusion by her?), they would feel themselves fine and at home with the biggest systems, they would alter the pattern of the little pearls on their handbags and would feel themselves immensely original and unique. Exactly what governs the editorial choices of the Eighties, so complacently demagogic and concerned with content (the pursuit of the bestseller, of easy transmission, of communication). I'm not saying with this that the publishing industry must opt for post-modern poetry from Catania, where – since they daren't write occasional verse about something called *Cosa Nostra* – they go in for experimental writing on the Universe and God and everyone is happy, and no third party, even if he wanted to, could spy on the intriguers and guarantees of the Mafia's *nouvelle vague*; but a minimum of risk between the literary stupidity of the relative and the literary stupidity of the absolute (between the bestseller and the Cabala) is something the publishing industry ought to run. Cultures too are rotated and there are fields which from time to time are reclaimed. If the problem of the publishing industry is to make money – a legitimate one – it is all the more obliged, along with all kinds of industry, to restore dignity to *the word* if it wants to continue to exploit its products. A publisher cannot, in the long run, be less far-sighted than the latest idiot.

⁓

I should have liked to follow the Italian soldiers to Libya as a sexy camp-follower, a big shot shoe-shine. In 1940 I'd have had another mental fascist badge on the Youth Front – I'd have painted my lips and I'd have imitated the *femmes fatales*, everything would have been more Etruscan, more neo-realist, more on the lines of *your cow of a mother*. When I came back the people who go about at night – in packs – to beat up homosexuals would have courted me, then on the doorstep my mother would have calmed the coronaries and I, to be precise, would be part of the jury of the Mondellocampiellocommissozeffirelli prize or at least would be in *The Caprices of Pauline* by that same publisher. Instead we are in the Eighties and I am what I am and not a member of the jury or feature writer for Fiatolivettitaltel, I am a man of sorrows, I am strung along with a series of revered publicist scribblers and maybe it is they who feel that I am an intruder. And I have to come to Africa to let them draw a sigh of relief.

⁓

Homosexual fascism: the gay identifies himself with the stronger so as to get more on top of him and get fucked. The reactionary banality of a gay man lies in the skill of his acrobatics in order to comply.

⁓

Progress goes ahead on its own and man remains always at the same point of inhumanity, of superstition, of racism, of sexophobia. Maybe progress serves simply to anticipate itself.

⁓

As in any country with a large number of unemployed, unemployment does not exist here; only ancient traditions which permit the very real work of idleness. In such a hot country, if they did anything they would not have the energy to reproduce themselves, which is the only task which universal tradition guarantees to flourishing human unemployment.

The Arabs and the Venetians – I might also say the Sicilians – are rich in valuable qualities which cannot be bargained away for nothing but can be so for something.

And I have no desire to get out of Gulimin and expose myself to the curiosity of the inhabitants. I have not seen a single European in the streets and the places I have gone over carefully in the last few days. I have been to the *hammam* – it looked like a sports centre, lit up as bright as day. There is a lack of public opportunities here and I am worn out by personal approaches. And then there is no such thing as one Moroccan – the moment he has stopped beside you there is already a swarm. This shows that a gay man is divisible by the inhabitants of the various house numbers: Street of the Camel-driver No. 8 (corrugated iron), No. 10 (crumbling bricks), Street of the Single Palm No. 12 (brushwood) . . . Here a piece of shit if it is white brings all the flies. And all the flies, all black, laugh at you. But even Mitterrand could go along the street and arouse the same hilarity as me. A European who comes here to Gulimin as a tourist *is* ridiculous. I understand them. A person stays here because he is prevented from going to suffer elsewhere – anyone who comes of his own accord is a fine specimen and can only be a ridiculous European. So let them laugh – I don't expect it happens to them more than once a quarter.

Now I am saying to myself that I am here because tomorrow there is the souk for the men from the desert. As if I set store by their blue turbans. I want to see them – the Moroccans – achieve industrial emancipation and keep their sex-appeal like the Germans or the Dutch. Very nice to play the *sauvages* Adonises now when they have nothing but their prick and don't even take the trouble to learn to use it, because in any case the tourists are easy fucks. Without the challenge of technology there is no sexual technique either. Do you want to compare a Ruhr worker when he decides to let you have the lot? All Arabs get everything wrong sexually because they lack the sexiest deterrent of industrial modernity – the fear of looking bad in the eyes of the contracting party.

The Arab takes for granted that an erection is sufficient to satisfy himself and therefore anyone he covers.

. . . This book is really of no interest if you love breeding rabbits and examining the problems of the heart.

***

The same ragged beggar as at midday. Chased off by the dishwashers from the terrace, he comes back at once and takes his share of my supper which I give him to make the dishwashers angry more than anything else. This time he didn't bring the bread. One thing I suspected is that here beggars cannot be chased away more than once every quarter of an hour for humanitarian reasons. Since the long-bearded youth is like a wild animal on the loose, and there would be no way to cage him by an invitation to table, I fill a nice roll with grapes, tomatoes, meat, cucumber and cheese, and, rejoicing, pay quickly so that he won't escape me. If I am a good lycanthrope it is because literature comes first and foremost.

He was behind a pillar of the colonnade and smoking a cigarette-butt with the manners of a great dignitary, tranquil and arrogant like any client. Fearing he had not noticed me – for he had turned his head away the moment I appeared holding the roll – I came round in front of him offering him his supper. He refused it scornfully as if to say how did I dare? and made a face. It seemed to me to be sacrilege to throw that roll into the rubbish and with it in my hand, dripping oil, I went out into the street. From the other end of the piazza someone was dragging himself along the ground with one leg – and not even rich enough to have a crutch. Genuine black misery. Instinctively I made for the figure that was scraping along, hoping he would save me from my embarrassment, that he would give me a hand by holding one out. He was a human pole snapped off at the knees, covered with rags and dust, young – he took the bread as if it were exactly what he had expected, as if he had seen the whole of the preceding scene from afar and had run to beat a thousand phantasms like himself to the goal. I am sorry that tomorrow at midday I shall be back in Agadir, the beggars here are so curious and so cheap.

. . . I shall die full of unfulfilled desires. And yet I have done my best – above all to have them.

~~

I am exhausted by this writing. I keep myself under observation without distracting myself for a moment. Some people will not believe it but the things I live are more frequent than those I describe as being lived. Every so often, to no one's benefit, I take part in the game over the lines of demarcation art/life, which don't make sense and aren't lines. The intolerance of every *unicus* like me for the populist vulgarity on the lines of 'What does a writer's life consist of?' It is like the life of someone who makes electrical equipment: full of burnt-out bulbs. It gives light for a little then one has to change the bulb. If it weren't for these scorched beards interrupting the electrons, the person who produces the light wouldn't even have the wherewithal to buy himself a candle. The life of a person who writes – apart perhaps from the favourite relationship he establishes with the dark (I have filled notebooks writing in the dark of hotel-workers' rooms where I went for the season) if he is a great writer – is made up of the things in the life of someone who does not write and, often, of someone who does not read.

~~

I have never met a smelly Moroccan – I would make long train journeys with them with the windows shut. But in this place, Gulimin, they have all come from the brothels outside the city and there is no point in letting them into one's own – it would tempt me to go as well and fuck a purple Arab whore but only for the joy of my liberated women readers.

To have myself buggered by a cunt-fresh prick has always made me feel a little sick. It would be like holding one's head a little to one side, assailed by metaphysical anxieties.

Veiled protests to myself as someone who is prepared for anything and who instead is prepared to stare at a wall and to bite the blanket until they finish the job.

Meantime, while they are having a good time, a few titles for novels: 'Chickens for sale, 1 km'; 'Too mischievous to say No'.

. . . to climb back up the slope there would need to be at this point a Prince Charming on a white horse . . . The white horse is at the other end of the blue men's souk, tied to a ring in the wall. The prince was missing. The horse was motionless, not on principle but because a rope tied its front hoofs together and another the hind ones.

'Italia?'

I turn round – a toothless, laughing old man on the back of a camel is looking at me, completely undoing his blue scarf round his mouth.

'Yes.'

'Me too. From Napuli.'

'What?'

'Yes, yes, me still have Mamma a hundred years old in Napuli.'

'Noooo!'

'Yes, you interested in horses?'

'But how did you get here?'

'Left to go to the war here – had wife and children in Napuli but Arab women more beautiful. But mussels *alla marinara*!'

'And have you settled here for good?'

'Have done well, married, got ten children. Was fifty-two when I come here.'

'And now?'

'Eighty-seven.'

A 'blue man' from Naples, I think.

'I went back to Napuli ten years ago – my wife dead but my Mamma still alive. For Christmas, for Christmas! Italian children and my children in Morocco now going to and fro – I don't know one from the other – and the grandchildren and the grandchildren's children. Ah, what a confusion! Goodbye, M'ssie! Damn women! *Jammé jammé*!'

The Prince Charming is half-an-hour late by now and I am tired of looking at baskets of citrus fruit and carrots as if they were rarities in the Orangerie. Perhaps he is giving his white horse fodder, shoeing it better so that we shall gallop into eternity, holding back the blue Mamma who asks him before he mounts: 'Did you put on your blue T-shirt?' Meanwhile I wander about among the sellers of trinkets and camel-bags with camels painted on them (to put the fodder for the desert crossings in).

And here is my handsome blue Prince Charming with his legs apart, 1 metre 90 high, dressed all in white and blue, extremely clean and fresh clothes. He signals to me to come to his house and sits with his legs crossed on a blue carpet where he has set out various pieces of cheap jewellery. Mohammed (but I shall have to start to give an almost cardinal number to this name) is a dealer in bracelets and silver- and copperware, and apart from his socks, which he doesn't wear, considers himself to be a perfect example of the blue style after a course in marketing. He has a beautiful tapering face with black eyes and petrol-blue eyes framed by a sky-blue turban and he says to me Oh Italian! buy bracelet, buy amber! Since I want to feel the thrill of being loved for my own sake, which would be Sci-Fi for me, first of all, since I am short of cash and my traveller's cheques are in Agadir, I tell him I can't buy anything. So he suggested that I stay a day longer, he makes a date in the Hollywood Hotel, and now here I am expectantly waiting. I even save money for a beer for fear of not having enough to buy him some knick-knack. He had sex with me with a look, madly in love with me, with my sincere reluctance to spend money. Ah the watery eyes of vendors of African trinkets laden with Fellini-style promises!

While I am waiting – but it goes without saying that the person awaited always thinks he is the first to appear – there arrives at the next table a permanent guest in the hotel, a splendid young man who laughs heartily with his companions and then gets up, makes his way up the stairs; on the landing turns towards me before disappearing. A lightning pursuit. I enter his little room, which is a metre by two and a half metres, undress him with a desire that astonishes me, he is so beautiful and well-made that I am afraid of fainting, he says it is the first time, he doesn't get excited because he keeps on laughing, he laughs and laughs and laughs, he is a dentist's assistant, he tells me his story while I take off his jellaba, his socks and underpants, as I turn him round and lick his arse and all his thighs, oh, he earns almost nothing but in the meantime he gets experience, and he talks, and talks, and then I take courage – I get up to his face with my stomach and I stop his mouth. He sucks and sucks again and laughs and laughs again. Then I tell him Get like this – does it hurt? I ask, but not at all, and I fuck him till he bleeds so that I could almost die on top of him – didn't I have a pair of trousers, a sweater, 10 dirhams? and still laughing about his limp prick, about how it hurts, and have I any idea when I'll finish and do I have presents for him?

Sometimes I wish God existed – it would be handy to be able to thank someone.

Interrogated about women, I reply to the question: 'I only talk about women under interrogation.'

In Arab countries the homosexual is not a substitute for the absent woman. Here the Arabs themselves see so little of women that they are not in a position to make the sexual superimposition or subtraction of considering someone else their palliative. But the Arabs see a lot of goats – a homosexual is the she-goat which, seen from behind with its head down, most resembles a woman (no one knows what a woman really resembles). But the homosexual mustn't be too hairy. Homosexuals with hairy backs, for example, make them laugh a lot because they remind them too much of men, and besides they are never even hairy enough to be a she-goat at least.

Story of an attempt at emancipation by a young Moroccan with the help of a French designer: two years ago, finally, the youth gets the longed-for passport and, bag on back, sets out for Tangier to cross over. In Paris he is awaited by his old friend in the fashion business whom the youth had phoned twice – on leaving Agadir and on arriving in Tangier. The young man, a modest employee in a haulage firm, full of confidence, although he has more than enough money, simply to save on a bed, goes to the beach and sleeps against a boat and on his bag.

Naturally in the morning he finds neither documents nor bag. The coastguards arrive.

The Moroccan, like all Moroccans, full of confidence and temerity towards the defenceless tourist but abject and servile towards anyone who is taller by a millimetre and is Moroccan, allows himself to be seized by panic and explains his misadventure in an excited and unlikely way (here it only needs a policeman to look in their eyes for an instant for humble citizens to feel completely guilty). He is put in the cooler, stripped, beaten, and no one pays any more attention to him for some three weeks. Moroccans are patient and the youth doesn't do much of his own accord so that he at least takes up his own case since, being without an identity card, he is convinced that he has no longer any identity at all; he eats his rations, sleeps and unlearns how to smoke because he doesn't have a single dirham. At the end of the fourth week, for the first time, he tells a visiting inspector of prisons that he really ought to go back to work and that the holidays are over and he really couldn't go on staying there. They clear up the misunderstanding, they send him back to Agadir and here he is sacked for turning up at work two days late. He is unemployed for a year, plunging his family into despair, and after a year is taken on again by his old firm because in the meantime it has come out in black and white that he didn't invent the story of the theft and that he has an identity etc.

Now the business of getting a new passport is in good hands and, if everything goes through normally with the documents, in June two years from now he will go to Paris where there are all these museums and Moroccans can get lost on the streets more easily than here. But this time he won't be so stupid as to go and sleep on the beach. He knows a lodging house in Tangier where one really spends little. In the casbah.

⌒

The most exciting thing in a man is his nervous system – if only he had one.

Oh, the good sex of the bourgeois pig! Proletarian sex on the other hand is too strongly linked to atavistic symbologies mediated by petty-bourgeois sex, which never allows one to do what one feels like doing thoroughly. An example: a good-looking unemployed man who goes out in his best clothes (a sort of respectable uniform made from European remnants) presents himself as someone in the sixth year of a course in literature and philosophy (what a lot of years they have in that faculty!) and when things are at a pitch (which is the peak when you can't wait to find an excuse) says: 'Watch out not to dirty my stomach, turn round but take care of my shoes.' And he was secretly a postman.

I make love keeping a little apart from myself, like a big goat ruminating on the impossibility of his part in the fun. Sexual proletarians see in the homosexual a little animal that has lost something, a collar; the sexual bourgeoisie, a little animal that isn't looking for one. The latter are sentimental pigs who permit themselves everything, because the sense of anything has escaped them, unlike the former, who do not allow you anything because if they have the sensitivity, they do not have what it takes, and vice versa, and so neither do you.

Popular mythomaniacs think you are a homosexual because you like men inordinately; not one of them has had the fleeting suspicion that you are one because they take up little space.

⸰⸰

'*Non, je ne regrette rien*,' says a famous song by Piaf. It strikes me as a great piece of humbug of universal bad faith. I am full of regrets. I am unable to interpret them but I know that they are packed into every statement of wisdom, of cynicism, of social satire, of intellectual weariness, of political boredom. But I do not regret the years (thirty or more, by now) spent denying things; they have been the most lively, the fertilizer of today's *I*. Today I affirm one thing however – I am more positively assertive, but my *Yes* is nothing compared to the vitality of my *No*. I wonder what these people feel who began to affirm the consensus from their first whimpers and have cultivated and precipitately espoused those aspects of society from which they can derive a speedy advantage, thanks to their *Yeses*, or in which there was something so clearly designated that they could subscribe to it without risk to themselves. They feel well, these people, what else could they assert? And no regrets/ None (or only of a very personal nature), they say in a peremptory manner, the little whited sepulchres, only that they said *No* too often . . .

⸰⸰

At moments of great danger for my physical safety, I am tempted to retrace my steps, but I dislike the idea of taking to my heels – and suppose no one were pursuing me?

It is a continuous process of elaborating images of sentences.

Wherever I am, I feel the aperture in myself which imperiously pumps out material for a new sentence to be refined. I do not think that the *senses* have anything to do with it, for they are not particularly acute or rendered so. Every sentence has meanings imposed on it; it feels and sees and touches and demands of me the synthetic finish of an expressive rendering which can only be *that* and no other, not an active participation . . . Sometimes I am sorry not to go about with a notebook and pencil, as at this moment with this other terrifying story that weighs upon me in this darkness – I do not know where nor with whom – and for the second time believe that the world will have to put up with my penultimate intentions. He climbed over a wall once we had arrived in that unknown village by taxi without headlights, a whole series of stumbles, a man with a little beard who babbles on and I feel it is all too late and find myself in a dark cave and then I don't know what will happen and now someone is knocking at the door, which is off its hinges. Shall I be accused of breaking and entering with accomplices?

(I could take as my nickname Lucky-to-get-away-with-it.)

➤➤

From this evening I am no longer here even if I must stay another two days because of the plane. I have changed hotels at last and have gone to a *résidence* where I would be able to take as many men as I want to my room, something strictly forbidden where I was up to now and where I had problems because of the *brother* of the blue merchant, almost two metres tall, who came with me loaded with painted saddle-bags, whom I could pay only once I was in Agadir because I had used up all my money in Gulimin and the two of them insisted until I gave in. I was sorry about this long trip and after giving him the money I invited him to at least take a shower; the porter came up and made a row and the frightened boy went off without either washing himself or eating. And so here I am. There is a swimming-pool and the water is dirty enough for no one but me to start swimming in it; which means that I have also the surrounding garden at my disposal (at six in the morning I do ballets in the water along with two frogs and a hen which comes to peck at the surface; the ballet is the one where all ten girls open up like a lotus flower and then take hands and dance in a round). I shall buy briar ashtrays, three ceramic plates which should drive the stewardesses out of their minds, a tortoise carved from thuja wood, three mats. I shall arrive home. I shall hang everything up and lay everything out, I shall do up my suitcase again.

I remain there for an eternity, relax, contemplating the pure material of my thoughts, each of which is interchangeable with other myriads of equal purity, which is a feeling of mine about happiness which is perhaps not to be taken literally nor to be undervalued.

Love is a descent into the lower regions of the supermarket of terrifying chimeras. It continues to be publicized from neighbour (female) to neighbour (male) because the bogus gift offers, the malicious goods at a discount, and the ridiculous postcards *No stamp required* of the 'Send in and Win' competition are in no way compensated for by the great waste of time in getting to the bank. The secret of outward success in love lies all in the queue.

There is no harm in having illusions and prejudices. Things go wrong when one forces oneself not to take them at their face value.

➤

Seven o'clock: the muezzin's tape recording sticks twice – the shutters remain half-raised and then finally the sacred tape starts up again and calls together merchants and dealers. The great bazaar of human activities is open.

I have come to the conclusion that here there are no unemployed as there are at home; there are only employed as there are at home. The others simply do not exist. The country more racist than France towards Moroccans is Morocco. As with homosexuals – I had to be born to become conscious of the political and social problems and all they need do is escape the notice of those directly interested and, when I can no longer cope, of myself.

This morning I intervened between a policeman in civilian clothes and a spy in uniform and two wretches in search of a quarter of an hour's employment whom I had stopped. I was searching in my purse to give them a little money without strings. I defended them with drawn sword. I wanted to follow them, come what might, because they were taking them off to the gendarmerie. I expressed in lively terms my disgust at this bullying behaviour, the two lackeys deferentially advised me not to interfere in 'their country's affairs'.

If one could at least delude oneself that one is aggravating a certain situation that would in itself be a not insignificant political hope. But here it is not possible to aggravate anything – there is no margin. Which is why I did not insist on the pleasure of defending them; they were already completely done for without me.

21.42: cockcrow. Time to wake up and go to steal soil, I imagine . . .

To agree to explain homosexuality to heterosexuals is like explaining the Gospels to children addicted to television: all that sticks in their heads is an ox, an ass and Mickey Mouse in the midst of it all.

One of the few cynical joys snatched from this country, which is such a happy place for slightly depraved Scottish ladies in retirement, is to display my elegant and sinuous indifference to those unfortunate people who have only the cowardice of the conquered not their vengeful inspiration. I know I am much desired by black eyes which put a price in dirhams on shirt, trousers, arse. Duration of a further stay between here and the airport – another thirty-three hours.

Helsinki – who knows how long underpants take to dry there? A whole hotel full of writers from all over the world busy washing underpants and socks after the daily outpourings is what we would have were I in charge of the apocalypse.

The Elizabethan Englishwomen have magnesia-white tongues; the Swiss female Tells continue to scratch themselves where they have hair; a patent case of Wilhelmine paraplegia would not give in although he had to be helped by his friends to open his thighs so that a greatly intimidated black could fuck him by numbers in a cove in the rocks (the German has AIDS, I learned later), the flying Dutchwomen have teeth as long as two hot-air balloons, and the Danubian Austrian ladies veins of varicose blue, and nothing is ever good enough for Italian superwomen. And a displaced gay man?

Young Moroccans are gymnasts, cunning and pugnacious. On the beach allotted to them they do pirouettes, manage to open a tin of sardines with their teeth, turn any inadequate material into the utensil they need. They are skilled at getting by, which is the indispensable antechamber to any great culture. In their extravagant constructions – bricks without mortar, sheet-metal from cars, cardboard, broom-handles serving as beams, tin-cans (Gropius seen through the lens of the poor) – the antechamber is in fact the most important chamber. Everything happens there. The other chamber is the neighbour's antechamber.

In all ways and for all purposes the homosexual should be as true as a bell – instead he is a bell with a clapper that belongs to others.

Writing has come to dominate the organization of my daily life (never of my thoughts) because it distracts me from the mechanistic fine dust raised every moment – day and night and dreamwork – by the social conditions of my sense organs. My writing must be arbitrary and unnostalgic like the fucks I did not manage to have which, so Don Juan teaches us, are (if you think about it) the best and most concrete.

I write, in short, to give sense to the life of others.

~

Today for the first time for three weeks I bought a newspaper. How many badly written crimes earn the dishonour of journalism. And the Mafia, always the Sicilian Mafia. The American Mafia spilt blood and set up IBM; the Sicilian Mafia spilt twice as much blood and – in a manner of speaking – built the airport at Punta Raisi. The Sicilian Mafia must be put down.

I have changed two hotels in two days. In the smart third one, the flight having been delayed for another couple of days, I think suspiciously about what intrinsic pattern my tastes have obeyed: from the hut in the High Atlas to this elegant mart of flesh for old Europeans and young professionals who arrive, hand in their identity cards, are assigned to the various floors, go into the rooms, come out again, come downstairs, go up into the room next door. Is this the *classic* route for a tourist like me?

(This is a no-travel and no-sex book and I am writing as I see fit – and moreover a book, even if a no-travel and no-sex one, which has some self-respect, is always of no interest to more than 99 per cent of humanity – clearly you are not included in this.)

There are pretty boys everywhere in the hotel and in the restaurant they are scattered here and there like obliging statues, which do not move unless invited to do so. Breathe and they breathe. Laugh and they laugh. Love yourself and they love you. The social system behind all this is so complex that I feel more cut off than in an ordinary museum.

I no longer run after the same phantasms but other ones. I want to plumb the depths of everything that has already been said, to found a new dazzling banality. I don't want to wear myself out with epigrammatical lollipops that people read like the things in Chinese fortune cookies. When wisdom does not become reactionary it becomes gluttonous.

Of all the terraces and balconies I am the only one exposed in the night. Of the four windows I can see all have drawn blinds. Everyone is doing something with someone. I am the only one who does not manage to come to terms with the Mafia of sex and I stay there alone. I who am ten years younger than the youngest clients, healthy, passionate, potent, something to be squandered. Once I explained to someone how I had never managed to take advantage sexually of anyone *in difficulties*, and that an invincible kind of respect had always prevented me from enjoying the *amusements* of prostitution, job by job, in order to concentrate on the real, genuine exploitation of a man *without* going through sex. In the sense that I have played the kept man more than once – and then had to flee just in time not to be completely cannibalized.

Since I indulged in too many explanations with this person, because I was afraid of not being sufficiently sincere, either with him or with myself (my high-class guilt complex at not being able to prostitute myself or to *corrupt* someone who prostitutes himself except by giving him money and then making myself scarce), the person in question cut me short and said:

'You don't have to make such a song and dance – it is natural, if you were different you wouldn't even have the personality you have.'

It was Celestino Lometto and I am grateful to him for this one compliment he paid me in all those years of going round Europe selling pantyhose. But I would have had another personality and no one would have noticed the difference, beginning with myself; certainly I would not in my own eyes be that *integral* writer I am because I *have integrity*.

Journeys, like sex, like writing, cannot be related, cannot be described, cannot be theorized, cannot be filmed to derive from them *images* that can be passed on: one makes them. If the journey is *true* there is nothing to be said, it is woven into the text and leaps out with the same low profile as everything else that has stayed at home. I like those people who take a month or so abroad and on their return change their style of life and import India, America, Brazil. It is because they had none before leaving. A style is not changed, it becomes imperceptibly integrated. Thinking minds do not know any road to Damascus, ethological, mystical or political, they know they have incorporated every blinding flash a hand's breadth in front of their noses, including the truths (great and small) that underlie them from São Paolo to Caracas. A *coup de foudre* is all right if it remains a *coup de reins*.

〜

My supermasterpiece has already been written and sent off; they are my letters of which I do not have a copy, because to me writers' epistles have never been of any importance. However, that apart, the thought of the duplicate of a letter, the so-called *flimsy*, blocks my thoughts. Thomas Mann, on the other hand, numbered them all – the horror of diaries which are already public before being private.

〜

If I had not discovered that by writing one can also earn enough to live and to dedicate oneself to almost nothing else so as to earn one's daily bread, I would not publish anything from now on, if only to avoid the typographical reproduction of my novels. The day that I become rich because of one work I become posthumous with all the others. In either case, I am the sole customer for my works. But in the second case I could finally, in peace and quiet, write *for myself* that novel about adultery in the provinces which I am so interested in and which would be called *Blackmail*

Has No Price and have a happy ending – I would make them all die a nice, happy death in their baths with razor-slashed wrists, the telephone to hand, but as I write I would first disconnect it and the characters would never know. The characters would be: the husband, an accountant in a firm dealing in spare parts, the wife working in her mother-in-law's boutique and the traveller in fur-coats who seduces both ladies contemporaneously in separate rooms without either of them knowing. They would all be strangely real, living, adulterated.

The three-in-one things which devastate an existence or nation are linked in part to the way the wind is blowing and two parts to rhetoric.

I fucked a third Moroccan, one who isn't from here, from the north, a marvellous footballer who played on the beach surrounded by male and female admirers. In bed, once his brand-new yellow jersey had been taken off, at everything I did to him – did for a change – he protested feebly *'Ce n'est pas mon habitude'*. He did not know the Le Chic boarding house. I was tempted to believe him. After all there must be a first time for them too. He was frightened, embarrassed because I paid more attention to the back than to the front, that solid and well-rounded bottom above the muscular and strong thighs enchanted me, as did the line of hair on his back right down to between his cheeks. I had to chat him up for two hours before convincing him and each time he opened his mouth it was as if the voice of protest came from his arse-hole. I gave him a pair of jeans with a broken zip – I have nothing left – and at the door he asked *'Monsieur, vous êtes sûr que c'est comme ça qu'on fait?'* Sûr, sûr, I repeated. Jeans are the equivalent of the necklaces of other times, but he deserved a diadem. At 7 I have an appointment with a sports-instructor from the technical college whom I met at the post office. But what was I doing at the post office? Whom had I written to? Sometimes I really think I have invented all the addresses on the postcards I send off. I look for a name I would meet when I get back and do not find a single one.

❧

Will I too end up joining those footballers who repeat year after year 'Football is my life'? and the singers who say 'Singing is my life'? Writing is not my life – I could perfectly well have done without it – and since it has descended on me there is no reason why I shouldn't shrug it off. I hate the thought that writing is *one and the same thing* as *me*. The quality of my writing is the result of a polymorphic compulsion; it is not specifically a choice or – that thing madmen have – a *vocation*.

Thanks to writing, which has been sent to the front but is too perspicacious to be avant-garde without also watching its rear, the society which sets me the task of *predicting* can calmly stay the way it always was and protect both its front and rear. The poet is the person who is sent off somewhere (so long as it is not *here*) – he knows for how much life he must provide a rearguard, leaving his own back unprotected, and he also knows that it is not particularly inspiring to find oneself caught between two fires when one refuses to be the prophet of both: the extremist imperatives of poetry and the tricks of the society involved, which disguise the writer as a fine Nobody so as to send him forward, and then those imperatives and tricks asking him contemptuously: What makes you do it? It doesn't work with me.

◆

The present age is certainly the age of Gorbachev as before it was the age of Mao, Kennedy, Castro, de Gaulle. It is him they are now making say the most important things for us all. Who would ever have thought that I would be undercut by the Politburo and cast in a secondary international role?

I notice that I am becoming hairily grizzled like a monkey in an old folk's home. I would find it anthropologically correct that the regressive cycle should fix on me and stop with me, the maximum expression of the evolutionary cycle of the species human animal. Or would Gorbachev have something to say about this too?

◆

This morning in the post office I telephoned Adele. I heard her little voice which muttered little cries of shy amazement. She told me I wasn't there any more and that the bowls arrive tomorrow. Which is a good sign – she still remembers me, has questions to put on the table. My sudden absence, if it has gagged my family, has opened up some holes in the rhythm of her day – halfway through the morning I take her to the tobacconist to get a sweet.

How on earth shall I explain it to her? I shall tell her a lie which will begin with: 'Once upon a time there wasn't . . .'

True griefs are classical: the death of a dear one, a financial catastrophe, the end of a love, a child victim of a *stupid accident* or someone you see dying along with yourself from hunger and can do nothing about it (the grief lies in being unprepared for the disaster of those others who are ourselves). Grief has no gradations, because the words of pain are clear and prolix like the silence of the tomb, which it brings into being. It is round like the earth without slippery corners for you to catch at, it is a form of Arcadian perfection in which from the animal there leaps out man himself, vital and rhetorical, like a mother robbed of her son, and the same at any latitude, in any language, any ritual of grief. Of true griefs there are no more than three or four in the whole world, and they are its genetic guarantee, a perpetuation of the original matrix of man which does not undergo mutations for its own survival (up to now no one can prove the contrary). Without the straitjacket of commonsense, grief does not exist as a feeling truly experienced, and someone outside of you must be highly dangerous for the joy he causes you to change its sign into grief. But I am all here, in here.

Mine are not properly speaking griefs because they are not catalogued – they will become so if the diabolical god of the Encyclopedia of Received Ideas snatches them from the limbo of neuroses on the instalment plan without citizen rights.

How I could be prey to a *grief* which might descend even on me seems fantastic to me. Only the death of Adele could cause me this neutral kind of true grief, great, irreparable, *painful*, and it would be positive for me and my parched sensibility. Grief recalls us to life, it gives you energy to carry out the usual trivialities, it spurs you on to be content to make the same errors again so long as it assures you of a little full, intense, illogical happiness . . . But that would be fatal to Adele . . . She is the only human being truly dear, truly *me* outside of myself, and how cruel the hypothesis is that I could return to life at the price of hers.

(But for pen and paper I would not be able to formulate these atrocious sentences even in thought, and it would be better thus for everyone; but if in life I can be as stubborn and reticent as anyone else, when I write no – because the word has the last word; not my fears and bogus exorcisms. And the word does not allow half-measures, halts, retreats.)

However it is not said that I must love her for ever, indeed it is good that I should detach myself as soon as possible to avert bad luck, for her safety. If she survives and emerges from the magnetism of my weakness for her, I shall put up with my *nonexistent* neuroses, which are magmatic, impetuous, and uncatalogued, packed with nuances which do not add up to a text.

Given where I am now what would I do with *grief*? There is no turning back not even head down.

～

Farewell. On the beach the ladybirds arrive in swarms from their meal on the eucalyptuses (also called 'fever trees'). These delicious omnivorous creatures being in their thousands are called 'mosquitoes' by the natives who, by the way, call '*putes*' those few women who are slightly obliging. And they too are convinced, like all linguistic gurus, that they are calling things by their right name. The inevitability of referring to oneself things which are no one's business – like insects and women.

Farewell. In the garden at 2 in the morning a little Norwegian gay shows off to the patrol passing on the other side of the gate. The little fairy, who has just arrived, skips about in his little miniskirt-dressing-gown, shakes his ash-blond ringlets, draws in his breath to hide his Viking paunch. At the end of his number he promises 50 dirhams to everyone who comes into the theatre to give him a hand in the interval.

One cannot judge a whole little tribe on the basis of the four or five million tarts who stand around it. *Ciaociao*.

～

Why, in the vague jurisdiction over the origin and end of being, is to be a writer often compared to God? Certainly not because he *creates* – everyone does that, God no less than any sheet-metal worker. The writer – unlike any other trivial being devoted to the *humanity* of the Quadrivium – is *divine* because he is the One who has no feelings of guilt. Which increases the feeling of guilt of the others – all to the advantage of the writer who, being incapable of considering himself the Prime Mover, is content to describe them himself, standing in for God – who, not giving a damn about the sense of guilt specific to each man, not only doesn't laugh at it but doesn't even smile at it. For anybody to become a writer (an author-ity) he must first get rid of any falsity towards himself, he must challenge his own sense of guilt (one at least is guaranteed to all without distinction) and contrive to brandish his own guilt in the rays of the sun until he blinds them so that there are no longer any personal barriers between him and the sun. The sun – or God – becomes his only possible mirror.

God is by his unnature stripped of all guilt – neither Good nor Ill exist for Him, what is allowed and what is forbidden, Creation exists, and the promise made to men not to let them know it. If God were not neutral how would men be able to savour their sense of guilt? And if a writer continues to savour his personal sense of guilt how will the guilts of his characters be able to emerge in all their fetid but uncontaminated purity? And with that I have arrived at the *point of view* which, according to Brodsky's saying that 'the autobiography of a writer consists in his ability to perform gymnastics with words', is the fundamental point of being a writer.

There are few men who have at their disposal a point of view in life which is not other than *their own*; the writer, on the other hand, possesses them all, all both historically and socially – Creation, *all that exists*. Indeed what suffering and wretched humanity, in its need of *conscious* feelings of guilt relative to its being carnally *imperfect* and socially *non-conforming*, calls God so that He will remit even its impatient little acts of sin, the writer calls *the point of all-seeing vision*. Thus not only will he have all the points of view but actually One more.

If God cannot be of use to men, because he would be shown the door straight away, then at least let Him be of use to some good novel on men written by his sub-God, the writer. The writer is God because he is someone and no one; if then he wants to be something more – a great writer – he must be a hundred thousand and God one of the host.

But at this point many aspiring sub-Gods will ask themselves how not to have feelings of guilt and consequently:

How is one born a writer?

You are born a writer as you are born a piano-tuner – the moment you have become one.

You board a whaler bound for the North Pole, stumbling and puffing as if you were late for a bus. The voyage begins. All you see is ice – a penguin, a polar bear, a seal in an album you have brought from home – the same ones as you would see in a zoo and nowhere else. Ice calls to ice – is that all there is to the polar voyage? Until one fine day you begin to interpret the veins in the floes and by interpreting them you engage with them. You can also decipher the ice in your bedroom slippers in front of the television set, but it is better if you catch hold of a shoot of a tree so as not to go and crash into an iceberg – like life; not indispensable but better than nothing.

Writing needs to dress up every so often in the bullet-proof vest of *reality* rather than in the dinner-jacket of realism. Sublime and geometrical things can be written while you are on the deck buffeted here and there by a cyclone and you are going all over the place. Watch out that the pages don't fly away. Rhetoric for rhetoric, the tempest of *reality* is no less strong than the breeze in an Hôtel des Bains.

One has vocations if one takes a lot of trouble
to invent them for oneself

I have already said how you are born a writer, now I shall set out the layette:

(1) The conception – not haphazard on the lines of 'one son brings another son' because my folks had plenty of men already and wanted a girl at all costs (to help the other males in the house, not because a female is beautiful). Fathers who go off again for a trench war and mothers who rejoin them on foot and borrowed bicycles and in a cottage, during a leave which gets down to business, gland to gland against plane-tree bark, while the mines of memory flare, still have a need to express a transcendental wish: 'Let's hope it's a girl.' Not even Madame

131

Rousseau with that fine example of a husband when he was there (rarely) could ever have formulated a 'let's hope it's a writer', and neither of my couple did either.

The white and black mélange of the crocheted layette says a lot about the sex which is unwelcome to the betrayed parents: writerly. The desperation, the feeling of having been tricked for the third time, will contribute to giving the taste for first and last causes which, since they do not exist outside of popular-religious iconography, are nevertheless at first the inky beauty spot and the storied feeding-bottle of the new-born babe. In fact, at a little distance and after much erudition, he will discover a third kind of cause – the lost ones. We are already almost on the brink of a goal.

(2) The infancy of the writer – without books of fairy-tales about the place, only a calendar from the priests hanging on the up-to-date stove with the gas-cylinder built in so you can't see it. Herbal cures, riddles, proverbs, habits and customs, the priests have an infinite supply with their way of making of every herb a detail worthy of description. They live on them, retail. A picaresque sense of time and space – feeling oneself different almost out of spite – they are all too alike. The first and definitive aesthetic-sexual stimuli are already clear (a writer knows everything immediately, there is nothing fundamental about himself at forty that he doesn't already know at four), he clings to a hawthorn bush until he has internally explored mimesis, he imitates the kneecap of a peasant woman on a bicycle, of a patch of white violets, of a piece of stem-stitch embroidery on a cushion.

The feeling of being everywhere without belonging to anything, because there are other things that press forward and ask to be re-identified by you: the emerging and setting of the sun, dressing up by moonlight until you fall into the ditches with it. To say *no*, to act as if other people's days were cellulose compressed between *n* and *o*. If you deny, you affirm; if you affirm, you affirm nothing. The other children don't feel like this, you soon notice; they are not writers. And you also think of two immediate things: what a pity that I shall never be like them – just think what a light and easy life; the second: what a pity for them that they will never be like me, what a burden of a life.

A thing like this can last for decades and, as if by magic, you find you have three manuscripts to one side.

In your late childhood, typical reading matter for childhood: Freud, Poe, Baudelaire (*Pauvre Belgique*) and *Peyton Place*. In other words, one childhood is very much like another, the writer's childhood is less important, that is to say it is what it is.

(3) Adolescence: in early adolescence it is important for the stripling writer to collect around himself all the pre-texts for making himself noticed, to create scandal and consider all the other boys and girls sexual objects to teach, in vain, how to kiss a hand and so on. He launches the dramatization of *himself*.

He will never stand in the middle of anything, he will not have a sense of measure and will not even aspire to do as well as others what he does badly so perfectly that it constitutes a sure safeguard against football, the boy scouts, the catechism, the classical secondary school, the first motor-scooter, the first girl, the first boy, the first cigarette. In this sense it is better for him to have everything behind him and to opt right away for being numbered among the octogenarians. The stripling writer must be *different*, feel himself unjustly excluded from the human company of trips with the priests, accumulate a store of mortal insults, and, perhaps a touch of jealousy and envy, maybe. The important thing is for anger to grow, and grow all the more when it is chiefly allowed to explode and be scattered in all directions – to formulate hate so as to avoid the calamity of repressed and unexpressed ill-feeling. The writer will be full of weals, he will be made to pass from one assailant to another, he will come back, his bleeding head held high, he will contrive to triumph in the hardness of his unacceptable defencelessness, and he will leave home before he is fourteen. Otherwise if he is confronting his *difference* rationally, constructing it at the little table in the Municipal Library, he might as well resign himself to being the same as others; so he should ask his godparents or parents to be enrolled in a school of creative writing and to be held at his christening by some Italo-Calvinist.

I am of the opinion that a little sexual discomfort does no harm (to understand the flesh of others so as not to understand anything about your own any more), but it is not an indispensable condition for being born a writer.

First wanderings, always further and further from a phantasmal nucleus – the writer learns his syntax by detaching himself from it. He detaches himself from his own sensibility, which is the fertilizer of writing and certainly not the fruit; in order to describe the chimera one must have consumed it in any amount of ink, one has to make it exist as long as necessary – not all that long time that is never enough. As a youth, the writer lives in a state of suspension between being and not being *himself* – and of searching for a safety net, because in either case the imagination has to turn somersaults. His poetic life suffers from the frustrations of being made di-versely and without any real status, social or academic. Let no one intervene to help him. One cannot do anything for a writer but everything against him.

Fall hopelessly in love with love enough to not repeat the experiment; prefer to one's own great and absolute passions, which extinguish the independence of writing, other people's medium-calibre ones which *amuse* you enough to write about them. Oh adolescent writer! Don't stay shut up for months in a hutch for fear that anyone you meet in the street is happier than you, and meditate on this other concept of *happiness*: if you are writing already what need have you of happiness? If you are writing already what need is there to live?

Learn to let those live who have nothing else to do.

Rendered incapable of writing organically (a house, an income, 'a room of one's own') but already dialectically on the right road to alienating oneself from the *bon ton* of the false writers, several of whom are *maudits* – for whom it would be possible to live and write, whereas the two things, being mutually exclusive, are one and so let us forget it – the novice writer lives fiercely, gives as good as he gets, changes jobs, bosses, cities, countries, centres of infection – he will have an iron constitution combined with laments worthy of Leopardi over pimples mistaken for gangrenous lumps. The writer reads a great deal and in the only fitting way – untidily – so that he will not be forced to be the product of higher education and show it even when he is expelling the smoke of a *gitane*. There is much more gipsy in him than that; he knows right away that he will be the greatest author of his century. If he does not know this or turns his back on this moral obligation to the supreme illusion, after some failed efforts at a *novel* he will become a publisher's editor and will be reduced to being a snob – and what groans every time you hand him *the* manuscript which he too could have written If.

(4) or (5) Maturity (optimum age for Anon – eighteen, nineteen? but what if at three I already knew that I preferred the little prick to the little slit!); the writer will begin to understand that what he wrote in all these years makes sense only to himself (poetry!) and so he will get shot of it, he will see the yawning gap between propaedeutics in language and writing. He understands that his own brain is not enough for writing; he must work with everyone's brains. The moment (decades!) has really come to do something which will have meaning in its own right. The effort to achieve a style is perforce painful; without a morality one does not even learn to turn in one's flat feet. He will therefore have to make one for himself. By feigning a morality he will become thoroughly ethical, because morality is an analytic effort by narcissistic thought to formulate an evangelical language – not a question of a spurious, vague, approximate morality, however exemplary in its good intentions. On these foundations, which cost blood (if blood had a price and were not free when shed), the style can be grafted from one sentence to another; the style of writing is all the less solid the more shaky the writer's moral architecture. If the writer does not have at his disposal an interesting *ego* to act immediately as *narrator* (and therefore has done nothing in life to make himself *anything other than himself and every self*) he would do better to give up the attempt to narrate his own life immediately. If it is still his, it responds to a single neuroplexus without a mirror and is of no interest to anyone except himself; a reader wants one to speak about his own life, and in this subliminal sense I accept the notion of customers in literature: that anyone else is preferable – if one really must write about and of someone – to the writer who writes for himself. The question, obviously has never occurred to me. It is better for the writer to train on a love story between a shoe-box and a spare shoe-lace, otherwise he will run the risk of becoming a minor nineteenth-century Russian or eighteenth-century French author like almost everyone in the West.

(6) Some years *later*.

Since the writer writes and does not publish (if in addition you are handsome and finicky like me it is still more difficult) and wishes at all (his own) costs to enter by the front door of the publishing house, so as not to leave behind his back skeletons of gratitude in the nepotistic, political sexual cupboards of high society (it really looks like that and I too would have stories to tell – from the big firm to the hand-press run on family-incestuous lines, everyone who deals with the volume touches him up and he puts up with it, he puts up with it), he has learned in his time a couple of foreign languages and now offers himself – almost gratis – to translate works of a certain literary and publishing prestige; Goethe, Heimito von Doderer, Christina Stead, John Ashbery, Flaubert, Lewis Carroll, etc.). Six more years, let us say, of apprenticeship go past and here he is all cocky (and shattered) with his first work and the testimonials – always necessary but with this difference – that he has done them for himself.

By now there are so many publishers who are forced to expect the first work of this antipathetic, assuming, stubborn champion, who is also, it has to be said, an excellent translator (punctual and really extremely meek – be meek whenever there is something around that has to be learned) that, perforce or from love (always perforce), they have to endure the mortification of knowing who he is, this 'writer' and will still have to take up a position *against* his first work, perhaps precisely by publishing it. The typescript, that is to say and as a result, is read right away like a tooth you take out with a tug. It is published – to the fury of all those involved in the business who had lazily rejected it, turning up their noses. The first work is a success – all the better if not only *d'estime*. If it does not have one, that is not in itself a bad thing, but it is better if it is a success; future generations are already sufficiently overburdened with failure-now-certain-glory-later and one must give them a helping hand *at once*, material outstanding which has been waiting for centuries to be dealt with, truckloads of stagnating glory.

While the first novel is being printed, the writer will have the good sense to frighten everyone with his prolific seriousness, organic strength and determination; he will present *en passant* his second work – of 700 pages – without saying he is already writing the third. It is not true that publishers are upset when confronted by production which is intense and of quality; they are upset that you can do it and the others from their stables can't and it is impossible to redo one's thirtieth anniversary catalogue just like that. The literary figures will be upset however, but they don't matter; you must understand that if they don't say a word to you it is because in their sleepless nights they have used them all up, cursing you out loud to their partner (who is often a male Libyan who makes Japanese haikus for them).

The publisher who bets on you has to win. Perhaps you won't but he will – at all costs.* The real publisher – the one of great entrepreneurial quality – if he is perfect – disappears in the end. For a Sainted Nonentity he does everything and even more. On his side the urgings to moderation and to an editorial strategy ('One must space out the works . . . By the way when are you going to hand in the next novel?') are routine, but woe betide you if you take him literally; from you he now expects self-abuse. This is why he leaves you *free*, because no one knows better than the writer how to destroy himself with his own fingers; he is the autistic cannibal creature who eats himself and chews his own cud and expels a work. In fact the writer bites into his own flesh and from his own flesh produces works and knowledge. He does it not because he is a butcher who has taken over the shop or because he is incapable of any more banal comments on his own inclination to write; he does it because he likes to eat himself. To tear oneself to pieces is the only way to fill the void between words and things; to suffer the incurable insult that 'Milton's *Paradise Lost* does not exist but Milton's *Paradise Lost* exists once it costs five guineas.'

(7) Friendships: avoid so-called influential friendships. True, influential friendships are inscrutable in their influence; so they may as well be disregarded. Frequent those friends you like and even the enemies you like – not those who are useful to you because it is not said, in any case, that those you don't like are those who really count or, if they count, are those prepared to pardon you for your effort to suffocate the nausea they inspire in you and to ingratiate yourself with them. Follow your instincts

*N.B. note on p. 141.

(make sure you keep one of them awake), do not keep company with anyone involved in the business, no writer, no intellectual, or not as such. You only need to have once helped a writer to cross the street to understand that even the shyest writer ardently desires friends at twenty-four, contents himself with an accountant at thirty, and from forty on has recourse to a lawyer.

And so too with sex: apart from the ecclesiastical career or little blue films, I would advise you not to begin on any career that crosses a bed, far less a literary career – unless you are really ugly and repulsive; in that case accept with a light heart, not for your career but because you find yourself confronted by an *amateur* and it is a golden occasion to make something of yourself.

(8) Dispatch of manuscript to publisher (don't send manuscripts to writers – if they are real ones they have no time for the ambitions (*sic*) of others, above all if well concealed; they have to think of their own; each time you make direct contact with a writer ask yourself what you can do for him – if nothing, as is likely, avoid making contact).

(A) (remember that a B must follow) Send a letter to the dictatorial publisher and inform him of your intention of submitting a literary work to his judgement. Usually a circular letter from his representative invites you not to send the manuscript (which will be a typescript) because the publisher's lists are full for the following three years and the author would do better to turn to another publishing house with less tight timetables, however . . . the aspiring author must seize on this chink and exhale the manuscript and not scruple to ask the approximate time for a positive or negative answer whichever. He must invent for himself a contractual power, right from the first failures; he must not give the illusion that he is letting himself fall like a dead weight into the arms of Orpheus plc.

The letter accompanying the typescript must be laconic and formally polite, not a sample of writing, even if in its own way it is. A basic letter is the most appreciated, most read in depth, thanks to its lack of information and of one's own opinions and the (supposed) opinions of others – the more supposed the more they are backed up by photocopies of personal letters. A letter like a police summons – if only for a moment – makes the imagination of a person, who for decades has been used to getting packets accompanied by as many other packets called 'accompanying letters', take wing. The ideal letter of introduction – if one has overcome the barrier of the 'however' – should be like this:

Dear Sir,

Thank you for giving me your attention and it is with pleasure that I am sending you my novel . . .* I shall be grateful for an answer by the approximate dates mentioned in your letter of xyz. I can assure you that I shall not be hurt by a negative outcome nor even by your failure to return the typescript, which is something you must not feel bound to do. When the dates you have indicated are past I shall consider myself free to submit the same work to another publisher.

Make sure that in the meantime the 'Dear Sir' has not become a 'Dear Madam'. And it goes without saying that meanwhile you will have sent the same work to as many publishers as your imagination (and the funds for photocopying) dictate. Anyone in the business will tell you that this something one does not do for the same reason as, in a little town, a boutique wants exclusive rights to the shorts with the little red fish on the fly: competition. Forget about them! This clause is valid everywhere *after* the same boutique has placed the order and stocked the article and has committed itself to terms of payment and never before. *First* the firm's salesman goes round all the boutiques, leaves the sample and then gives the shorts with the little red fish to:

a) whoever places the order first,

b) whoever orders most,

c) whoever enjoys the most credit.

I do not see why a publisher should demand favourable treatment contrary to all the laws of the market.

The ideal mentality of the ideal publisher is that of the dealer in hunting and fishing tackle who sells worms for bait – both *love* their products and their business, but that alone is not enough to make them change their mentality.

So I would suggest to authors not to allow themselves to be moved by people without scruples who sell bait for readers holidaying by the sea. One need only be there when the annual

---

*What a title!

accounts of any publisher are presented to realize that literature, as Nabokov says, is a lie.

But to come back to your letter presenting the typescript and yourself, I would not even put the date of birth or the profession of the aspiring author (who usually has a *profession* but cannot resist the anxiety to create for himself a writer's pedigree; he feels himself bound to believe that there is a difference between the misfortune of having a social status rather than having none), nor would I specify whether it is a case of a first work, a second or a copied work. Here too the cliché about true love holds good: anyone who loves you has all the deep-down excitement to seek you out and take you as you are while lamenting the fact. Leave an address – a recorded delivery note to be sure that the typescript reached its destination, that it has survived the most inaccessible reefs of the term *Printed Matter* – those of the Post Office and the porter.

The rest, where you are concerned, from now on is either very easy or impossible. To go on knocking at doors, which by definition are not already wide open, is compromising.

Do not commit the shameless mistake of linking your non-existence as a writer, who has simply wormed his way in, to the unique existence granted you as a telephone user – one does not ring up the editor-in-chief beforehand and rarely *afterwards*. Learn to wait – it is not said that what went badly over ten months may not succeed after eighteen years of exemplary lying in wait. Faced by a negative letter from the publishers reply with a courteous one, because in any case the secretary who typed it and who will read it has nothing to do with the case. On the contrary; learn to be grateful for this unfavourable reply – an opinion costs money and a negative opinion costs still more, and you have not yet repaid the paper and the stamp you cost to say *No* to you. The publisher who says *No* is more generous than the one who says *Yes*, because the *Yes* is capital invested and the *No* capital lost. Publishing is not a charity. A publisher is only to be praised if he publishes commercial rubbish, do not condemn him for refusing sublime masterpieces. If no institution of the State has yet thought of sending him to the gallows for his crass greed, don't give yourself judicial airs, unless you have caused him to earn enough to allow you to send him to the devil. But console yourself and don't despair: something always gets through the editorial filter – even oftener. Me, for example.

Don't lose hope, rejected author – but seeing that you will never have the chance of being Aldo Busi because I have beaten you to it you must at least be Lado Subí and then you may offer anything you can. Be that as it may, as the Marquise de Merteuil (PR executive) advises, with the publisher confine yourself to parading those virtues which you simply cannot contrive to do without.

P.S. The elegance which strikes a publisher favourably will cost you a pretty penny in the accounts department if every time you decide not to insist on the return of the typescript. If you cannot make use of my luxurious pieces of advice about *use and throw away*, which always makes an impression – by not creating false responsibilities or deadlines for someone who has asked for nothing from you, you will awaken his good humour and therefore an identity for yourself which is already less anonymous – contrive to be, precisely, already at home in the publishing houses, having learned some foreign languages and translated for six years; in the end they will actually have to recognize that they have seen you somewhere and you can scrounge all the photocopies you like. Furthermore, without being anyone's grandson, since you are there already, go into the secretary's office and ask for Mr So-and-so: you were passing and if possible you would like to have your rejected typescript back.

Faced with Mr So-and-so who is trying not to yawn as he tells you by word of mouth this time that the pearl which he has been sent and which they have refused to take on 'unfortunately doesn't fit anywhere on our list', don't let him feel all your hatred nor the exasperated arrogance of the failure; look him straight in the eyes, explain to him that you have nothing extra-textual to explain to him. He will feel himself knocked out and – in an instant! – he will begin to be afraid he has let slip a masterpiece (of sales) which thousands of publishers, from the very next instant, are about to have taken on by their guys . . .

Anyone can allow himself to lose – even the publisher – not the writer.* Therefore it is not possible for alliances to be established

*The exact opposite of what is stated on p. 137.

141

in which the writer does not occupy by natural right the highest point in the hierarchical ladder, because the writer is there by convention born of the conventional necessity to exalt his own work at the expense of any other factors (editor, publisher, critic, bookseller, reader etc.) and I do not see how it can be possible for an author to be the champion/agent of himself (of his works) if he begins – badly – by allowing himself to be ousted from a position of conventional supremacy by giving in to the inevitable trivialities of human beings, who in any case have really no interest in exposing themselves more than so much and who would sit *up there* and do nothing. Writer, help them to stay in their place and to avoid their dangerous ingenuity as trapeze artists who have no real turns to put on. Where possible also with delicacy and discretion. However, if you are not made of good theatrical stuff (the author should prepare himself by attending in his late adolescence a 'workshop' where he will learn to simulate gaffes or to project a certain *stupidity* of facial expression so as to leave the others with some illusion of a kind of superiority), don't ever force yourself to conceal your personality if it is the only one you have: tell them crudely to fuck off. It is positive to be disliked by someone, you would be so in any case and moreover you wouldn't be liked by anyone.

Remember, dear writer, every time you humiliate yourself in your guise as writer, cutting the Achilles tendon of the man you are, if you suffer passively it is your work that will feel it and that must not happen. So create for yourself little free zones or no-man's-lands where no one knows what you do with your human nature and suffer them there – a man's routine humiliations – without ever bringing the writer into it – not to mention his works. Don't go and get involved with *commitment* and *opinions* which are always the commitment and opinions of the Prince and are a presumptuous way of imposing your needs. If you want to make a university career or, precisely, one in publishing, you are excused: but then you will have the good sense not to write – that is to say you won't have it and there is no point in your going on following my advice.

(9) Literary salons and literary parties: Don't go to salons or to literary parties. I was at one once – it was early days – and literature didn't come into it: the building trade, ministerial

portfolios, sugar and cement, quotations on other people's money, yes. A few literary figures arrived too – 'shy' ones according to the favourite definition used by the creeps of feature writers – and the German wife of an ex-publisher electrocuted in circumstances which are only too unclear – they spouted and spouted all of them and talked about bestsellers (books naturally). All that was lacking were the bonfires and, sad to say, the clients.

As for the literary prizes, go to them only to receive them and only be against those they don't give you – seeing that they always give them to someone worse than you, deprive them also of the satisfaction, too, of being at least worse than you. This is usually why they are awarded the prize – for no other reason.

(10) Editing.

The one support which a writer must find for himself, displaying all his perfectionism, is someone who knows his language thoroughly and carries out an active first reading of the text before it is sent to the publisher (or the printer's). It is no easy task to find someone who has a feeling for the plastic materiality of a page of a novel from the lexeme (alliterations/assonances) to the sentence, not to mention a feeling for the organic nature of the work. One needs years and years of practical, brutal work as a labourer on language to know *what it is*. Personally I have not yet found anyone who satisfies me as being capable of at least correcting the typing errors – not to mention the grammatical ones (anacoluthons, often semi-intentional) which every writer makes (in my case the difficulty too of coming to terms even with the *given* facts of language – the desire to force the prepositions and all the transitivity/intransitivity of the verbs) and which usually betray an unease of a psychological nature at what he was writing.* Very few proof-readers are able to distinguish the musical difference between two syllables with the same vowel and it only requires a strong regional spirit to type what your ear dictates. I, for example (who else?), working with foreign terms or turns of phrase which I wish to alter or to distort so as to give

*I have in fact found one, he is a little wizard!

them Italian citizenship, very often deliberately and mistakenly distort them and there is no proof-reader clever enough to recognize that the error lies in correcting the error. But apart from these typical and arbitrary linguistic idiosyncrasies of the writer, which are of little importance, so far as the language and the laws of the novel go (in my case those of the *point of view* not only of the narrating or narrated 'I' but the 'I' of the language which is a kind of signifier to the power of two), it is easier to dig out someone very well qualified in a little hamlet than in a university faculty or in the heart of a publisher's. The great experts are: an old bigoted schoolmistress who lives alone with her cats, a parish priest with a weakness for nettle soup, people who write romantic novels on commission. Why? Because they are without shame and have a strong attitude to the business of language – that is to say, a capacity for synthesis in the shortest possible time. Capable of any linguistic hallucination, they are equally capable of critical vigilance and immediate reaction to false notes – they underline in red. Which puts the author in the position of being able to intervene or to accumulate awareness of the permissible topos of obscurity (stylistic or syntactical) to the point of leaving it as it is.

Distrust academics who do not consult dictionaries with the excuse that they put them together themselves – when two years have gone by they know no more about the language and less than ever about spoken language if they have taken as their literary models their own vocabularies. Besides you cannot expect someone who talks all the time and never listens to *have an ear* – to evaluate the phonology of the verbal expression. Moreover a university professor reads himself in everything and is incapable of following a text that is not his own. Academics have made a career by dint of quibbling over the little tasks to which they have, in theory, been called: to teach, which is only a grubby way of getting a chair and holding on to it until you transform it into a throne. You cannot ask of them that they should be able to make distinctions between a grave and an acute accent.

Do we want to say what literature is? According to Tzvetan Todorov, right at the beginning of an essay (which means you don't even have to read it to the end), 'Literature is . . . an opposition to utilitarian language, which finds its own justifi-

cation outside itself; it is, by contrast, a self-sufficient discourse.'
I entirely agree, even if I would have some objection to that 'by
contrast', which seems to me damaging to the self-sufficiency of
literature and limits its utilitarian indifference. It is like when you
talk with a hundred shades of meaning about your personal lack
of interest in religion and an institutionalized God and they tell
you briskly, 'Ah, I understand, you're an atheist', underlining
not your absolute autonomy but your dependence in a negative
sense, in terms of opposition, on the only entity that exists even
if it does not exist (for you).

I don't want to linger over this point – like anyone who has
discovered an elementary law of physics I should also like to
appeal to the objective prerogative of every exact science: 'in
short, one understands it'.

So from now on you are a writer.

Don't think that the omnipotent magic power of writing
transfers itself from the sheet of paper and transhumes into your
life once you have finished writing that page of that novel. There
is no transference from work to author, there is no mobility of
possible liquids, because the unity of both in a single being
ceases with the conclusion of the work and has never even
existed as soon as the work is published. *Grandeur* does not exist
in a living writer. The grandeur is given by the *hero* who conquers
or loses because he is one with his sword, in fact he is a hero if he
dies, not if he continues to live. Writers live – indeed they do –
and most of them live long because the average age of a writer
has not fallen, even with the introduction of radioactivity, into
the lot of ordinary mortals.

A writer can, however, also be polite and well-mannered –
complacent never. He is the object of flattery in his own person to
the degree that he is learning something of the madness of others
and will make an effort not to send his public (the public that
concerns him) home disappointed, but he will know when it is
the moment to kick someone out and without bothering too
much. Pay no attention to anyone who *loves you* because you are
a writer and not a house-painter. Sentimental idiots identify the
work with the person who has written it so as to be able to make a
better claim to know something about the writer – not about the
work. All this is superficial and makes us envious that we are not

house-painters because they undoubtedly have better luck. It is not possible to flatter a writer, even for fleeting gain, unless it is to make him feel bad.

I have had the experience of finding myself facing someone in a public garden by moonlight; we were handling each other but he was looking at me in a strange way and it was as if he was afraid to come to the point – manipulations by hand only tire me and I probably wasn't in the mood but had it out. I realized that I had been recognized and said to him 'You know who I am, don't you?' 'Yes,' he replied. 'You are Aldo Busi.' I sighed (the minimal odyssey of disgust) and said, 'Right, let's pretend not to know', but it was impossible for him and I was about to button myself up again and he says to me, 'I'd like to make love to you', imagining who knows what difference in the alchemy between making love to Aldo Busi and having sex with me. I fell in with his linguistic rejection and said, 'Let's settle for sex.' 'But I love you – you can't imagine what I am feeling at this moment.'

He was making an identification. Which, if it increases the potency of the reader, reduces the writer to impotence.

Probably I never had a more sincere declaration of love than that (I had it in my hand) but the fact is that I went away. A.B. may very well write harrowingly of his need for love, or of the hysteria of love denied, but then he is a practical being and goes about exactly like me to be tossed off and that's that. The boy had lost all sense of proportion and distance between me and *me* and *me*, which are – yes – single, double and triune – but at my whim and not at the whim of the receiver. So not only did he not toss me off but he lost the chance to love me, perhaps exactly as he understood it.

To fuck someone enchanted by your work or, usually, your photogenic looks in the rock reviews, is a possibility that gives me goose-flesh – and certainly false writers do so, they profit from their false nature as writers (in fact they are merely public men and well-known like so many others) and from their innate predatory and summary falseness which has an *end* in view . . . neglecting any style.

A true writer, when he goes out, leaves the novels he has written at home because a joiner doesn't go about with the chairs and tables he has planed in his past. If he does so, if he uses his pages to give himself an *allure*, they are no longer literary works but toilet paper and his volumes latrine walls (maybe luxury ones, why not?) covered with graffiti for mostly highly improbable appointments and facilities.

Those really smart people who attract the attention of the writer as such are well-bred readers – the ones who would like to say something to him in public places but refrain. A smile or a gesture with the chin from the distance and in a Prussian manner have the power to move me for days and be sure, if we should chance to meet another time, it is I who will take the step of getting to know such an extraordinary person. But no one must take liberties with a writer which he would not take with any other person in the street. Only stupid public men are always public and live to be recognized as such. A writer goes around not to be observed but to observe. A writer, since he does nothing specific, works non-stop. And no one likes to be interrupted when they are working.

If I should meet myself on the train (oh, what a temptation!) I would not conduct an interrogation on the dozens of interrogations he permits and far less would I give him a little bow – I would leave the compartment at once if I felt I couldn't bear to be in contact with myself: not to be there is stoical. And then, who knows, at the whim of chance, a second train, a second fortuitous encounter . . .

Write and be as great as you can be or wish to be and, for the rest, go on doing what you always did. Writing is a reason for living only if life puts its trust in other reasons. It is not worth while constructing a personality as *writer* if one is a writer, who does not have the duty of representing himself outside his own works. No *look**, you are not a singer, an accountant or a soubrette. Writing is a luxury one pays for and not one that pays. If it pays – and usually it does (that depends on your personal demands, on the writer's milieu) but, if it does, watch out; it can become a profession and therefore get better. Others are making you take on that career which is contrary to the neutral condition of the writer, which is that of not *rising* but of not sinking, and not moving away from where he has always been. If you cannot

*In English in original. (Tr.)

do without *ambitions*, stop thinking in terms of *glory*, *eternity and greatness*.

If you become a traveller in cheese and mortadellas packaged in hard covers, learn to recognize this so as to avoid ridicule right away and, obviously, try to derive as many advantages as possible from it, give your name to a square or a literary critical column in a woman's magazine – but leave *literature* alone. Indeed it is very sad to write in order to *have success*, to sacrifice everything else and then not to have success. I said to forget about *literature* because there is no worse sacrifice than to continue to delude oneself that one is sacrificing something one has never had. Result: a guaranteed fiasco even with the sale of mortadellas. If you are fainthearted, you will produce the right book at the wrong moment; if you are good businessmen you will produce the right book at the right moment; if you are writers, you will produce the wrong books at the right moment; if you are geniuses, you will produce the wrong books at any moment.

Be suicidal – the rest comes of its own accord.

••

The writer is no more desirable than a shopping bag once it has been emptied. It is foolish to expect from writing those things which make life bearable in terms of its normal activities and render the awakening of ordinary men important: a love, a journey, a mirage of charm, thirst for justice, a vendetta that has struck home. None of the sublime tittle-tattle about the life of people like himself is possible for the writer who is recognized as such, and the very demands of life of those who are (so to speak) his like lose any sense for him if they encroach on his anonymity as a man. There is no safety nor abandon for him outside the mechanisms of the printed and composed word, which brutally exercises its power to keep him free and puffed up by the nominal expectations of his characters. The writer has a new (not recent) awareness of the fact that being an underdog prevents him from getting any compensation from the fact of being a superman in terms of self-destruction. Everything that cannot be brought back to writing fails – it is not consoling, but that is how it is. Moreover, woe betide the future serious reputation of the

148

writer who commits suicide – he will have had to do it at a given moment and people will not understand why he did not do it earlier, and seeing that he did not do it *now*, they will not pardon him for doing it at some other time *later*. It does not make sense for writing to exist *as well as* life, a real writer knows it and does not make a tragedy of it – least of all a personal one. He rebels against it with all his strength (goes to Morocco, for example, or to a conference on himself which has gone to Morocco, knowing that he is going to the same place) because he feels the servile pettiness of devoting himself to anything – including writing – but does not manage to escape from the same cage which changes shape to let him move about temporarily by moving the bars without his knowing it. In spite of this, the writer does not lose his sense of proportion (which comes in useful for his characters), and does not feel himself the slave of a particular *destiny*. *Destiny* and *unhappiness* are for him rhetorical figures no less than the desire to revolt and for happiness. It is not possible to leave one cage and prefer another, in the end it is only a change of names and a means of enlarging one's vocabulary. One does not turn back from a vocation – if you make a pact with God you cannot break it to make a pact with the Devil: this would be part of the pact with God and the Devil would know of it but would never tell you. All this is called *the real writer's literature*; take it or be left.

∾

A real writer does not take notes in the street or in the café because it would mean that he is stealing time from the *internal* writing which must never stop – and which is always concealed. No lover of a writer who is not aware of this permanent betrayal – of which the notes are merely mouthfuls of sulphur in a sea of oxygen – will ever succeed in having the upper hand over writing. Once it is there it does not admit rivals; it inks them out. Writing tolerates only accomplices, or better, extras – lovers, wives, husbands, even if I do not understand any of the three either looked at from one side or from the other side of the partners . . . A writer, according to me, not only has no need of a companion (male or female) but not even of a stagehand, a being at his service to see to him and his most elementary needs. A

149

writer should wash his own underpants or not wear them. I cannot imagine the life of a writer forced to gratify a person somehow because that person washes and irons a pair of underpants every day and presents them to him laid over his arm like the sacrifice of a whole day of doglike obedience, dedication in person expecting a sign of gratitude, as if to be allowed to wash them were not a sufficient honour. I cannot imagine the life of a writer in the company of a wife or a woman friend with whom he makes a couple. In fact they are always all particularly monstrous couples: a headless and tailless quadruped, with four paws which all go their own ways – all four of them, treading on each other. From a writer one must not expect anything on a personal level – he, if he is a real one, uses and throws away, and does not accumulate emotional, sexual, sentimental etc. debts.

A writer is loved only when he is adored as a stone idol whose image does not give the original measure of his humanity in the imagination of whoever takes on the task and responsibility of adoration by renouncing the right to love him and by giving up so many fine things in life *elsewhere* and with others.

To be a real writer is not a happy state. Everything runs out of your fingertips if you type; and neither the keys nor the paper nor the characters are consistent to the touch. Yet everything goes that way. The writer *is* his fingertips: a bridge, which by itself does not link anything, nor is it touched by the banks it links, nor lapped by the water which passes beneath it and carries it off. The writer crosses himself to allow his tribe to cross and if he had imagined it previously he would not have been there. But he is a writer only when and if he is a bridge and there is nothing else to be done or to be, and like every other human being he has a longing not to be a boat or a bicycle or a van – longing for the lost paradise that has never existed, a longing with clenched teeth which reduces the size of any bridge to a line, in fact to something like nothing and even to less.

~

I have lost the tooth which I had put in in Florence I don't remember how many years ago. The dentist had cleaned out the cavity of the nerve with the patience of a Carthusian monk, a whole business of inserting thinner and thinner needles and of fixing another appointment until he ended up using invisible needles. One could see that he was keen on it and I was pleased to fall in with him. To sit and wait for my turn in the waiting-room gave me the sense of a calling.

It fell out when I was sunning myself on a bench in the Giusti Gardens in Verona, I felt the tooth going down over my T-shirt because I am inquisitive and was bent over looking at my prick (it is still a funny little thing) and a fraction of the fall to earth of the man on the monument down in the plain.

I had been walking there on the walls for an hour, towards a dusk that was tardy beyond endurance, waiting for all the ladies with dogs, the old people with dogs, the children with dogs to remove the leashes so that I could take off with my wings in my right hand and my prick in my left, even if it neither stands up nor lies down because there is no reason for it to do so. Sometimes I try to get excited with the fine dust the cypresses or the moon by day leave behind the eyelids when I shut my eyes tight, but from a vegetal and cosmic point of view I have impossible masturbations. But at sunset at the beginning of summer in a relatively public place with the din of the traffic from the streets down there round the slopes, I like to try other, unknown kinds of desire. I have even tried to concentrate on a little bag of rubbish, a syringe in a white hawthorn bush, a pink condom with a knot in it. Besides, it is boiling hot, a heat different from that of the June haze in a steaming landscape. The heat of a desire, perhaps of a violence. The heat of an untamed hate of oneself.

When there are no longer either dogs or human beings I have my usual little shit beside the bench, which is the one highest up of all, because as a boy I used to go and do it in the fields and *nature's* reflex deals with any constipation. I come here too to pay homage to the earth burnt by the heat and the invisible poisons which destroy it minute by minute, to give it a little syphilitic hors-d'oeuvre in the shape of my modest, final manure. Here now I look into the dark, eye the silhouettes which move about on the central steps and cannot see me. Then I smoke.

A marvellous atmosphere – a post-nuclear one – nerves that have grown over the invisible asbestos suit that has become part of us. A new kind of human being – contaminated by the here and now. From here no one sees me, were it not for the burning ash of the cigarette, because my favourite bench, half-uprooted, has its back to the bank which rises up to the metal fence of the gardens. Beyond the fence there are the avenues to the railway station, the enormous parking place with the gypsy caravans, cars coming and going because of the transvestites. A gypsy woman comes out and hangs up the washing, she sings a plaintive song and at the end of the lament I hear a shattered laugh. Not even from down below could anyone see me because I am hidden by the trunk of the cypress and would have an eternity at my disposal to put everything and nothing back in my trousers or leave it where it is in the non-event of my mind and the mind of whoever might approach.

I never pull back. Have never had the habit of sparing spermatozoa to perpetuate a senseless erection. As when confronted by death, I am debtor for a single ejaculation at a time – then my prick goes back to lie down in its coffin. Once someone came up with a nice little old man, well preserved; they had not noticed me and this young man unsheathed a fantastic weapon which, erect, reached to his trouser belt, blue dungarees. It seemed a waste to regale a fussy pensioner with it because the young man was more or less my age, a metal-worker with the brilliantined parting typical of somewhat *démodé* gerontophiles looking for emotional satisfaction. Of the two it was the little old man who made least effort, kept on kissing his neck, frowning like a sceptic in evening dress, they disgusted me, the young man handled it halfway between them, leaning a little on one side so as not to dirty his ironed dungarees – the trouble some people take to calculate the direction of the spurt or those who close their hands like a trap when you are going to come – all this sense of afterwards in the present moment; with one eye they are here and with the other they are trying to avoid a dry-cleaner's comment or a remark by some domestic washerwoman. Well, I felt it my duty to do something, to give them a hand, to show them how it is done. I rushed up to them – they did not expect it – they gave a little start of fear and after a first moment of embarrassment I set to work too. I was very excited by the big prick of the thirty-year-old with that face that spoke of a wage a few points below the national average, the red fibrils in his chubby Venetian cheeks, the black amusement in his eyes of the young husband caught in the act. I took it in my mouth without by your leave, he came in the same instant along with me, since I had waited in vain for the little old man to let me feel the grip of his gleaming, slightly horsy dentures, but that was asking too much. He demonstrated in silence the insolence of a person who is used, as of right, to being served and that's all. To demand contractual power at his age! The young man brought out the haughtiness of all the nectar of this retired office-worker and they did not even shit on me – that's the truth. I immediately became a phantasm again which returned to its place among the brief shadows of the trees. It was a good job that he had come right away because if I have to go on and on sucking off I begin to giggle, I feel I have a dummy in my mouth and I am not a mummy's boy, I spoke and walked at nine months and ensnared little boys and girls when I was only two. Then my sister was born and my mother suckled me over again from four to six because of an innate sense of thrift and of the home-made.

At this time of day someone arrives whom I might describe as an acquaintance – a teacher from Macerata a little older than me, an academic prick, averagely impressive. I feel no physical attraction for him, perhaps because I prefer to teach him Italian as it is spoken today. I have in me a bit of the schoolmistress insistent on the red pen; when he takes it out I let fall a correction of his relative pronouns, which are too levantine – a didactic way of saying No which is a little pastoral but efficient. We also talk about politics and school, government programmes and scholastic sex, of the I'd-like-to-but-can't of so many students who, where the poetry of the nineteenth century is concerned, follow only the movement of the teacher's hand on his fly and his little scratching prologue. I do not remember having fucked him here – I really don't – the rare young ones have all this dream patinaed on their anus of interesting bed-dim-lights-a-record-a-little-whisky. The bark of a cypress would seem funereal to them and instead it is precisely their psychic chintz bedrooms which are cheerless funeral parlours. People are full of tics called good taste – get to know them first – and please be discreet. All so *different* half-and-half – ah! the pretence of making an omelette without breaking eggs!

There is another well-preserved old man here – I have excellent sight and manage to see in the dark almost as much as in broad daylight, I could count fifty moles in a face which thinks it has none: the important thing is to be conscious of this ineluctable *pretence* between the one who sees and the one who is seen – he has an astrakhan hat, a witty person who unsheathes an incredible weapon, knotty, worthy of a convict sentenced to forced labour, and he goes around like that offering it to the ladies with dogs, without shamelessness, indeed I would say with a discreet professorial preamble worthy of someone selling relics for a third party. All the ladies shake their heads as if to say 'No thank you, I am all right for today.' From the ladies he goes on to the boys with the same air of an attendant with a torch going from row to row in the theatre with the programmes asking 'Anyone want one?' when the show has already begun. As evening is falling he finds adolescent crises, crises of abstinence, matrimonial crises, and walks out of the gardens with someone towards a supper of crises and cress.

Here only the young and the old – few in between. For me who don't please the young gerontophiles because I am not old enough and don't permit myself affairs with the old ones because I am not young enough – here there is nothing to be done in the way of interchanges. Too decisive, too direct, too much of everything at one and the same time, a sexual quality inspired by frankness and immediacy. Which is extremely elegant and extremely rapid. It is with difficulty that I deign to follow someone whom I have not caught up with at the first step. There is nowhere to go. Towards 10 at night the waiter from the bar in the station buffet inevitably appears. He is from Salerno and imitates Celentano, the pop star, in his free time and takes it up his arse non-stop, from panting fatsos – even when they're sitting comfortably on the benches. He does it all. He sits on you, talks about the weather a little, about the strikes on the railway, about the delays for travellers, takes a serviette from his pocket, the one for the brioches in the buffet, cleans himself and runs off to start serving again. He leaves behind him a wake of bacon and coffee, the grubby fingerprints of thousands of tickets stuck on the spike like an automaton, all conditioned reflexes, having already moved on to a later hour when he will finish at 2 in the morning and will run here again. He is smiling, in a stationary way, the skin drawn over his temples and nose, huge eyes – like a skull. It is odd how I am moved by his frenzy which no mirror would be quick enough to reflect, all bench and buffet and smell without head or tail of great rivers of travellers.

How I like to sit here, how soft the texture of this darkness, the fragrance of a night with me.

Once the old men with abscesses disgusted me, I was for the rehabilitation of the third age only in the sense of as many prayers as they wanted and thermal treatment for all. Even to catch sight of them by mistake having sex horrified me, and then so insistent, babbling about everything and nothing, without history and with all the histories in the world, to come to *this*, the gouty corpulence of a fantasy behind each 'Have you got a light?' If there was an old man standing there watching us I could not even manage to get a hard on. But now I at least manage to ignore them and therefore *to include them*. If they don't give in among themselves, I even like them, all this pulling up and down of zips for the boring old country-dance that is over in a flash, the beautiful high-explosive shells of once upon a time . . . Complicity in the Italian rout at Caporetto in World War I.

If they reach out a hand I snort, hoping they will understand – it never happens. Sometimes I let them get on with it, inventing for myself a love for father figures which I don't have while I think up a good excuse. Nothing stops them, not even a finger of processed cheese on the knob – they are capable of pulling out a slice of toasted polenta from a hidden pot. And now this incisor of mine has fallen out too – it is better to exaggerate certain intolerances to the point where they become perfect acceptances, not even I am so young any more. Maybe tomorrow I shall get out of bed and find myself there, in big close-up, with a senile cataract or a madness a little deeper down, Kafkaesque, a loss of memory or the recovery of certain horrible badly buried memories or the mystic stench of a conversion.

I see a figure against a tree, a pine, from behind, a great mass of long hair, chestnut, I think – now I can also see the colours. An American beatnik? Blue jeans, a big hat with a wide brim, someone from NATO perhaps. I approach him, a lovely little bottom, slim hips, and instead it was a very young girl with a barbiturate complexion; she was watching without interest three or four fat old men with their trousers round their knees who were licking each other's bottoms and pricks like a number put on by an ex-servicemen's circus.

A touch of femininity would not come amiss in certain meeting-places – a woman where there shouldn't be one gives sense to the event just as when I go into porno cinemas and see there, alone, sad and rigid, a wan woman whose mind I shall never be able to break open. I knew one once – a Slav, dark-haired, a fine good-looking woman, who used to go and beat up the homosexuals in the English Garden in Munich, she would arrive on the stroke of midnight, very beautiful and terrible, leather trousers with the zip *behind*. She was an *anonymous* woman, a marvel with her brain the wrong way round, a rare being, proud as a god of war against her likes, without the timid prissiness of heterosexual women, oh I would willingly have made a comrade of her because she inspired in me a lacerating tenderness, bending over, clasping a tree . . .

When the girl made to move, shaking in the dark her long stringy hair, I saw that she had a little pinhead of a tummy, I said to her Don't be afraid, don't you feel well? She burst out laughing – the senile pyramid undid itself in an instant to fasten up its trousers – she said she wasn't well, she was six months pregnant and that the baby was kicking angrily too and yet she had to go back down to the street and turn at least two more tricks and if seeing I was there I were to help her with the little spoon and the ligature and was I an arse too and why did I whistle when I spoke, didn't I have front teeth either? For her too the teeth were a fine problem, they were almost all dead and a molar with the nerve exposed – ah! what a hellish pain – and now I should fuck off with the others because she wanted to have a little peace.

In the flat bit of the Giusti Gardens then there is this Monument to the Fallen, three statues in one, in a bad way slipping towards their single and joint fall to the ground. The first man in an erect position leaning slightly on the shoulders of the second who is half-bent over the last one, himself almost touching his own feet. He is naked with a cloth round his loins, his covered pudenda are supposed to move one to pity and safeguard the sacred nature of heroic death in civil iconography. I wanted him to pull out his prick because maybe one doesn't know what to do with it but has it even when dying in war, because the prick is also one's only fatherland and maybe one pulls it when pulling the trigger to fire the last shots. One carries it about with one like a very thick roll of parchment lined with rivers and mountains, cirrus clouds and caverns, men and women, and nothing will ever conceal the indecipherable nudity of its impossible flight out of oneself.

～～

Here in Finland the landscape from Helsinki to Lahti is hundreds of kilometres of Lombardy before the discovery of fire and the invention of the wheel. Birches and birches and birches without a human presence. Then the English and the Finns are still arguing over the prize for rain – and for madness, I think. We get out of the taxi – I and the other two guests of the Committee of the International Writers' Symposium – and I take possession of my room in the Scanhotel in Mukkola.

What a lot of writers and critics in the hall, I have never heard of one of them.

From my window I see a mini-golf course with boys handing each other the club. Hours later they are still there, maybe they are not the same ones but wherever the first ones are they won't have noticed that they are somewhere else. This is the pattern of feeling about a whole nation that will accompany me.

Here nature is perfectly organized – camping by the side of the lakes, property held in common and available to all (from the electric iron to the cup for the handicapped), cabins for undressing. I go into the woods round about hoping for who knows what Viking encounters – nothing, always and only woods within woods. There is nothing in the landscape that surprises except the age-long patience with which the $4\frac{1}{2}$ million inhabitants have resigned themselves to loving it.

And all this light which fades, soars, stretches out, thins and is always light. Water and vegetation everywhere and wind, rain, one excess of nature after another – today hail as well. I don't know what the centre of Helsinki is like but I have heard it said that at the weekend the city empties to go . . . to the country. And Helsinki is devastated with green exactly like here. And now as I walk about I look at the blinds of the houses scattered here and there and wonder: once the excitement of putting them up is over what remains for whoever lives in them to fill them with? When the inhabitants emerge from the interiors what is the difference between this Sunday exterior and a holiday exterior? Folk costumes? In other words are there such things as Eskimo passions? I find out – yes, for social climbing and for horses.

There are many scientific meetings every week to search for the cause of the national curse, alcoholism, but they never find a reason why people drink. In the evening the experts finish up under the table as a result of forgetting what they never knew – that the lack of reasons is the most mastodontic reason for taking to drink. But the memory of this ignorance would ruin the voluptuous pleasure of the alcohol and of the popular and congressional benders, to be alcoholized without a reason is certainly more exciting, a form of national mysticism under the banner of which people can recognize each other with sobs and confer on each other a tipsy collective identity. I have never met so many people with alcoholic breaths even in Friuli – where I don't think I have ever been. At 4 in the morning, that is to say in broad daylight, I grasp the artistic dogma: a writer who does not drink arouses suspicion, he is looked at askance, he doesn't do anything to connect with people. So many wavering figures who take each other home. Alcoholism equals a common clichéd transgression and therefore equals a guarantee of respectability. I stand apart at once. Here one has to ruin one's liver to get approval, it doesn't do to turn up sober anywhere, exactly like the hostesses in nightclubs. Or perhaps it is different here – the *real* artist is more of a somebody the more he is a nobody (but not in the good sense that I mean it), that is to say, deprived of any autonomous personality in his transaminases, because a writer who does not drink would not understand the national soul, which is profoundly melancholic, with neither object nor project, (Russia at the door) and this at minus 50 degrees. It must be all this nature that is depressing, this neither day nor night which impels everyone to the neck of the bottle – the Finns would never understand the novel of a non-drinker, it would be like signing a document of political espionage, of national betrayal. The Finns are very lyrical, just like the Russian poets of the regime – before versifying the little house in the woods ('Come, there's a road in the wood, I know its name, do you want to too?') and the inner life between a sauna and a fiord they have to knock back something. They're all like that. I try approaches here and there among the tables strewn with bottles of whisky and beer and port and wine – if I come across anyone again who claims to influence Freud (of whom there is a lot of interpretation going on: *Treib* drives and myth, Jewishness that doesn't do much wandering and academic chilblains, vodka and 'solitude') I won't speak to another person until the end of the reunion. At dawn, so to speak, even the Portuguese, the English, the Nigerians and the American deconstructionists, the Hungarians, the Romanians, the Turks, the Cubans, have become Finns. I feel that four days would be too much. I am heartbroken to see so many writers suddenly reduced to human beings arm in arm, sitting on benches and singing 'hollalahihi'. Topic of the Congress: The Crisis of Seriousness.

~~

Today an old lady professor was watching another old lady who would have been drunk since yesterday if she hadn't been drunk from the day before that. The old lady was crooning something and moving her head from side to side along with other Norwegian and Swedish intellectuals with bleary eyes who were trying to have a party.

'Oh how stupid,' said the old lady professor, scandalized by so many men around a woman exactly as if she had found herself in front of Salome, veiled, determined to get her cunt licked by the Baptist, who is doing miracles not to fall off the salver. To move one's head from side to side like this, lowing, must be considered here to be pendular anarchy in an artistic lady.

~~

1st Intervention (fragment) at the president's table:

Since we are already in a state of depression I hope the symposium will not be transformed into a shambles of incompetent neurologists but may remain in the ambit of semi-serious writers who like to lift their elbows. A serious novelist – because I do not want to consider the writer in general, *écrivain* or *scrittore* or *Schriftsteller* – is never in crisis like a man of letters in general. A novelist champions *life* – that is a text, a structure, a rhetorical figure, that is up to date and in itself timeless, as is *life*, while a man of letters busies himself with a context and supports a specific *establishment* because he has an entirely pragmatic *end*: a certain social power within the usual social class. The two economies could not be more different – the writer draws on *collective* money, the man of letters on private or, worse still, public money.

The novelist does not obey any pre-established power and lacks self-censorship as he indiscriminately censures every power which comes to limit the elementary rights of *life* – that is to say, any conventions concerning the social liveability of life under any flag or system. Every novelist who consents – even indirectly – to take on board a power declines into a man of letters.

If there is a moral duty above all others for the serious novelist, it is precisely not to be in a state of crisis, while the inevitable right of the ordinary man of letters, in so far as he aspires to being serious, is to be so permanently. I can understand that a critic, a historian, a journalist, a philosopher, a poet *laureate*, a scientist, a Prince's secretary, can be in a state of crisis – indeed the crisis gives them credibility (they all have long faces, they grow round them and the commonplace of *doubt* as if it were the mask of a profound dignity because it is painful), a novelist does not understand it at all. He has no need of it – if he *is* one he cannot be one in a state of crisis.

The novelist has a vision, the man of letters has the mugshot which is stuck on his brow so that he can be defined as such. The novelist forges the brand which the man of letters suffers at the hands of his masters.

The man of letters finds support in what Marx calls the *superstructure*, which in our days has been reduced to a plastic overall to be put in one's bag for sudden cloudbursts, while the novelist works and finds support exclusively in his own work and in the models he forges for himself and for whoever wants to adopt them because, as is well known, the *structure* in the capitalist countries does not exist, has never existed, no longer exists, will never exist any more, in short is ready for anything except existing – so much so that no one knows what it is or where it ended up, and therefore the novelist is forced to do as best he can in the interior of his *vision*, which is the only structure ideologically pertinent to his work.

Since in the last fifteen years of European belles-lettres men of letters have spoken only of themselves and of their intellectual philippics with their monthly payday assured, I shall dedicate the next fifteen minutes to speaking exclusively about the novelist (applause, even if the novelists here are one in ten) and about the nature of his seriousness and about the possible crisis that follows from it.

To be serious (for a novelist, I repeat) presupposes the inclusion in one's own seriousness of a certain amount of necessary crisis so as not to become enlightened idiots, or reactionary idiots, witty idiots or depressed idiots – 'soap-literature as opposed to nostalgia literature' – that is to say, with no one *opposing them* they are the same thing. A serious novelist cannot but have thought of it beforehand. A state of seriousness in crisis is a tautology if we are referring to a novelist, who ought to be the enforced interpreter of his present, if possible not affected by erudition and fascinated very little by his navel, which is in the middle of his belly, as you are, wrongly, thinking of me, seeing that I always turn up in a T-shirt because of the simple fact that I can permit myself to do so physically. But I prefer to be a moralist, and not to be fat, to being alcoholized and by now so unhappy as not to be able to do without jacket and tie. Physical ugliness is the corollary to the snobbery of the overseer of criticism.

Intervention interrupted by cries and whispers.

〰

I don't mind stating something then sceptically turning it upside down and into its opposite – this forces some fifty participants to quickly correct their prolusions before coming to the micro-phone. However before dinner, having just got out of bed, they are still almost all sober and they do it very well. I felt sorry for a Nigerian writer who was complaining because in certain African countries writers who actively oppose the regime are imprisoned

– just imagine! I jump up, seize the microphone and say I'd very much like to see the opposite – if someone uses the pen as a sub-machine-gun it is clear that he is making war and not just literature, which is a sort of war in the home, and therefore expects to be captured, imprisoned and tortured, as a simple barber would be who decides to use his razor directly on the jugular vein. Seeing that I am a *guerrilla writer* and do the same as my imprisoned Nigerian colleagues – but in a country where the snobbery of a presumed freedom of thought and word rules and since in order to be imprisoned as a writer a flood of warnings are needed first – I feel very frustrated for the opposite reasons: they keep me prisoner by leaving me at liberty.

Quite a little scandal – the press reports in headlines my famous line: 'Why must barbers who engage in revolution go to prison and dissident writers not? What is a barber that a writer isn't? Why should liberation committees for martyr-writers be set up and not a single one for the liberation of ordinary barbers? What does a writer with a toupee have what a bald barber doesn't have to have if they are both making a clever military use of their art?' With a fine photo of me in a T-shirt yawning, half-asleep, among illustrious American critics with bits of paper in their hands and a staggering Nordic beauty looking at them with a rapt expression.

A lot of sober conversations, very intelligent ones, even, but thanks more to the critics and the correspondents of the Scandi-navian dailies than to the writers who, as is well known, don't like to talk to each other but to talk badly of everyone and always in particular of anyone absent. I don't – it wouldn't amuse me; the best scenes are those face to face in public. It ends up with us all telling the usual fairy-tales about literature's *internal* reasons: life/death; high/low; love/hate; seriousness/hamming – how many pairs to say something more!

I try to keep in a disciplined way to the external or materialist reasons such as royalties, relations with the publisher and the media and the pseudo-freedom of the writer which is the real freedom between being established and marginalization . . . but all this to append a theme:

'No significant work of art is produced in the state of margin-alization as it is experienced – often a free territory for dilettantism and for foxes and grapes. It is too easily habitable to be the humus for an aesthetic project, the inspection of which is permitted only by the Establishment and not by a caravan of damned and bitter gypsies surrounded by their dear ones with the claque's tambourine.'

But even these discussions bore me, I don't manage to connect with anyone, at most I get as far as half a beer while apparently most people make connections with each other, drink toasts, know each other already, invite themselves to the next meetings all over the world, have a good few drinks together etc. I seem to be burning in an exchange of opinions all the experiences which anyone else in my situation would set fire to little by little, perhaps because, being on the brink of the publication of my second novel, I feel I have already been overtaken by myself as a writer. Just as the development of me as writer has been so slow, so now the destruction of the recent role granted to me, as it is right it should be, by the fact of publishing, but which I am already finding restrictive, is rapid. I should like to make clear to myself that it is not definitive, that there exists an unknown Mecca of roles before me and that I must not stop at this one. In fact I am preparing to spoil the other side of the written word: the *unspoken* silence.

I should be pleased to be here – after all it is the first time I have been invited to an international conference, the Cuban and Russian delegations are already asking me if I want to go to Cuba and Moscow to their conferences, I arrive as an unknown person and one unpublished in foreign languages and there is no edition of the papers that does not deal with my awkward absences, with the uncommon dust I have raised with a grimace, and I have quarrelled with almost everyone – specially with the integrated American negroes and the high-society queers and the academic critics and the psychoanalyst ladies. Instead I seem to have been here for years, a prisoner in a bottle, and feel they don't let me reach the shore. I like to write, I wear myself out, I destroy myself, writing is the only interesting thing about writing, immediately afterwards comes publication – all the rest is a great burden and intolerable: conferences, exchanges of ideas over a void, dinners, presentations, interviews. I go along with the publishing machine because I thus feel myself freer in relationship to my publishers if they suggest to me that I do something euphoric which, according to the press office, does honour to their capital invested. I have no *strong* opinions on the subject of making propaganda for oneself, personally I am of the opinion that there is no difference between a thousand interviews and no interview; let them decide. When *Seminar on Youth* came out I begged them not to take photographs of me; the photos I had brought (all the five I had had taken in my whole life) were ridiculous; it wasn't possible, without a photo no interview, and the publisher insisted too, so they persuaded me, I didn't want to disappoint them in their part of the work, and with one done all the other thousands were done too; through shyness, through shame, I became an exhibitionist of the worst sort, because from now on only in exaggeration would I be able to find the lost balance of a person frightened by himself. If I had been born in the eighteenth century I would probably have had to go into a few literary drawing-rooms between Venice and Turin and Versailles and Vienna even against my will. Today Diderot and Voltaire would go on the Wogan show if asked to by the publisher, and since they are authentically famous would not screw up their faces, not even if it came to them spontaneously. The truly great have this natural inclination to do violence to any given context from the *lowest* to the most overwhelming from *on high*; their text wins out everywhere and in all cases even when strewn with sequins. The true hell is not marginalization where vain and unverifiable illusions can continue a holy war – the only hell is integration for someone who had made of marginalization a reason for being part of literature. Formally I am no longer marginalized, on the contrary, although in substance I am more so than before, because I have lost my world without discovering another, because what is offered to me now in the role of *writer* repels more than the old one. Yet if I have not cut off my balls in rage and desperation and hate for a society which marginalized me, I don't see why I should cut them off now amid the ardent indifference and the success denied and the tolerance with clenched teeth to which I give rise. Or perhaps it is precisely because anger desperation hate keep you alive that your balls are useful? What can you do with your balls if everything ejaculates for you too? 'You will have happiness or power' it has been written. The first I have never known, I do not see how I can aspire to the second. Should I proceed in an orderly way meantime? But even the fact that the system goes to the trouble of castrating you in order to deign to annex you is not bad as an attention received – it is also the only one, for the system is incapable of any other kind of attention. A pleasant castration as a substitute for ill-gotten happiness and power.

~~

2nd Intervention

Let us demolish some myths about writers and writing, biography and text, before moving on joyously. Oscar Wilde wrote his worst text, *De Profundis*, during and after prison; therefore we can say that to be persecuted is not a guarantee of getting away with things in literature and that Wilde's best works (I am also referring to the essays) developed when he was not in crisis at all. Cervantes, on the other hand, being decisive, did not allow himself to be in a state of crisis even when he was in chains. So much so that his wrist ached more because of his pen than his irons. Boccaccio gave us his masterpiece with the *Decameron*, a joyous artistic act for all times and all places, and then disappeared as novelist because he felt (was stupid enough to *make himself* feel) guilty of lack of *seriousness*, so much so that he began a new career (of man of letters) by giving us extremely boring little poems which are today completely unknown. Of him we might say that the only time he was *serious* was when he was not.

Another myth to be demolished concerns the narcissism of writers – it is a matter of fact that a true writer is narcissistic and does not see an inch in front of his nose because, being a great observer of life in its every aspect and nastiness, he is the true, the real exhibitionist of his own interpretation of life itself and, once again, if he is a true writer he is conscious of his own mental limitations and we all know that writers who are mentally limited and short-sighted are narcissists – so much so that they do nothing to anticipate or conceal this calamity. The point is not to be or not to be narcissists (we all are) but either intelligently *idiots* or idiots. If a writer's narcissism is too intelligent we must be on our guard; he risks not being aware of it with the excuse of the myth of intelligence and therefore cannot be a true writer. There is no salvation except in sensible narcissism of an *idiotic* kind; idiotic narcissism is, yes, idiotic, but programmed like everything else into the neurology of the true novelist. His idiocy will never run the risk of escaping from his control – something which on the other hand often happens with his intelligence.

As regards the preceding criticisms (which are not mine) aimed at writers who deliver monologues – I have nothing against monologues because the alternative with writers in any case is to talk about money and young women readers. So a welcome to all those people who give monologues and who talk at the microphone because, while they are holding forth, they allow me to contemplate this stupendously mortal landscape – something which would not be possible if someone was speaking about rights and royalties and censorship and literary climbing, things so damnably interesting that they would end up by distracting me, titillating my eardrums, but would also end up by making me forget that all that counts here is the birch-tree – yet another – to lean against when one is totally drunk.

Whistles, applause. The Chairman, turning to me in a temper:

'Can't you manage to spell out some foolishness without making it look intelligent?'

Oh, finally the undulating nymphs arrive, the television cameras which have been shooting everything from a distance. They come close behind my back. One of the operators, completely sloshed, confuses me with another person with curly hair, an Englishman, and addressing me by his name does an interview with me about the outlook for British literature. It is too amusing, I let him get on with it, holding him up from time to time when he is about to fall to the ground.

➳

3rd Intervention – still on the martyred state of the *false* writer:

Man's private or political suffering fortunately has never furnished society with real writers but martyrs and heroes of whom we all have a growing need; if it were not so, the prisons would regurgitate frustrated scribblers – who have been up to their tricks again to earn some further instrument of torture provided they get to the Nobel Prize – and be completely empty of heroes. Where a true writer is concerned – one who aims at glory but above all at the *novel* – not only is it not advisable to be put in prison, it is not even serious . . .

～

Looked at with increasing suspicion I have managed with very few interventions to make myself hated by everyone. Not a dog at the collective tables who addresses a word to me, I eat quickly, go out, walk, think of Leningrad (where Anastasia claims to have been born), read some novels I have brought from home, the best-looking boy I meet resembles a sole worried about the mercury in the seas. One of the organizers approaches me to ask for an intervention tomorrow as well, I feel flattered. The fact is that I make them feel more united among themselves against me if I have the good taste to attack them and then to stand up for myself. That is to say, I keep up everyone's morale. I am thought to be so eccentric. But I say to myself, am I really Aldo Busi and not someone else they gave an air-ticket by mistake in order to send me in his place?

～

4th Intervention – 'Closing Panel' – goodbye till next time.
    '. . . if the ways of being an *organic* intellectual in Italy have become less well defined today than those of the Sixties and Seventies, this does not mean that his function has become less important in the public institutions and in private industry. Today, alongside the old organic intellectual of the political parties, we have the new extremely organic intellectual of *Made in Italy*, the intellectual of the textile industry and the advanced technology firms, intellectuals of high fashion as well as IBM intellectuals. One says *organic* because his organic nature is at the service of an organism which finances him *to be part of it*, not to be a whole or an autonomous nothing in himself. By organic intellectual is meant generally an educated person at the immediate and totalizing service of some power or financial system or other, I do not believe that the Scandinavian countries are an exception to this, I am sure I am talking about a touchy subject, but I am tired of being interrupted by Scandinavians asking me what an organic intellectual is. Let them look in their mirrors. And the more organic he is the more he will try to hide it,

167

redeeming himself by a *creative* production so as to indicate that he enjoys the maximum liberty and calls to witness his little productions which are subversive in intent, the opposite in integration. His *artistic* testimony is usually considered such by other organic intellectuals who have every interest to mirror themselves in it so as not to see.

To come back to *Cosa Nostra*, to Italy, I personally know some organic intellectuals of the Communist and Socialist parties who would never admit to being such, while they are to all effects and purposes in the usual way. With their 'works' they don't pick up a penny – they're too pure to dirty their hands with the laws of the free publishing market, in any case they have a university chair, they therefore *create* for the cultural prestige of handing out party cards to a world that is still unreformed. They are organic as things go today – transversely in order to muddy the waters and cover up their gains. Periodicals, meetings, literary prizes, the conference circuits, publications for banks, movements in support of life, scholarships abroad etc., chances which have never been offered to me and which I once accepted for the experience, that is to say, as a prank. Every so often these erudite people give us a little work, they feel at ease with their artistic insubordination (how much fascism is hidden behind the new fetish of *linguistics* and *narratology*! 'Languages are the science of fools,' the Abbé Maury thundered back in the eighteenth century, perhaps not referring only to the deciphering of inscriptions) and sit down once more at the table of their Amphitryon, dispenser of obscure membership cards. Their generous host usually allows these petty artists to spit – veiledly or openly, it makes no difference* – into the plate in which they gorge themselves so that the illusion of heraldic freedom may be perfect: the pigeons are caught with the bait of imitation beans, which are thus saved.

These I would define as pecuniary intellectuals in crisis without being serious; they are in a crisis of seriousness as others are in a crisis from giving up nicotine or heroin or grappa.

*Nathaniel Hawthorne: '. . . persons who speculate the most boldly often conform with the most perfect quietude to the external regulations of society. The thought suffices them, without investing itself in the flesh and blood of action.' Read *The Scarlet Letter*, which I intend to translate.

Seriousness is the fount of health, as such it cannot fail or go into crisis, but the lack of original *organic* seriousness is original, is already in itself an incurable or hereditary illness, and therefore we cannot take an interest in the highs and lows of a fanciful crisis which has none of the marks of health.

I do not feel myself in crisis and nevertheless I feel myself to be serious, just as this table must feel itself to be a table if one presupposes that it is conscious of its own nature as table. I do not believe that writing a novel is any more or less necessary than building a nuclear plant or an intergalactic bridge or a space station, discovering the anti-AIDS vaccine or preparing for the sake of a quieter life to stem the apocalypses of the nuclear reactors which will blow up. A real and serious writer must accept the burden of his own illusions of ferocious liberty right up to their extreme consequences and be serious about it: he has sought them out, he has wished them on himself, he cannot now be in crisis because of them, he must take them on like a steward who finds in himself his own justification. A writer cannot complain about *losing*, losing like some man of power who is required by statute to *win*. The writer's crisis cannot be located in his defeat, for it is congenital to his battle and woe betide the writer who thinks of fighting mills which are not strictly wind-mills, and if this is not his true defeat, the cause of his crisis is presumably elsewhere, in the lack of recognition of his merits by the Prince and the court. The writer in crisis reveals the plan for a mission therefore, for a way round obstacles which have proved useless. A writer is an explorer, therefore he goes on a voyage of discovery; if he goes on a mission he is an employee.

My personal mission as a writer is to have none and I never know if it will succeed in coming into port in its perfect absence. In this carefully guarded and vigilant negation I feel serious and not in crisis, I feel myself to be a writer and a man.

A certain amount of stupidity is required in order to be intelligent as writers: true writers metabolize even the stupidity of their nature while the others, the courtiers, remove their stupidity for fear of the Prince who, being usually too stupid, will not give up the myth of intelligence and will demand it from others. The literary figures of the court go into crisis because they have had to renounce the long-sighted intelligence of their natural stupidity and suffer from all the castration undergone by their cunning intelligence without having any longer the marvellous fodder of the uniqueness of the *stupid, idiotic* character. They can now only create by halves, definitely on commission, and, having been rendered incapable of limiting themselves to the laws of the novel, flutter about in the stupid clouds of omniscience, totalology or whatever. They are not sufficiently serious; they will continue to talk about *writing* without ever doing any or doing too much, without knowing what it is (and what is writing if not that entity which cannot be defined when it is there while you can tell at once when it isn't), and will insist on continuing to torment us with their crises of short-sightedness.

I have always known that a true writer is a Man without Qualities. The power of a lighthouse in a port lies in having only one beam; if it thinks it is a fairground it falls short of its function. The ray is often coarse, monomaniacal, but it lingers, probes into the storms and points the direction with immense force of inertia and perseverance. It may prove useful or not, it may or may not be followed and taken into consideration, it may or may not exploit its flirtation with tempests or with fine settled weather. It is there. To the lighthouse, as such, that suffices. If style lies in constraint, as Goethe writes, today style is *being*. It is not much, but in the constraint of being there is enough to be serious about. Writers who are no writers, or those already dead, may be in crisis; their illusions are as *non-existent* as their certainties. I am and I am not sorry – seriously. . .

~~

Yesterday evening, which is a time by name only, the day met the night, there was a moment of dawn-dusk and then light in abundance till midnight or two in the morning. I was on a little island along with two American critics, a pair of Finnish women translators, an American writer (a black whom I rebuked during the debates because the moment he jumped up with the same old story about racism here and there in the world I asked him to worry more about the racism that the integrated blacks of Chicago impose on the blacks *tout court* of the ghettos) and some liberated women at the university of Helsinki. But people kept on arriving – the party was the second of the *evening* for me and I was electrified by the constantly renewed opportunities for scandal and provocation which land at my feet in avalanches. The women obviously delighted, the men too ugly to notice. I had a sauna, I whipped myself with birch twigs, I dipped in the fiord – the water is neither fresh nor salty like everything here. At midnight the fiercest of the American deconstructionist critics whom I have brought to his knees a couple of times with a blow and a counter was still talking about post-modernism to drunk *women delegates* who had been in Italy too and looked at me with the expectation of a woman going out alone in Sorrento after 10. One of them was trying to pass off an unknown Neopolitan scholarship holder as a star among theorists. It was clear that the lady had left an orgasm in some faculty in Southern Italy. I asked her what else she did in life apart from being a woman. She taught. There arrived African writers in miniskirts and other Finns. I have learned to feel good and at ease everywhere, so much so that I feel favoured by my sexual fate, and all these educated heterosexuals were frightened of the others, the women, as if they were *the* earthly minority. The women with mascara on their chins as the result of radiating erotic desires and the men there discussing the processes of writing and cod codology. I feel that the humour I give off from my comic isolation – at the official dinner I ate quickly, I couldn't bear them any longer, to me it felt like a club for *Alpini* – is the only experience they will have had from meeting each other. They talk nicely about *eroticism*, poor things, and put back the drink between a Lacan, a Bataille, a Barthes, without ever screwing each other. Eroticism is the candied cherry on the cake when the cake is missing.

It seems to me that their desires, deep down in their machismo and feminism, which is shot through with spiritual speciousness, are as defective as mine – with this difference that they are ridiculous and I am not because not decipherable. What reason can they have to justify being so neurotic? Why do they all go home alone, drunk and empty with their seduction that sighs and lurches? In Helsinki the streets are invaded by staggering men and women who look at me askance because I walk straight. One of them grunts something hostile behind me – 'queer' no doubt. Here homosexuals are constantly attacked and are *sovietized* in terms of legislation, that is to say, the police attack them fiercely, as everywhere – yet it seems to me that in this respect the Italian police in the last ten years have had a witty attitude that could be the envy of several civilized nations, and the *Carabinieri*, who are manifestly complicit, are so numerous that often, but for their colleague in tow in the patrol car, not only might documents be checked but people searched. Good boys, keep it up, and maybe, before searching us, tip us a wink so that we know to move on a little. In the lavatories at the railway station in Helsinki the entrance is 2 finmarks, that is to say 700 lire, which is why there is not that same fine coming and going of men as in those countries which in their town-planning culture have taken into account the violent need of all males to indulge in confrontations. Here everything seems torpid to me – the benches full of silent drunks who nudge each other and then go back to sleep with folded arms. It is the etiquette of academic circles, an unsexed spirituality immobilized on a cloud, a trunk shaped by the tides, a blown glass. In their works of art, murals or sculpture, they have the nerve to get their inspiration from *nature* . . . I too have been living for a week without sex, and those taking part in the congress not only did not keep silent they were also not desirable. In Finland you can be charged with obscene behaviour in public by the man you have looked straight in the eyes. In fact I have noticed that the passersby do not even look at each other fleetingly – they go straight to their destination, but the tragedy is that they have no idea where they are going – they will go to the 'Wines and Liquor' store . . . Here it is indispensable to have a partner so as not to cause the natural function of the eyes – which, good heavens, must after all look at other people from time to time, they can't always lose themselves in the beeches and little lakes – to go mad.

News item in English on the radio: 'This morning 22nd June the sun rose at 23.30 yesterday and will set at 0800 on 29th August.'

Oh, time which slackens its bite day and night and makes the storms of the human passions fall headlong into the darkest despair of not even knowing the hour when it happened – or if the hour then not the time, and if the time then not the night, not the day. A region of nothing but space. I am here bored with walks, with the open air, with botanical gardens, with gulls and mosquitoes, in this amusing time of waiting to finish writing, to become a husband. A parenthesis in one of my acclaimed interventions said: 'Ulysses, who not by chance is called No One, is Ulysses so long as he sails and fights and suffers to return home, or perhaps not to return home. But once he has put in at Ithaca he is no longer Ulysses; he is a husband. The same goes for a writer.'

I buy *Silk*, a homosexual magazine with an English translation at the back. I should like to know what it means when it says that homosexuals are 'attacked at night' in Helsinki. Do those beaten up and the beaters-up make appointments to agree when it is night, that is to say, when it is day? I make contact with someone who works for *Silk* and he makes an appointment with me. Surprise – it was one of the staggering television correspondents at Lahti and he had never shown a sign of interest, at least as writer, seeing that in my fifth intervention I had stated, on the subject of writers who say they speak in the name of France, of Cuba, of Russia and for the good of mankind: 'According to Karl Kraus, if a writer has something urgent to say let him come forward and hold his tongue. There is no role a writer has to fulfil in the name of a country or a cause, however just. He will do so – if at all – as a citizen not as a writer. If that is not the case he is lying. A good writer does not take on the responsibilities of the irresponsible, he underlines the need to distribute them and for each to take his share – or else go to the bottom, country by country, citizen by citizen, even without him. If a democratic man or a perverse woman is sufficiently good-looking and has a prick of at least 21 centimetres (I translate – about 15 inches) he is invited to come forward: he or she will certainly be provoked or amused, at the same time he will have a wonderful time and can expect every imaginable Russo-Cubano-Ghanaian position from me, not because I am fulfilling my role as writer but because I am fulfilling the needs of my arsehole and filling it.'

You can't put it more delicately than that. Instead this journalist ignored me and I have the feeling of various compromises between the fact of being homosexual and collaborator on a homosexual magazine and at the same time being an employee of State television. We chat without any reciprocal interest – he explains about not interviewing me: 'On television it is not possible to talk about certain things – in the magazine yes, because in any case no one buys it.'

There is a knock at the door, a Finnish professor who lives in Paris arrives; he has with him a lot of articles from various papers and magazines on the development of retro-virus (*Recherche*: the structure of the virus, photos of sarcomas etc.). Fatal cases of AIDS in Finland up to today, June 1985 – six. How they managed to catch it, what kind of transfusionary adventures to get so far is a mystery. Or else it is not true that it is sexually transmitted. A nice article: in a zoo, the female giraffe having died, the three male giraffes became gay. The experts say it is not a good idea to alarm public opinion and the population and it will take more than three hot-arsed giraffes to undermine science's credo in male/female complementarity in nature. I say goodbye to the character and his friend, he gives me an address in Leningrad and a letter of introduction in Cyrillic script to be hidden so that it isn't discovered at the frontier. I demand that it be rewritten in French. He looks at me in a puzzled way, rewrites it in French, I leave and throw it away anyway.

Finland in its time was covered by a layer of ice two kilometres thick. Then the ice melted and here it is. There's no need to be surprised that the faces of its inhabitants are so smooth and the lineaments swept away. Because the great thing is this: they are Finns, they live in Finland and aren't happy about anything. They have parks and museums and old-Bavaria-type bars – only gloomy, like lunatic asylums – and legend has it that Helsinki is a Babylon of spies; but who would come here to spy? Whom can it really interest that Finland is not independent?

And so I walk on.

Women: who look at me, smile to me, slow down in their highly chromed cars, turn their heads, stop the car, radiant, very beautiful, with very accurate make-up, refined gestures of the hand, fluttering silk dresses, extravagant and very short, asymmetrical hair-styles, eyes and cheekbones rainbowed with purple or maroon. Their extraordinary punk haircuts or a pink or yellow pony tail down to their thighs. Obviously one ends up hating oneself because, being a homosexual here, one doesn't know

174

what to do. How many lost opportunities and I have been here for eternity, dulling my senses with walking, and my departure for Leningrad has been put off another day and there isn't a woman, or hardly one, who doesn't smile to me and walk more slowly. Women in twos, threes or fours, who greet me, waving creamed fingers with varnish on the nails, bizarre make-ups which communicate a desire to live, for Latin gaiety, pupils of every shade from green to blue fixed on the man with curly hair who, always alone, takes the same route port – beerhouse – hotel in the centre of the city, clearly an Italian.

This nation, unlike any other, has more beautiful women than men. For those who might not know it, the Finnish girls are the most beautiful in Europe. But Tom of Finland, the famous gay porno-hero, will have been inspired by whom? That is what men are like here – shapeless.

Finland is so full of anxiety without form, if not the very archetype of universal anxiety, that I am made anxious by it too minute by minute. Infinite signals of fear from a young organizer at the congress; he has come twice to visit me at my hotel because his post-congress functions keep him there. He takes me out and about and is afraid that people will guess that I am homosexual; Helsinki is a small city, fear that prejudice may sully him for having been seen at my side in the street, he spouts all this madness – that of an inadequate steward – and I listen in terror and he made me swallow down the wrong way the only beer we have had together (quickly) until I told him I was too old to be burdened with his guilt complexes and we laconically said goodbye. All he did was to inoculate me with fear of this and that, forcing me from fatigue – the excursion to Leningrad is fixed and it is not as if I can decide to go there whenever I want – to keep on inventing his suspicions and anxieties. This empty city, myself forced to wait for Monday which never comes, the only disco shut, chuckers-out in every bar and restaurant who look me over from head to foot – what the fuck would it have mattered if the young dandy, lover of refined food and invitations to Italy hadn't repeated to me dozens of times this worrying terror of the 'homosexualizing look'? To me who am trained to look at close-ups from a distance and to pretend there is no problem close up?

And why are they all alcoholics here? How many are so because the State does not permit a sexual option? How many violent and murderous gays only because they cannot manage things in a civilized manner with their arses? Of if only the arse could produce children, at least in countries with a low birthrate!

Museums shut, churches shut, everything shut, everything desert-like and tree-lined, in the street drunks of every age who inveigh against the passerby, the only feeling of beauty is imported: an Indian with legs crossed on a flowerbed meditating, a Japanese man in traditional wooden sandals who beats out on the gravel his carefree feeling of being a rash tourist. I go back to my room, turn on the TV, but lo and behold! I had to come to the North Pole to do things I never do even in Italy. Video-clips, Russian films from the Twenties to the present day, and then teleplays Swedish, Lapp, Bulgarian, beeches and long icefields, a whole parade of reindeer and birches, birches and long icefields, and dramas of jealousy and alcohol. And on the TV newscast, the usual news about the sun which has risen and who knows if it will set and how.

\~\~

Tomorrow at last we leave for Leningrad with the Finnish tourist guide, with Anna, the most beautiful Anna in search of highly placed acquaintances, European or Caucasian millionaires. Anna looks like Greta Garbo. In Helsinki I was three days without a word spoken, without laughter or sadness, with the leaden feeling of waiting not to be here any more – killing the hours, forgetting I have been here, recovering a little of the human code of behaviour. The birch trunks – white and then as it grows the birch splits into black sharp ridges and with the knots above and below they form giant eyes on the edges of the arteries. Impossible to make out a single expression from among the thousands of them.

The papers continue to give ample accounts of my interventions at Lahti, the invitation has been extended to me again but I refuse it, my photos everywhere, the usual wry mouth but in all of them a tranquil air, of concentrated serenity, just a tiny bit suffering, of histrionics in the embers, I shall come back to

Lahti, I say, only if and when my novels have been translated. A writer is the custodian of his fate – to be in the bookshops, then in the libraries, then in the archives, to and fro in a century-long fuck; and now not even one of five minutes.

***

Appointment at the train. My party is made up of sixty little old Scandinavian ladies transplanted to America. I am the only young old lady of the group; I am so unique and alone that I might give the impression of not having ended up by chance in the midst of this noisy party of old American women in miniskirts who immediately elect me Mister Lenin, collecting the votes coach by coach. My God what madwomen! How impertinent! They undo their curlers and comb their hair in the coaches, they chatter, confusing languages and childhood dialects, I think, and one of them winks at me and smooths her dressing-gown on her thigh. When I am fed up with the double meanings of the liberated merry wives I look out at the landscape: birches, those damned birches, always and only birches. Why do I hate them so much? Why do we get paper from them?

A thread of smoke far away – so a chimney exists. A thread of smoke caused by a fire of dry birch trunks – the eyes burning from one piece of bark to the other. A roof, a little station, where I am bewitched by a Russian woman erect on a bench, blonde, too tight a coat, tall, statuesque with the look of a lost child, such a beautiful woman, so lost in her spiritual alienation that I swallow instinctively. Then Leningrad.

Apart from the colours of the old Kalevalesque ladies, recycled by Disneyland, with whom I share meals in the Hotel Moscow – by colours I mean those of the dyes: hair white/violet, white/platinum, white/purple, white/whiteish, white/silver, lots of curlers at all hours pressed down by scarves – the first thing that leaps to the eyes in Leningrad leaps to the eyes on the second day: the balconies of the blocks of flats are bare, without geraniums, and the windows rather than closed one would say locked, for decades, as if the interiors were uninhabited or filled with the useless parchments of uncontested inheritances. A far cry from nice off-white colours! The façades follow one another opaquely and only the district round the Hermitage is newly painted in a fine bright orange. I have come to Leningrad more than anything else to take a trip to Anastasia's lie (Anastasia who will not set foot here, to the secret delight of Signorina Scontrino). And then, by dint of going about, dazed by the relentless beauty of the houses, of the palaces, of the castles, of the enormously wide streets – as big as the Champs Elysées even in the suburbs – I keep on repeating to myself what a pity about this dead city without living souls, who knows what they were all doing in August 1917, ideal for international torchlit parades or for imperial processions, something human simply had to fill them. The Hermitage square recalls Place Vendôme and every-thing, moreover, recalls Paris, but Leningrad is more beautiful than Paris, more grandiose, so uselessly uninhabited, a beauty adrift, a massive museum of itself and without visitors. I too am caught in the monstrous grip of the organization of tourism in Russia – hotel-warrens, the ambiguity of paying in the restaurant outside and in the shop inside the hotel so that you never know whether in foreign valuta (preferably) or in roubles, no contact possible with the Leningraders, bar inside the hotels for tourists scattered here and there and where I end up always running into the same Ugro-American hearties who acclaim me, fight over me and want explicit turns from me while they show me their varicose veins from New York and San Francisco – the space between one nostalgia and another to which I cannot give a name. It seems to me that a revolution that does not contemplate public lavatories for good-time people and Chinese restaurants is not worth while. What, a nation overthrows a dynasty and then forbids itself sweet-and-sour pork ribs? Here the Italian tourists are all happy (including the usual smart little industrialists who pay the trip for trade-unionist workers to make them tear up their party cards), they have come to have confirmation, they have, and they get plenty, not like me, who am collapsing hour after hour under a heap of *démentis*. The streets are full at fixed times for going to work and for coming back from work; apart from this obligatory transit they have no social function, people run for the underground and the tram, run more than in any other metropolis where normally people run a lot, and I do not measure the degree of civilization or the viability of a people by the beauty of its architecture but by the quality of life in the public places, in the open spaces, its fashionable little homes don't interest me however well furnished and comfortable they may be. Here no one must have ever lived through anything outside his own door by chance; these avenues, traversed in the name of socialism without exchanging a glance or a greeting, hurt; and these marvellous parks with mute motionless little couples, unable to bring out yet another sentimental formula, to loosen their tongues, for they are without social projects, without any direct political aim in which they feel they can participate . . . I ask myself, as an ex-proletarian of an undisputed libertarian and anarchic grain and a left-wing communist in my bones from despair, if it was worth while overthrowing tsars to replace them with ghosts still harder to dethrone. I think I shall leave here with a lump in my throat. Would this have been more or less the fate of Italy if, after the war, Togliatti had won instead of De Gasperi? What difference would there have been, please? Why, by living, does one end up by despising what one is no less than what one ran the risk of becoming?

On the black market (which by the way is there in front of everybody and in the public square with the connivance of the police who stand and watch) 1 dollar equals 3 roubles, in the bank 1 rouble and 60 kopecks. With the roubles you can do nothing or almost nothing, apart from asking the Russian citizens what on earth they are good for and, after a little, knowing what they are good for. There is little to buy even with dollars, apart from tins of sardines and rectangular sweets to suck, preferably in a group, so big are they. And wooden dolls. No flowersellers anywhere – this lack of flowers obsesses me, frightens me. That there are no lavatories to hang about in, all right, but that there are no flowers is inadmissible. If you want cigarettes that aren't Russian – which are disgusting to my palate – you have to pay for the others in foreign currency. What a humiliation for an anti-imperialist system to have to bow to the dollar to pay for cereals and technology. On TV: propaganda, propaganda. Army choirs, military parades, films of Mongol *descamisados*, tables with microphones and black people, no one who ever lets out a laugh. Let's hope they let me leave. The press – celebratory, as with us. The most sold books in the bookshops: the life of Lenin among the essay series, *Open Space* in the nonpornographic version, Marx's *Capital*, first instalment, among the novels. When people feel they have no earth under their feet they turn to the moon. Reagan on the one hand, Thatcher in the middle and the Nomenklatura on the other; but how has it been possible? There is something that doesn't work in this century, that is to say, which works less than in the others – or was Napoleon, too, seen in his time as an actor at the apex of glory? And did Fabrice del Dongo, that sublime imbecile, play a part? Have we become all Fabrizios sublimating behind the screen of how we will be received by a listeners' rating? What has always mattered has been an ovation by men in chains not the dismissive smile of free men.

Hermitage: thank you, thank you, old Reagano-Scandinavian lady Beowulfs, thank you for fighting over me at your tables, thank you for being there in the evening, for pulling me here and there by my sleeve for your own ends, thank you for clapping me on the shoulders and thighs like all-in-wrestling midwives, one day I shall come to the States and will come and visit you all one by one, promise? Promise. Addresses scattered in every pocket, the liberated grannies add dedications under the telephone numbers. This evening I am taking them down to the cellar, called 'Night Club', and in the meantime, make them all dance. Cries of joy and they begin to sing. One of them – wiry, a bit neurotic, more discreet, moves her hand a little further up my thigh and inadvertently squeezing my balls tells me I am really a good boy, Ah, these Italians – fabulous, fabulous!; a sudden attack of rheumatism in the soles of my feet makes me decide on slippers before setting out – only the bus set me down a couple of kilometres away and to complete them is torture, I have to walk crookedly so that I end up by walking barefoot and running up to the third floor of the museum before collapsing on a sofa to massage this sudden swelling on my left foot. And I can't get up again. I get an attendant to bring me a catalogue and look at the Hermitage in the Hermitage exactly as I could have done by staying at home. The huge dancing Matisses I had already seen in Paris some ten years ago.

And now, two in the morning, with this listless lager orchestra on the stand, my Never-Tire dancers – with the ample grip of their arms that fall round my back and on my shoulders as if they had to snatch me away – make me drink another toast, with them sober, me undecided, and the toast goes to health and youth which if it isn't there any more the best is yet to come.

~~

Yesterday with Anna – who walks with her toes turned out in black pumps size 44 – I was at the lido on the Neva and had the impression of good, tranquil, polite bathers who wouldn't invade their neighbour's towel far less Afghanistan. Anna says, impressed that I don't open my eyes wide at her one-piece black costume which enwraps her extremely slim, haughty figure and giving a brush to her honey-coloured hair:

'They are like the Germans the Russians, they do how and what they are told. They look good to you but . . . Self-censorship is no longer external – they have made it part of their flesh and blood. They are like angels, aren't they? Capable of anything when you least expect it. But what are you doing, going into the water? Are you mad?'

I had a swim in the maroon water in spite of her warnings – after the Ganges it is the most polluted river in the world. Nothing must be more polluted than me – I'd like to see anyone try.

Anna is a person who makes an effort to do something out of friendship without a return but she doesn't succeed, she gets tired right away. If there isn't a man to love and fleece at the same time she doesn't manage to pretend; and in fact when I come back from my walk along the river to see the young Russians in bathing costumes – hardly clinging or not at all – she is finished, horizontal, under the hot white sun in the haze, a woman adrift who wants to go back to the hotel to receive a compliment from a man as soon as possible.

I accompany her to the tram station where each of us takes a taxi, I invite her to supper but she says No, or perhaps doesn't know, must give instructions to a new group that is arriving. We will never see each other again.

There ought to be carriages and horses in this square, bars, a brothel for single men only, a baker's, fine *vespasiennes* like those in Montmartre, seamstresses with sloe-black eyes at the window, a merry-go-round! Non-existent, without volume, bodiless, I wander here and there from one part to another of the immense forest of petrified beauty.

As a reprisal I send some deliciously anti-Soviet postcards: 'The best thing in Leningrad is St Petersburg', 'First religion now mass militarism; and the prick, when will the prick become the opium of the people.'

Another day of boredom, the last, Gorbachev willing – with the Russian boys in the metro who look not at me but at my sports shoes, rubber and canvas with on them geographical maps in three colours. I have the world on my feet, they a room for four, that way they can keep an eye on each other better. If they speak to you they do not look you in the eye and a policeman goes and checks the documents of a youth who had been staring at my shoes for five minutes with intense insistence. I was sitting on the steps of the Hotel MOCKBA and the policeman came to inspect me, trying to make me understand that it was not decorous to stay sitting like that and then, seeing that I decided not to go away, he turned round and asked for the documents of the first passerby chosen at random. But this is pure Orwell. One will have to explain that in Italy there are no communists like this, thanks to the failure of the hard men of the Italian Communist Party, but that those there are would corres- pond to those chic, bespectacled young ladies of the American university campuses who are precisely called *liberals*. The Italian communists have no sense of humour and in their commitment give themselves the same revolutionary airs as a ladies' hair- dresser busy on a permanent wave. Oh, the little professors, male and female, who hymn social justice with 2 million lire net a month without doing anything more than stylishly carry a briefcase around in some faculty. This little trip to Russia was exactly what was needed and so it has been without Russians around, without joy, without exchange of ideas and of spermato- zoa, without laughter, without weeping, a little balalaika in the basement of the hotel where they put on 'variety' – all of which is the same. Now I feel myself more firmly based in my anti- capitalist rage, less between hammer and anvil, sickle and baptismal-profit-and-redemption font. Standing apart from the mucky pap of the ideologies of those who think they are *the better sort*, without illusions, except the old ones of doing the least bad possible but with political determination, full of hope as a programme and a way of stepping on the corns of more people as soon as I get back to Italy, those from before plus those from now on, anti-ideological manna.

I get back into the train with the same old women. I can't stand them any more, tired of feeling their bottoms and tits to make them laugh, the simperers. But I will be clownish and polite again until Helsinki. For the rest, life is a golden moment passed with one's feet dangling from a top couchette, the ideal dimension to shut out of sight the obstinate birches of the return journey and to sink into the gloom of these thoughts and this reality without falling into exhilarating whimpers. I am in the province of the story of the ugly duckling which is allowed to redeem itself provided, please, it remains the same as before. Helsinki, station – kisses, embraces, cheeks daubed with pastel rouge with maroon lipstick, I drag myself to the hotel opposite, another night . . . and tomorrow, at last, the aeroplane.

As I wait here in my room, almost in a corner, waiting for the dawn to be official to go to the airport, Finland is a country to be able to live in which one would need to live eleven months of the year elsewhere.

I walk, at midnight, I am still here walking, only a cemetery near the coast is open, I go to have a swim but there was too much wind and I dress again, what a strange light on the beams of the wooden houses, and the graffiti in the cabins remain a mystery, there is no one, the sand is damp and cold under my feet, and nothing, the sky which enwraps the globe coming down as if from beyond the hemisphere. And now more hours and hours in my room waiting for time to pass. What do you mean you are coming home tomorrow? You've just left! Do you know what time it is? The electric light bill has come.

The positive thing about certain countries is that, not having ever existed previous to being visited, they cease to do so once you get to know them. There's nothing like travelling from land to land to realize that you are living in the clouds. In Agadir a pair of writer's pants dry in half-an-hour in April, in June in Helsinki a pair of pants, washed in Leningrad, in four hours twenty minutes. I was forgetting – often you put them on when still damp, whether in hot countries or cold ones.

And now that I am home? I go about my room singing aphorisms to myself like a pedlar selling alienations in the market:

'No injustice or social persecution will ever equal my most unpardonable sin, which is not homosexuality but comfort.'

(Roll up, roll up!)

'There are honest people who are honest but no less conspicuous for that.'

'There is no one more dishonest than the person who devotes himself to honesty heart and soul in order to get away with things.'

'Hey, Sanremo Song Contest!' my mother shouts from her room, 'Give over singing – you're waking me up.'

~~

Taking into account the fact that eroticism is a super subproduct of sex, true sex does not derive from any specific and mutual consciousness of one's partners but from the spiritual readiness of each individual to trust to the genetic and unreflective memory of their own sex organs, of sex. To abandon oneself to the immediate mechanism of the fingertips, of the eyes, of the ears, of the palate and of the *tongue* (words *and* silence are sense organs) is the maximum expression of *homo venustus*. I am leaving out the nose in so far as the best smell is not imposed – sweat, perfume, deodorant etc. – but is the one that is created in the instant, at the command of the particular body before one, to merge into a *smell of a couple* at the so specific and unrepeatable second; the functioning of a relationship can be established by the originality of the odour which the intensity of love has elaborated from the bodies of the lovers. The utmost elegance in terms of libido is provided by the sexual immediacy of the species, not by the interminable preambles of the separate animals which require so much intellectual exorcism. Everything that does not accumulate feeling in the sexual organs but *creates* it is civilized pleasure of the first quality. Seduction is not set in train beforehand but during. One has to be effectionate.

All the rest is the white-collared routine of salaried employees with problems about housing or the perpetuation of the race.

The man of your dreams is not the one of your dreams but the man you have in tow this instant. At this moment you must respect in him your own inexorable imperfection which has immersed itself in the reality of a need. I don't go mad about dwarfs, for example, but if I am in a circus, why not? Seeing that the magnificent trapeze artists are tall but always up there, so much the worse for the trapeze artists and the idea my desire has formed of them. I shall abase myself and become at least as tall as a dwarf.

Here in the pizzeria one can set oneself to forging aphorisms under the impulse not of an illumination but of a beery hiccup. It has always been the weakness of the *creative* intellectual to subordinate a burp that does not come to intelligence that overflows:

(1) the mystery of sex is dead. Long live the (dead) mystery.

(2) to make it feel like the first time don't meet a second time.

(3) my ignorance is not equal to my knowingness – it is inferior.

(4) intelligence has nothing to do with intelligence which has nothing to do with its own stupidity.

(5) ugly men are like beautiful women – they are preferable.

(6) an ugly and intelligent woman is just as irretrievable as an ugly and stupid woman. From a woman one demands much more than mere ugliness.

(7) there are at least two types of man – the strong man, the weak man and the man.

(8) last night I dreamt of Sarah Marcos cross-dressed as Imelda Fergy. No one could have done more.

(9) the politician's wife was so attentive that she laughed only with her husband's wisdom teeth.

And meantime, skating over the fibres of mozzarella, I watch these new conversationless triangles of the present day: a blond man with long red/black hair and bulging eyes between two girls with long green/purple hair who look elsewhere, at each other's pizzas.

And meantime my heart beats the while: chuff, chuff, the leathery pulse . . . Yes, I admit it – in my youth from desire I too went in search of my assassin. If I am still alive it is because at that time I found an infallible one. He was someone who always felt out of place, always embarrassed, he whistled away like a male without needing to, always worried at not being up to things, always almost frightened not to be noticed. All wasted effort. For a long time no one had been taking any notice of me and now that everyone's glances are converging on me it is still worse, because they are looking at something invisible which has nothing to do with me. It is like going to Rome to present a script with the title, let's say, of 'The frontiers of silence', the story of an Ibsenite girl in search *of an identity* among the mists of the Nordic fiords: they will make a few changes, the girl will no longer be sent in search of herself but of something else and the title of the film, which will not be made, will become 'The lady goes to Morocco'.

~

Everyone drifts in the same way, gripping between their teeth and dentures chimeras so different as to be the same. If other people's chimeras were respected out of due ethical neutrality and not out of acceptance, tolerance, smugness, calculation, goodwill, laziness, snobbery, fatalism, and fanaticisms of yuppies, even the river system of a nation would benefit enormously. Not to mention the sea.

Let us take this week, the polite drift towards places gleaming with corrugated iron under showers caught hours before from a sky full of pink horses over the Adige; and one sets off – distant rhinoceroses which swell in great leaden attacking clouds, warm humidity from the open window, leaves whirling on the windscreen, a by no means excessive thirst for happiness framed and hung up. I am a homosexual – but let's forget about the writer who does not depend in the least on the frequency with which a man changes his underpants when others are to blame – who is not attracted by heterosexual men, surrogates for homosexuals. If they stay apart with the women it is because they have essentially feminine problems which I do not have. If I had to opt for a heterosexual human being I would go straight for the Rib and not for Adam. In terms of virility a woman, while being inferior to a homosexual, gives greater guarantees than an ostentatiously *comme il faut* male. The thought of going with a man disgusts me 998 times out of 1,000, 999 times out of 1,000 he leaves me indifferent. Yet, even while taking advantage with one excuse or another of all 1,000 times the thought in regard to a woman is less drastic – there isn't one . . . Once more I am following a motorway . . . The difference between the squalor of the eroticism of the rich and the squalor of the sex of the poor is that the rich tell you what you have to do and the poor don't discover it by themselves. The only way not to go to this appointment would be if I burst a tyre. And the landscape: the usual astonishing one, amazed learning by heart of TIR number-plates, the beautiful white columns of the petrol pumps, the chestnut-coloured wind which ruffles the locks of the young pump attendant who for a half-tank – seeing there isn't much traffic – cleans the spattered blood of the November insects. In the services I sing to myself a little song dozens of years old which rises to my lips while I review toilets to read the new graffiti: 'Looking for cocks to come in my mouth and arse' and underneath in another hand 'in what sense?'; 'gentleman 43 seeks girls 12 yrs old maximum along with parents, voyeurs only. Discretion and good behaviour assured.'

I spent years understanding the congenital error of human existence – how when someone doesn't know what to say he asks *why*? Children say it and there is no word that is more learned, less spontaneous than this, a word that with an access of arrogant spontaneity sweeps away any possible poetry of being. If man's history were human and not transvestitely animal this word-inquiry would not have found asylum, it would have been struck out at birth, it would not have been allowed entrance to kindergartens, ruled by *why*? disclosed by the preceding history of *why?s*. It is a false word – one with which the West is born but one with which it – sets, with an explanation at its roots.

'Check the oil while you're at it. How do I get to Tavernelle?'

'You turn off at Montecchio . . . It's very low. A litre?'

It is raining, at last it is raining properly, weather permitting, summer is over. It has been the longest summer I can remember, I woke up with a longing for snow in October already and there were tireless boats out on the lake with people diving from them. Why may one not have the chance of dying at thirty-seven of a natural death? Death who arrives waving his scythe and you present your bottom to him so that he can reap you . . . I would whet it for him.

It was in Bardolino yesterday, I think. The lake was blue and indifferent like a sea. I said to myself, you keep moving from place to place and the place is always a bit further on, aren't you tired? Knowing you doesn't depend on you but on whom you meet, you don't get to know people, you leave them. You will never learn.

Tavernelle is where this enthusiastic reader of mine lives. The final thing that impelled me to fix an appointment contrary to my custom – and thinking about it what are my customs? Do I have any? – is that, after a couple of rather knowing exploratory telephone calls from him, at the third I fell for it – out of gratitude for his persistence. We had scarcely agreed when he informs me that two weeks ago he decided to have an operation for phimosis and that he still has the stitches. At this point I could hardly wait. Irresistible and new-wave, in fact, post new-wave because usually these people keep the phimosis to themselves and think it's the others who are defective. And now the rain and those gusts which buffet the second-hand utility with new motor full of rumbling noises and thuds and badly carburated sighs because of something brackish in the air, or perhaps it is my foolish palate which sends to my eardrum tastes of brine: all this makes this drive at seventy – I am late – more exciting, more witty, a mortuary chamber on the set of a film. Nothing to show.

It is a great relief an operation like this, I won't be forced to hurry things, I shall maybe have the time to notice that this body from Vicenza converses and this momentarily stuffed flesh produces from the silk yarn some jarring remark of which the longitude will have to be determined tomorrow. Another title for a novel that comes and goes: 'At what point of the ghost'.

At Cisano Bardolino sinister bundles floated here and there not far from the bank, but they were not the bodies of drowned people come to the surface in the off season when one could see them and inform their dear relatives. Nor was it a case of very recent suicides; those who horrify themselves do not kill themselves, they kill. People ought to commit suicide more and with less fuss as if it were something to be got over with before evening, in between things . . . I had better stop, torrential rain. Many jewels of cats' eyes gleam from my headlights in the darkness unleashed by the rain . . . The points of light might be the hem-stitching of a wait to be prolonged and on which to do some embroidery . . . And then he is a reader, enjoys my admiration, my suspension of judgement, I understand him; he loves my novels. There is something so intrinsically disgusting about someone who prefers the contemporary novels of another . . . I am incapable of assuming this intellectual, moral, aesthetic burden. And who knows what a proper phimosis might lead me to do; to transform the scalpel cut into the opposite of *taedium sexus*. The thought that the Latins declined sex in the accusative from *a* to *m*, the dative of machismo, the vocative of the final cry, the ablative of the movements from and in a place, to remain motionless inside a sleeping man for a whole night of expelled genitives . . . A silhouette passes drooping under an umbrella, a male of the storm. Marvellous for anyone who swims along the paths and floats among the leaves, the bitter-sweet desire for a furtive ecstasy without surprises . . .

. . . At Bardolino: movements of devoted fishers, how they make the line undulate and the swish of the nylon in the air which blinded the seagulls attracted by that gleam. A whole business of squatting on baskets, of getting up and readjusting the genitals in the plush of the trousers, of changing the bait, of searching in the can of worms for the tastiest successor . . . The appointment is at the railway station. I resist the temptation to slip into the fortress of the lavatory on the *autostrada* under that flash of lightning like an oxidized artery, which for an instant laid bare stupefied inhabitants, faces swollen with the stolidity of stolen drunkenness, robbed of trousers, deprived of underpants, doing it quickly, the desperate hunger with the dropper before relaxing the shoulders and lighting a cigarette. How I love you, my heroes of our agonizing void.

Tavernelle will be a hamlet with an inn and a bowling alley, the station hidden behind hedges of rotten laurel, a streetlamp to light up feebly the times of the local trains as rare as teeth. I stop to ask the way in a baker's where they also make home-made *marroni*. The baker's wife is on the old side, she will have two children enrolled in Sociology and will have been twice to the

Sanctuary of Loreto to ask for a lot of favours each time. There is a customer in Terylene who is pointing at the refrigerated counter. The lights are on a little this side of darkness. Not many varieties are left, yes, there is some fruitcake left, that iced one there is melon-peel, the other one lime, otherwise there would be meringued cake with quince jelly. From the layers of puff pastry there oozes a gleam of gluey ice-cream, the lady utters haughtily a Terylene Yes, but demands a wrapping with ribbons, she has guests to dinner this evening, and as *entrée* will make something very very simple, raw salad with whole stalks. Salad Niceways. Very new cooking, as the French say. The baker's husband presses the filter of the coffee machine well down and the sugar must pierce the crust of the cream. I have to go to the right, he says at the door, raising his hand in his apron, to the bus-stop on the left, then to the right to the end of the street, no, there's no street-lighting, catapults are in fashion again, keep right on, the second traffic lights on the left, but what is happening this evening, the Flood? Wonderful weather for the snails.

'Thank you.'

'At your service . . .'

It is raining and it is so hot, I open both windows, it feels as if I had been running all the time. It is the mind free-falling around itself. Now I understand why I write – so as not to think of anything, to escape from the conditioned reflexes of my sick mind, dirty with astral obelisks which cartwheel ferociously on the sarcastic screen of pain. Being unable to avoid not having a life, I have that of my characters.

Seven fifty, an odd time for a tryst, and one is hungry for it. To clasp him to me, to kiss him and by the mere pressure of bellies to burst his stitches, to feel him bend over to the rhythmic covering of his twenty-year-old Jewish hole, his hips rigid from the grip . . . this he would be able to accept, what blame would be mine if the stitches burst, a kiss to set against two hundred kilometres is the minimum.

I park among piles of sand and a few shovels and a cardboard pail, foaming puddles of mud and train tickets. He's not in the long narrow waiting-room and there's no one else. I wouldn't mind if he didn't come, there's something wrong with a writer who meets a specific reader of his. He turned up in front of me about a month ago during a presentation of *SLofaPHS*, on the telephone I even remembered his name, Egidio, because I had signed it Egidio as I had been told to, after which on the telephone he tells me that Egidio is the name of his friend who lent him the book, as if to say that use is memory for when you remember properly it is reality which is different, and is called Iago, that's right, Iago. Iago was taller than me, blonde, a punk chicken-just-out-of-the-egg gel haircut, black raincoat, I don't remember him very well, he could send his cousin Desdemona and it would be all the same. So long as she was chatty. Chickens are chickens and there are so many young boys and very young ones who stare at me as I write the dedication. They keep their tongues pressed against the inside of their mouths and the soles of their feet at an angle, hands in their pockets, they would like to laugh and I feel that the inside of their cheeks is an alcove of alchemies ready for insolent escapades . . . yes, I am greatly loved by my public, less by other people's.

You'll see I've really been had . . . Better, better, it is a catastrophe for me if I realize that the anonymous person standing in front of me comes round the back to stick it up the author's arse. It is an inkwell of protests. The vaguest of doubts and I go away, a certain misfire. As a youth I passed some years impotent and didn't understand why. I found out when I was already resigned to it: it was not acceptable to be queer and unemployed, that was it, too many misfortunes all at once, being marginalized in terms of work made me more melancholy than being marginalized sexually, I felt cheated out of the right to exist above all as a citizen who works. As an unemployed person I was forced to take from society whatever it had left over for me that was cheap: my *private* life, while my project was 1) to take part at all costs, 2) to set myself apart *by choice* – that is to cultivate a narrative vendetta, a rhetorical pretext for cultivating in peace hatred for the wrongs suffered. It is the *reaction* foreseen by the marginalized that legitimizes the *action* against them. And, as always, I got to where I wanted – to a political-sexual life made to measure, to action where before there had been enforced stasis. But now impotence assails me for the opposite reason: the excess of integration and of interaction which my new existence can awaken in the eyes of someone who does not know the preambles to my feigned *consensus* – the consequence of *success* and *notoriety* – inhibits me, paralyses me, no *I* is *I* any more, they will become image, projection, falsification of my most secret, most bastard, most unreproducible impulses. And here I am continuing to prefer the area of chance to frequenting literary hostesses, chance with its recurrent mythomanias, its fixed stations . . . Outside the narrow waiting-room the station is dim, the tracks flooded with rain. I am putting myself to the test; here under this trembling of a neon lamp I have brought the person most difficult to reconcile with me, Aldo Busi, let's see what his mistakes will be and what I must suggest to him in his representation of me. Will I succeed in that vital emotion typical of the lost anonymity of the animal with an intelligent heart? Or will it be another kind of humiliation which I haven't yet experienced? To expose myself like this, with a cold in the head already, little burst of coughing, a little hoarseness, a boring scenario . . . Will my cold, restless and soaking eyelashes manage to correspond to the indecipherable interpretation which this reader has elaborated from my novels to me and from me to my way of making love? Can a writer's prick live up to his fame? And fame – how can one know what it lives up to? Like when that bookseller said to me on the telephone: 'You should give me a present! I have sold two hundred copies of you. Do you know how many two hundred copies are?' I do not realize what two hundred copies are and don't know if they are two hundred copies nor whether I have to start learning my tables again to make up for this gap.

This is really late. A shuffling sound. I go to the door, appear at the entrance; it's him. A big white umbrella with gilt Greek-key design, white bolero jacket with kimono shoulders, white trousers tight at the calves, three-quarter sleeves, bracelet, gait not hurried, not nervous, careful about where he puts his feet, as if he were early, cheeks devastatingly smiling, little classical dance shoes which go up on points so as not to be changed into boats by a puddle. A little jump. I know everything by now; I could have put up with anything but not the little jump. I should like to be in my own house, this morning I had the nerve to make the butcher wrap up the rosebuds on the counter along with a chop, what more did I want for today? And with weather like this? Firm roses which will no longer open in time, and to lie under the duvet looking at them, aiming the table lamp at them to interrogate them. Instead here I am in front of a big effeminate youth who into the bargain makes people lend him books and says Hello in a singsong voice, very beautiful and useless, with all the paraphernalia on display of an inclination to belong, to lose a desire he doesn't know what to do with! The boy's face leaning into the cardoor as he gets in and I am brusque has the astonished expression from a silent film of the star who is loved on the spot for what she is, a star of the silent film – one who knows no other expression, because up to now the market has not come up with other demands. And so the writer is supposed to be the Mother Earth, the Mother with the round prick . . . Some suitable ceremonies, we go to a pizzeria, I take as little time as possible to go off without hurting him badly – I linger over the mushrooms and threads of mozzarella, seeking an inspiration to render the laconic quality of my lack of interest creative. Effeminate men dismay me; I mean those who try to arouse an erotic state with feminine attitudes and rhythms, while I myself make use of femininity for sexual alienation, as a comic way of engaging with the incomprehensibility of the genders. My being gay is functional for myself, not a spiritual compromise to give satisfaction to loving couples and to the man but to *amuse* myself, to project myself towards the unknown of a self-mockery which pleases me. I am effeminate as Totò or Keaton could be – not to seduce but to make me laugh. But in this boy there is an expressive histological module, without irony, monstrously nice and pretty and simpering, without the greatness that goes with the *madness* of a desperate sensibility that is still capable of a can-can.

No impetuous move on my part, nor any invitation to confidence; I chew the *pizza alla margherita* correctly, I have no wish to put up with his questioning glance: full-stop.

On the autostrada once again, in the petrol-blue of the suddenly blinding tunnels, my heart is sounding its klaxon within me and says let me pass, let me stop, let me go faster. And then if two hundred copies are two hundred copies – let's suppose – why on earth must I give him a present? Haven't I already done so with that turnover of novels?

Those seagulls of yesterday, I think it was yesterday, I did not understand them, why didn't they agree and, diving in unison, dispatch with blows from their beaks the defenceless contemplators of their own mental void called fishing? But tunny-fishing I would go to willingly even with only one leg, the lure of the living blood under the harpoons, the trapped shark which at one end savages with its teeth and at the other voids because its guts are open and it hasn't noticed . . . The gulls seemed already stuffed when alive in the landscape, their orange beaks slightly open, they screeched stupid and presumptuous messages of liberation. Then I heard that old theme come up, because the old themes emerge better flying over expanses of water which embroider on the sentence of which I am most ashamed: the hope of understanding things outside myself. Little red flags – danger. Rocks. The seamstress lying in wait . . . Here I am in the little square of the first parking place.

What a liberation to drive along in the gloom spattered by the portentous spray of the trucks and singing to oneself: 'That bunch of flowers . . .' in English, German and French! . . . We are three vehicles silent and shut. The mental word, its chemical formulation, is man's great safety valve: one goes on and on and then when all seems lost there it is intact, gleaming, witty: *your* word winking at you. All the rest is erudite shit. Not to be trusted. Or arse and prick on a platter offered by Power – which is mellifluous and unseizable, slides all over the place, a serpent of smoke which nests where least you would expect it . . . In the South the queers are only the poor and down on their luck and the feminine ones, the others, the rich with the junior football teams in their hand, are only *signori* and that's that. What does it matter if they take your sons and daughters so long as someone takes them and keeps them? Old patriarchal dreams of the south: everything is permitted and owed to the *Signore*. But I who am supposed to be an *artist*, what am I doing here, under the peals of thunder, leaning against a wall in front of a sewer which erupts with shit from picnicking parties and families, the broken handbasin which has flooded the place, the Kleenexes which attach themselves to your soles, what am I supposed to be doing here sharing the same condition in the same condition? By now I could, in terms of social status, aspire to a whole village of unemployed all for me, to play at football among the syringes, to offer screen-tests and talk about communism, invoke Italy's mammas . . . They would throw themselves into my arms, all these families of disinherited people to whom to prostitute oneself or to prostitute seems the only luxury which costs nothing – only one's life . . . It oppresses me to enjoy privileges when the real one is not to have any. But ordinary people are mean, they know how to hold their tongues when it suits them. The sexual complicity between big shots and silly geese in Italy is an institution in C major.

A fourth car arrives, very big and black, it slides in under the branches and lowers the window, it seems uninhabited. I already have my prick out, I show it to the driver, whoever he may be, along with stature, age, bearing, what I might be if anyone ever paid attention to what we think we look like – even going by sports-centre standards – and gave up the idea of that phantasm people keep looking for even when they are at home listening to the conch-shell of desires. The occupant neither shows himself nor gets out, the idiot, we aren't whores out here lifting up our skirts with them inside examining the goods with the anonymity of a customer. I go up to the window to allow him to take the measurements. The phantasm in centimetres. Sometimes I find it difficult to get it hard all alone – there really isn't anything exciting in yet another shadow printed like a transparency on a car window in the dark. Not at my age. No reaction. A little while ago I did the same thing for a good half-hour, back and forward my cock out in front of a TIR, in it there was one of these Vikings with long flowing hair, Danish numberplate, enormous shoulders, a lit cigarette in the corners of the mouth, fuck-all to be seen. Then an angry little voice says: 'Listen, miss, me need to sleep, fuck you!' It was a *woman* driver, a big blonde in a T-shirt, biceps like this. It happens these days with the new professions. Now that women are emancipated, they too are allowed to drive for thousands of miles and offload dairy products . . . If at least he let me see him feeling at his crotch a little, showing that he is game, I can't go on like this all on my own. Things started badly. You have to give them hygienic guarantees even to be tossed off with you here and them there. He lowers the window, I lean on the edge of the window like a guillotine. He takes a good look at it, looks at me. 'Get in,' he

says. 'About time,' I say. He says: 'You don't waste time.' 'Why –
is it obligatory?' 'Let's talk a little.' 'I've nothing left to say. I want
to come.' Struck dumb, doesn't touch me. Just to give him
courage I say: 'I'm full of come up to the eyelashes.' I feel it
harden. Damn it. I put a hand on his prick, feel it, move and
remove and move again but don't manage to extract it, an odd
lump, I give over. 'Take it in your hand,' I say and have to take
his hand and put it on his fly – something that feels to me like a
cold shower – it is like guiding a blind man while pretending
there's no stick. 'Let's move away from here. There's people,' he
says. 'People come wherever you stick yourself – we might as
well stay where we are,' I advise him, nettled. I can't see him
very well, he can't be bad, regular features, perhaps he's one of
the ones with a wooden leg who don't get out of the car because
they have a support under their bum and the moment they get
out they are like table-lamps. Oh, it wouldn't be the first time,
once there was one who had lost both legs but he wasn't satisfied
by my immaculate wonder, he wanted to take me home, and
when he took the lift, being so low down beside me, he made me
think of a messenger with a lump in his throat delivering a lamp-
stand. But there are times when you can't pull back and if he is a
bedside lamp you must give him the chance of turning himself
on. Then there are those who have one in a twist, like suckling
piglets, or a spastic daughter, and then they have to talk a bit
first. 'The only way not to stand out is to put oneself always
where there is most light,' I go on. He gets into gear, reverses, I
sigh . . .

Yesterday: I have moved from a bench to a rock, I saw the Lady
rise from the muddy waters, she had grey and orange boas
round her neck, a rusty scythe. The allegory was witty, it kept
the shudders at bay, the instant under control, the mouth which
must after all in the end relax and present a theological smile. The
things on the bank looked like newly cut waterweeds determined not to become hay. If there were amphibious rabbits the
problem would be solved, the banks would remain clean. So I
shall no longer be there and things will continue to keep to
themselves the meaning I have been unable to understand, I like
no other. And I have already pushed much further on.

He pushes down the seat-lever, we slip in, he bends his back

196

over me, cunning of the teeth and the throat, the smell of recent shampoo and the bitter, good-quality perfume behind the ears. I detest complicated men who forget they have a sex and leave it to you to have two, one for them as well. How many wretched homosexuals there are about who would have made a woman happy instead of reaching forty without learning anything about the rules of the variety and are not even straight. I try to unbutton his trousers, how come that they always think that a man can forgo that prick of theirs? Why don't they produce it first of all and then, perhaps, the rest? I feel under my fingers once again this odd spherical and extremely hard shape, I undo the buttons; nothing there. Yes, this boy lying prone, licking my balls, has no sex, not one catalogued as such, but a round tangled mass of nerves, one of these elastic balls which poor children use to play with. Somewhere there will be a urethra, a slit for urinating through, and you would look in vain for a scrotum, oh conjurer with masculine balls. This week this is the third one I meet with a special sex which is not a sex, a bag which is not a bag, and I am unable to feel myself either homosexual or homovegetal or homomineral or homoanimal, only homoastral and at most homoelementary. No doubt they are creatures from a new planet somewhere near here, the one with mothers who smoke or booze during their pregnancy and make a mess of things, do prenatal exercises in the streets, watch 'Dallas' and then have the courage to call them Felix or Bonny.

The other two had: (1) a curved branch which when it was hard kept a dorsal thorn, (2) a cigarette filter, a male clitoris planted like a nail between two immense balls, which made him a packet this big and they were all great big floating glands. They are sexual beings on the sly with whoever comes along and who distribute their misfortune equally to men and women, but above all to us saints and to our never-sated weariness, to our chimeras capable of hanging on for another thirty for that night of love thirty years ago with a little boy cousin in the hayloft and tomorrow, the day after tomorrow in the nearest parking lot we will be rewarded for the good we have done here and now. But this week I have done enough good works, I don't feel like a third – the point is that I haven't the will for it and so why should I force myself faced by a horrendous cyst? I close my eyes in my shut eyes, it's over. The notice above the flooded handbasin says 'Not for drinking.' Who gives a damn. I am back at the beginning. Like when they discharged me from the Infectious Diseases Department and told me (a truck is arriving with an Italian army numberplate, I make towards it with my pants soaking): 'Remember you can't play games with hepatitis – no smoking, no alcohol, eat boiled stuff for a year.' I went into the first trattoria on the road, pasta and Barolo, stewed donkey and piquant cheese, and so on for all the months needed for living or dying. I had defeated every after-effect by rebelling against psychosis. With HTLV III as well . . . The doctor says to me: 'Listen, Busi, everything is in order, you don't even have syphilis, not even a healthy carrier, but there's one extraordinary thing – if we had better instruments for the job we might be able to establish a sort of deduction I have made – that you have had everything and got over everything – time after time . . . I don't know how many times in a million it happens but that's what it looks like.' I thought – now what will finish me off? . . . At the window of the cabin there is a type with thick moustaches and red eyes – sleep, the slightly libidinous red of enforced wakefulness. They are those trucks that go back and forwards in the night loaded with bombs and ammunition, I know. I go round, the fact that he lights a cigarette is a good sign . . .

I say: 'Hey, chief, a stormy night, eh?' 'A Walpurgis night' might have had a devastating effect. 'It's blowing great guns, what a wind!' 'Feel like a bit of company?' 'Depends,' he throws out, shaking the ash from his fag but his elbow rising and falling in the interior says a lot. 'On what?' I say. 'What can you do?' he asks with the voice of a counter-tenor. 'It depends on how much room there is in the cabin,' I say. He laughs. 'That is?' 'Whatever happens.' 'Ah no, not whatever happens.' 'Whatever you go along with,' I lie, but meantime I have climbed up on the running board and take a look inside: a twenty-five-centimetre rod, direct evidence that I won't have to write down another ex-voto. He has lowered his trousers down to the end of his thighs, hairy, a clean smell, hard stomach, muscular, everything is long and substantial, a sensational cock, one of the old-fashioned ones you still find every now and again. This soldier who is busy digesting things looks older than he is and is younger than me, a big head, lips like sardine tins in the grizzled moustache. 'I'm getting soaked hanging on out here,' I say. 'Get in.' I go round, the click of the door being opened. He draws the blinds at once, I keep my eyes down not to be confronted by the usual photographs – 'Drive slowly, think of me' – she will have climbed up on to the fork of an olive-tree at Sirmione in her white wedding dress or the little toothless boy laughing in front of a cake with candles, the little girl all plaits, a frightened look. I would put on the dashboard a photograph of me typing. He begins to undress with some difficulty because of his gaiters with laces half a metre long. A couple of hundredweights of man all muscles but ones that are lazy, sweet, not aggressive, a good corporal, a barracks softie. 'Once a fortnight,' he begins, 'this comes over me I don't know why.' The cabin has a pleasant smell of pots rinsed out with the hose, copper and water and soap powder and also of corks and petrol, of breadcrumbs and liquorice. I feel that I will love him with enthusiasm, the sexual desire to use someone and surprise him, to flush him out, to give him a going over to take him out of his lethargy. It will be like writing the same sentence seven times over, never removing enough of the superfluous matter which bewitches me and making the words mobile, impregnating them with that absence I know of and which is the most arduous result to obtain: happiness without question. I am a statue at once mercurial and calm, trembling and respectful. A festival that feigns satiety with an empty stomach. I hope he won't let me down because I want to do this one a service he's not expecting, and unwittingly has been dreaming about for goodness knows how long. I delicately lift up his thighs which are those of a Japanese wrestler and begin to make inroads with tongue and saliva, he tries to repel me flirtatiously, as if finding this attack scandalous and not agreed on beforehand, but you know what negotiations are like, he gives a chaste little gasp, curses himself, says 'Well – anyway' as if he were rallying an outpost of repentance. The little red light above our heads scans the depths of the blood in the whites of his eyes. 'Come on,' I say, 'don't play hard to get.' The expression of a good-natured ogre is turning into that of little Red Ridinghood, the tamed male, I have to clench my teeth to prevent an overhasty disaster, I let his big thighs crash down and get up on to his chest, all that soft hair downy against my hips, I take him by the hair, turn his head round, strangled he says weepingly: 'No, tell me, do you all do this, you arseholes?' with sportive good manners. I adjust the silver sardine tins, I press, the lips resist and then open to close at once. I bounce my balls on his moustache and under his nose, 'But Jesus,' he says and I with all possible but authoritarian caution say 'Come lick the spunk out of me' – bits of dialogue borrowed from Sicilian cinematography – and this tongue emerges like a cobra's head, with fingertips all saliva he takes hold of prick and balls and begins to work me over, to get excited – he takes up an unsuspected space. Turning a little on my side, I take in my hand his enormous rod which is still betwixt and between, *soft-boiled*, as a first violin at the Scala used to say, but completely hard. The impotences of others excite me, they are messages in bottles, one is of more and better help if one pretends not to notice and the bottle is thrown back into the sea as it is. Then I begin to give orders. That a cabin should be transformed into a company office with dimmed lights is something a sexual soldier ought to expect.

I know who I have under me and why I dig into him with such ardour and determination; it is as if I had a wooden rod and not a sex organ stuck into my waist, I know why I am playing the game of making him suffer so as to make him have pleasure, he must remember me, an anonymous man at the peak of his immortal splendour unleashing subtle, memorable details. I know what words he expects from parading between mess and garage, a wedding and a confirmation, a trip to Comacchio and a 23-inch television, a game of rummy during manoeuvres and a Mass celebrated by the regimental chaplain – every truck-driver has a faith, two if an army one. I pluck at his turgid woman's nipples and then with my teeth pass from one tit to the other, under me he sings the hymn of the breasts, and how he is shaking his leonine head now and is putting out his tongue and opens his mouth wide and wants me to spit into it delicately. His tongue is long, pointed, stretched out towards mine, a tongue with a stereoscope hidden within it, which knows the secrets of the guts and the lungs, of unselfconscious putrescence. I leave him with his sticking out, imploring, without taking it and, in the same moment as he withdraws it, my mouth plunges on to his and I make the tongue mine and suck hard and he struggles, wounded, and then I spit it out, I thrust it back, tongue to tongue, force it back down and follow it into his throat, into the stalk of his female desire. Because these men think in roles and it would be unthinkable to have illusions that it isn't like that: all they want is to feel what they think a woman feels under them. 'What is it you carry about? Rockets, missiles, munitions?' I say. 'Oh yes! Dried beans for the army.' 'Ah.' At home, when I get back, I have this little vase of brown onyx with in it the rosebuds which won't open in time any more, says the horse-butcher, so he gathered them, a luxury – roses in November, in any case they would rot on the branches. I pull the toilet paper from the roller which hangs from the roof of the cabin. 'Listen how it's coming down,' he says. It has started to rain again. 'A great fuck,' I comment. They set great store by a sprinkling of vanilla. 'When I am with a man, oh, not often, my cock doesn't ever work properly and yet with my wife . . . But with a man it is more . . . odd . . . mo-o-re . . . more what it is – I don't know if you understand.' 'You bet.' Each one pulls back his part of the blind. 'Goodbye then, chief.' 'Ah, after a good come I manage to stay awake at the wheel another three hours.' 'It's the truck-driver's adrenalin.' '*Ciao*, lovely arse, and if you see me with some man on the road . . .' 'Don't worry – I'm an arse-of-the-world.' 'And yet if you see me in these parts knock on the side-window.' 'I'm always here,' I say.

Like a fungus, a snail, a luminescent little dwarf in the subliminal garden of the highway authority. And off I go as well. Dark, beautiful dark, beautiful rain, the moments slip away from one part of the windscreen wipers to the other, and so too this business of living, a poetry without attributes, poetry without question. And the heart too that *beats*, beats better if it beats for nothing.

The notice in the papers says: 'From 1st April direct flight Bergamo – Mombasa.' It's like saying Montichiari – Tierra del Fuego. Irresistible. I board the plane.

My fellow travellers must be a confraternity of pastrycooks – fragrances of butter and milk and caramel, a commotion of windcheaters and jerseys which disappear and underneath there appears the zabaglione of summer clothes with the labels still dangling from them. I fear, rightly, that I am the only single tourist on the organized flight, I feel like an extraneous odour among the nicotine and the garlic and the general andropausal smell of the incontinent. In the exultant flood that takes its seats the familiar essences which bind us or estrange for ever are rubbed off. I must think of something, how to cope.

'You, Busi, next to me,' says a woman's voice while in the midst of the gangway I am searching around for a seat, for three if possible, so as not to annoy anyone. I turn round – her glance is frank and authoritarian; 'Don't try to run away from me, Aldo Busi. And you,' she says to the adolescent beside her who gives a start, 'be nice, clear off. I hate youths who don't even wait ten minutes to start up absent-mindedly with their knee, I could be your grandmother and an eight-hour flight won't change my distaste into resignation. Since I shall be very nasty after take-off and will slap your face not more than quarter of an hour later you may as well spare yourself the rest. Go to Mummy because I have to smoke with my right hand and not hit people.'

The youth – nearly six feet tall, callow, erection very visible in his shorts – gets up without a blush because he has preferred to go as pale as a corpse and joins two mates who are sending him up from the queue.

'Come on, Busi, sit down, come on. We are the only two human beings who aren't paired off up here and I am one of your devoted readers. You owe it to me. Don't worry.' And she looks behind her and to the side.

My neighbour at the window is about fifty, she wears sunglasses with black spangled frames – a typical heroine. She is dressed with austere lightness, long sleeves, high-necked blouse, wide trousers, if it were not that everything is pink, flesh-coloured. In fact she looks naked. Hair copper-red with a few white strands.

'Just for once it won't be you to tell stories about other people. I want to tell you a good one – a *real* one. You will have everything to gain from it . . .'

If she really has read something by me she has learned her lesson well: to hate descriptions of landscape and presentations.

'. . . and to get down to brass tacks, I shall tell you right away that your method of being sexual is like my way of being criminal. I have discovered, thanks to my husband and to the provis . . . – providential end he met that I am an assassin *manquée*. It's the same with you, isn't it? A queer who detests men! That too! Clementina Gnoccoli – pleased to meet you.'

She holds out her hand. An energetic shake, summary pink enamel.

'It's the first time in my life that I have made such a long journey, apart from those damned Canaries, but then I have refused to go back there for the last six years. Six years ago I said a *No* to my husband for the first time, no, this time you're going to the Canaries alone. I told Faustino, my husband, Faustino Gnoccoli. He had taken a one-room flat there in Las Palmas, always bogged down there, me and my daughter, among the prefab holiday homes, to save money, year after year. No Canaries? No holiday, he said. I wasn't bothered. My maiden name was worse still than the one I got when I married: Passera* – can you imagine? And all because mine is a family of bird-catchers, but I've never really understood what it means, what sort of a job it is. Do you know? Did they go and set traps for birds in the snow? Well! A friend of mine in the factory, when I was young, as a young woman I worked in a meat-canning factory, well, she was called Melalavo† Domenica, she ended up marry-ing a man who travelled in soap . . . Yes, yes, it's my first real trip alone as a . . . widow and not to Tenerife. And after the tragedy, you might say, tragedy because I let it slip out, you understand, but no – even earlier kept saying to myself what's the use of travelling, what's the use of taking things easily, what's the use of it all, and one thing's as good as the other, and one time I said to myself – a week ago – Oh yes? Then it's good as the other just for once. And here I am. Don't look round, you're not taking anyone's place. Then I'll explain how I am alone. In any case between me and that person matters are quite clear, oh, as clear as matters can be between relatives from Bergamo, she was so

---

*Passera has various meanings: sparrow, currant and cunt. (Tr.)
†Literally 'I wash it.' (Tr.)

203

determined to come too. Then I said to her: Together but as if each one were on her own . . . In short it's too long to explain . . . I have an underwear business. And do you know what I have done? Exactly what poor Gnoccoli never did – I sent a circular to everybody, clients and agents, and shut up shop. In any case in summer it's not as if there was a run on knickers and in any case they could have thought of it sooner and then the new samples don't come out before the middle of August. Yes, dear Busi, I have the biggest stock of intimate uni-sex underwear in the district, and I shall gradually explain to you the relationship there is, because a relationship there has to be, between the ins and outs of the misfortune that overcame Gnoccoli and knickers. You can help me. Isn't a writer a detective in words? If you give me a hand to get them to come out properly I'll give you a stock of mid-thigh ones for as long as you live. Because the murderer, the one that took Faustino out of my mouth, hasn't been found yet and you can think if you like that they'd had suspicions about me even if, oh yes, they have had them, I wouldn't be here, they certainly wouldn't have let me go among the Zulus . . . But according to you, these ugly people round about us are they all hairdressers or ice-cream makers or hairdressers for ice-cream makers or ice-cream makers for hairdressers? Don't you smell a funny little niff of lacquer, of burnt hair and raspberry as well? My husband was, you might say, such an insignificant man that he embarrassed people. In some ways he was a real intellectual, he took good care never to lift a book all his life except the ledgers – and apart from the last two years always in the black for thirty years – an easy life. But to go back a bit – what does it matter? eight hours' flying is a long time – it's up to wives to read for their husbands when things are going well, because if they have an educated husband they tell him the gist of what they've read after they have turned over and gone to sleep. Well what was I saying? Of yes. Naturally I have a fortune, we – my daughter and I – have a fortune – poor thing with hips that look like a Volkswagen – but that's for later. As far back as the Fifties Gnoccoli had begun to take a census of the bellies and body-belts of the women of Bergamo and province because *ladies* were his speciality, men we began to introduce a few years ago because of my Loredana and yet there was so much to do with *ladies* . . . It was Faustino who introduced it here . . . *there* in Bergamo and round about – beginning at Cornate (d'Adda) because his mother had a tobacconist's there and I went to live there when I got married . . . the fashion, a very rewarding one, of interviewing people in the street, who all thought it was something to do with a quiz on telly. Oh what a lot of questions the girls who had the job weren't allowed to ask! The replies were always the same and consisted of crosses. When you got to three crosses you could be sure that this one was a bit of a slut – I mean one who didn't put much store by certain things and not even by hygiene, in short someone who hardly bought any knickers, there. Do you know how many women Gnoccoli looked in the mouths of with that system of 'Excuse me, Madam, can I ask you a question?' More than twenty thousand using local official records as well and latterly the favours of council members. And with size and all, how often changed, preference for material cotton mixed, quality low/low, medium/fine, fine/fine. Fine with elastic or without, favourite colours if not white, if embroidered or one-piece – oh he made a fortune in a twinkling. We opened the first shop for knickers straight from the factory to the customer the moment his mother had drawn her last breath she didn't want to change the kind of goods even if she had a licence in those days so that you could have sold hand-held missiles not to mention Alfa-Romeos and ciggies one at a time . . . A fortune because Gnoccoli at the interviews, to show he was serious and that one good turn deserves another, gave the first pair free, the second at a discount and with the third made them pay for the free pair and the bogus discount on the second. Oh, we had a queue outside. It looked as if knickers had become a sexy line, caviare for the bottom . . . Hundreds of women who together in a procession discovered the intoxication of knickers. Not that then, after the war, it was uncommon to wear them but it was Gnoccoli who knew to go about it without seeming to – Oh, the official sound of the indiscreet questions but nicely put. He ill-used them all as he did me, cross after cross, making them feel guilty and leaving them holding their breath, their purse empty and packets of knickers for the next ten years in their arms and on the carrier of their Lambretta. What a life! I think that the deceased had something in his nose, that – yes – all that special smell of the mass of women gave him a dash of energy in business. Oh, in some ways he was a monster, heaven help them if one of his staff went through the shop with deodorant and that is why you, Busi, a person like you wouldn't have lasted more than a couple of days. He sacked all the gays – with the first twitch of his nose he knew those workers who were suitable or not. At times there were certain smells because a number of the women tried them on there and then, behind the counter or in the toilets. There were two of them – two toilets, both for women. You will wonder – what about the men? Nothing, the men either held it in or went into the fields . . . At that time there was a lot of green round the tobacconists, not like now. And then that mania he had of going and cleaning the toilets himself. Cleaning! The least one could get away with. If you ask me he went there to count the sanitary towels in the little basket for them. Oh he was a fine one Faustino when it came to women. Was I jealous! Look, to me Gnoccoli was always so unimportant that it suited me like that. And then there's a world of difference between sniffing about and cuckolding. Oh goodness, it's not really true that he never meant much to me, you know how it is, I had all that work to do, all that pulling up and down and getting the elastic right . . . I'll tell you calmly later how we got to know each other and what followed professionally. Let's say I hadn't the time either to be jealous or to betray him – how can you betray someone who unconsciously doesn't matter to you? As useless and unserviceable as a spare you-know-what- at a wedding, a whole lot of rejects that keeps you tied to a string and moves you for ever, makes you keep going like mad for thirty years, doing what he wants without batting an eyelid – he didn't even have eyelashes. A type like him you either kill him, that's right, or you end up ignoring him and being his slave day and night. Because Gnoccoli had a way of . . . seducing me. His bald head, such a very round little head . . . I got to know him when he was young and bald already, a big round head like a Mongol, little light eyes, but he didn't have a human way of looking, I'd be inclined to say he was putting a price on a piece of commercial-livestock business when he looked at a woman. Obviously I liked him almost right away and then in those days he was a good match for a working woman. But he never looked at anything or anyone and said: I like that or

I don't like that – that's how he was. He weighed everything up in terms of debit and credit. Without concessions, without feelings, even. When he was serious you could take a look at him, but when he laughed you had to look away. We got on well together, we hardly ever saw each other. My daughter was born by mistake, his not mine. In certain things he knew exactly when to hold back at the right moment. He said he was horrified at the thought that it could be a boy – God, how he hated men! He could scarcely put up with himself and only if he forgot he belonged to the sex. He would have liked all women for himself, enslaved in a supermarket-harem for knickers and bras, to do up and undo from top to bottom from here to eternity . . . Once he drew back while I, as usual, was pretending to come on because in the act he was not to look as if he were selfish and, for all that it cost me, I let him believe it. And he got what he wanted, our Loredana was born . . . He was very keen on exploiting women – women, where there was a female pelvis he saw a way in, an invoice. Apart from the women who did the interviews, we had nothing but men in the firm, because he said a woman mustn't work away from home and must think of her husband and children, if possible with her iron going to and fro and the washing-machine working with a load of nothing but knickers with a few T-shirts and vests . . . Let me explain – he kept me and my daughter down like niggers but he didn't feel he was a hypocrite, no, we were *at home* he said we didn't have to undergo the humiliations of women in factories. Overlooking the fact that he would see we got a good dose of humiliation from himself, if really and truly a woman can't do without it at home or out of the house. And as for me, do you think, Busi, that he paid court to a woman when we met? No, I was something that walked about to put knickers on. Oh, I'll explain that too . . . Obviously a woman could lose her head – other men talked about love and passion, he talked about gift packages of six. To him the undersigned Passera was not a woman but a tailor's dummy from the waist down . . . The hammer all mucky with Faustino's blood . . . Oh, are we landing already? In Mombasa already? Goodbye. I hope to see you around. Otherwise I'll keep the same seat beside me for the return journey . . . Have you got the photo for the visa? I've got everything already, go on ahead, goodbye, Busi, have a nice stay in Kenya and I beg you – be chaste and above all avoid going with white women! Don't risk it in the lion's jaws!'

A terrible pandemonium at the airport customs: since the officials don't give change for the payment of the visa (you would need to present them with the eight dollars in cash, if it is ten or twenty you've had it, they say they are not a bank, next please, and they pocket the change), I get through elbowing aside those (all of them) who, to cut things short, were leaving tips bigger than the entrance price, and confronted all four officials, black, extremely fat and surly or else extremely thin, priestly and bored, call them rogues one and all and tell them it is surely an offence they are committing stealing all that money from the tourists with this excuse about the change. If they didn't give me my two dollars I was ready to take off again right away. A middle-aged Italian very joky and very thick with the corrupt financiers says:

'I can't make a fuss like you, I'm resident in Mombasa, you have to shut an eye or you get a surprise the moment you show yourself even if it is three thousand kilometres away,' and he leaves the change, inviting all the others, all non-resident and defenceless tourists to do the same and to take me for an oddball, a breaker of black balls. I replied to him – the audience magnificent, great dramatic tension – that if one has a certain character one has it even as a resident, a guest, a tourist, a stateless person, an exile and that he was probably one of those Italians who had been sentenced in his absence for something or other and that it was a good thing for Italy to have him out of Italy even if in Italy he would certainly be having a wonderful time because he'd certainly not be in prison, and that I couldn't see the reason for him living *here*. With a lack of character like his, one can get money and the heart-shaped swimming-pool anywhere, can't one? He gave a little laugh and biting the inside of his cheek, asked my name and what hotel I was going to. Then I told him his name and surname, which I had learned by heart reading his passport over his shoulder, after which I have him the information requested with every sign of cordiality, supplying him too with the times of day when it is good for the black mambas to turn up in the beds of undesirables. And I told him that I would get in touch immediately with the Italian embassy, in which case they will trace him more swiftly and give him the bad good news.

I haven't arrived yet and already there's someone who is in trouble and I am to blame. Ah, Mombasas! Mombasas, where do you find the arses!

Outside at last, the Kenyan whores occupy all the benches and low walls: more beautiful than words, elegant, shapely and very very young, very few old bags – and all of them, like a flock of black swans in a carillon, rise up, circle round spinning, displaying their most unique trophy. They smile, all teeth, flutter their eyelids on their big eyes with their golden whites, with nothing whorish about them, black and radiant and of an enchanting infantilism, one feels that they would do a trick with everyone, even the boys of ten. It has seldom happened to me to fuck a man with that same silhouette and the memory is indelible. Watching them swaying in their long colourful cotton dresses I say to myself what a pity, what a lot of lost chances for bum-fucking. Who knows whether they too are hairy round the arsehole like the men from Belluno, who knows whether they too like to be licked there? My God, how they stare at me, how they half-shut their eyes an instant, how everything in their eyes recalls horizontal vaginas which suck in your image as an imaginary reward. And then they laugh as if they already had their booty in their pockets, they burst out laughing all together, great big curly, tressed dolls. Only the Italian genius can manage this: to discover Africa or Romania to have it off with real ladies. It is one of the few qualities which I appreciate in the Italian male – his love for exotic whores. The women at home – he doesn't even know where they live: they are *all whores* whereas it's sufficient to take one's cock for a bit of a trip abroad so that later in the story at the bar the women become madly in love and refuse even a cheap ring. Because the Italian male, since he has a credit card, no longer talks about cash. And now there are two of them, the nicest of friends, who suddenly strike up a conversation with three black women, they who in the plane had done nothing but talk about AIDS. Good luck to them and especially to their modern little wives in Negrar, Province of Verona.

Vision: from the window of the bus which is taking us to the hotel and which has stopped in a traffic jam, I see an extremely beautiful European woman who comes forward and sits on the wooden bench at a stop. A moment later a black man sits down beside her showing a certain indolent familiarity. A woman who has let herself go, wearing with an unusual regal air a pair of blue jeans, green and dirty, a superior female to drive mad any white man in his senses in any part of the Aryan world. Beautiful and with something astonishing in the discretion of her gestures, which have a natural good breeding, turquoise eyes, a tall slim figure, falsely small breasts, as if they were squeezed under the abundant jumper, freckles on her ambered décolleté. She smiles with a certain reluctance at her black friend of whom I feel she is the lover and the mistress. An uncommon personality expresses itself in her elbow which, held close to her side, now throws out the lower arm in a gesture of fatalism. . . . Not the least betrayal of emotional impulsiveness in the way she moves her lips and throws a totally limpid glance at her loved inferior. She must whisper with precision, measuring out her sighs like falling manna. A wounded vestal tried by the vulgarity that a woman born beautiful endures. A woman, a lady who, tired of being punished for her beauty and her spirituality, the fruit of a controlled pain, and exploited in the interests of total revenge or the blindest solitude, has come here to be the object of curiosity. She has taken off from her beauty the price-tag she never dreamt of using, having exiled herself here to love a being on whom one feels she does not depend in any way, whose imagination she reins in – which he perhaps does not have. He is the victim, I can't be mistaken. A woman capable of anything, even of removing a breast with a blow from a knife, of staying a week in a boarding-house room with two metres of obedient and vainly excited black man, whose services she pays for, which consist in desiring her without ever having her, while she keeps them at bay with a mere movement of the mouth and clasped to her without ever getting what they want. The barrier that leads to the hotel gardens rises.

➤➤

Gilded hotel prison. In Kenya one inevitably ends up paying attention to what one manages normally to overlook at home: parties playing rummy to kill time. You would think that all the members of my group and of the others have come to Kenya to mix cards, deal them and get to know people like in a pub.

Evening: sentimental tunes in the style of Julio Iglesias of the kind considered likely to relax the nerves and get people chatting in a *savage* country. Two lesbians on display and certainly many more scattered among the tables and divans while 'Pensami-i-i' and 'Strangers in the Night' pours from the little orchestra. Not one solitary wolf of the kind that knocks off man or woman indifferently with the middle European elegance of someone who wants a fuck tonight at all costs. To get a tan and to say one has got it in a distant place instead of on the banks of one's own river has never done much for me; it is like getting chickenpox in the tropics. First dip in the Indian Ocean – four sea-urchin spines in my foot. Oh how the attendant cut away the slivers of skin and then, with the aid of a big thorn torn from a dry bush in the dunes, extracted the needles one by one from the feet of the donor of clothing! My foot immediately felt loved. The singsong of souvenir-sellers who take it in turns alongside the beach mattresses – not to have arrived yet and to have recourse right away to memories: little elephants, tiny buffaloes, panthers, jaguars, hippos. Necklaces, earrings, bracelets. All the more since immediately after the occasion which gives rise to the memory, everything flows together into a piece of literature. If only I had been happy once in my life with a man I would not have written either like this or so little . . .

Thanks to the written word I polish those new clichés of happiness which I shall never have time to print. But this, in fact, is my life: a strangely physical happiness with myself, my psychic marathon which spreads at immense speed in an impossible torchlight procession from one cerebral ventricle to the other and then nothing more.

Why have I undertaken this new journey? But to vanquish the word with life! That is to dream. I feel that life won't manage it this time either, not this time, not like this, not in my time.

◆◆

The existential tangles of man as writer are not resolved in literature only because he filters them through anti-biographical characters of which the greatest is the total character *writing* – with its appropriate system of relations: the mother Capital at the beginning of the line, the father Full-Stop at the end, the sister

Inverted Commas, the cousin Comma, the twins Semi- and Colon, the bachelor uncle Exclamation Mark, the grandfather Question Mark, the Dots – distant relatives . . . There is no relationship between life and art, only the caprices of facile sentimental dialectic, and to me the idea has become clear that I write to mark this irreconcilability rather than to show, as I thought in the days of the *enfant sauvage*, that it is possible to unite the opposites. Opposites cannot be united because – apart from being opposites – they belong to two different worlds which, if at all, recognize an opposite not outside but within themselves. There is no salvation in literature, thank God, and there is no salvation in life, there is no need for it; one slides over both and rebounds from one to the other and one is always at the same point of damnation – at the existential whim of speculating on it.

Writing has never distanced me from my natural sadness and daily anger as a man and perhaps the great thing about being an intellectual and writer is that you can unravel in a character, in a novel, all – but all – the knots and untangle all the reasons for malaise without thereby being able to do anything as far as the malaise in your life is concerned. To improve the intellect is a poor panacea which has no or little influence on the rest. The mind shines but the body remains wrapped up – for the body to skin itself there needs to be more than one mind . . . When I am living I do not carry my literature about with me – I live as a living being not as a writer, just as when I write I write as a writer and the fact that I am alive while I write seems to me to be a superfluous – if necessary – accidental matter. As for my direct relationship to others, I cease to be a writer each time I leave my typewriter and am not one even if, at the wheel, I continue to think of a sentence, not even if I am going to a literary presentation, not even when I am discussing a contract with a publisher. At these moments I am someone who has everyday affairs in hand, a hydraulic expert, an engineer, an actor, an unemployed man – the unease arises, if it does, from the desire to communicate to others that the *writer*, as something under the heading of arts and crafts, does not exist or that they cannot count on me to have the security of a *role* in which to cage myself. Everyone expects me to end up in the Presidential Palace because it would be on a higher social plane. The mad ideas of people who reduce to myth certain simple, wonderful ordinary beings! who are naturally accomplices – but not I.

Art has not permeated my body far less my social life; I feel I have become the greatest writer I could become by putting everything into it (to the point of repudiating myself, in the sense that I have given all my physical energy up to a future perfect to the present work of writing novels) not *within* but *outside* myself because I have no *inside* and live on non-existence, without sophistries, with the indispensable amount of cynicism to put the pedants to silence. My void, after three novels which have left me apparently exhausted but in the end weak and strong as I was before I girded myself to the task, has remained the same as always. My thoughts and desires are the same and my emotional longings and emotional waves too are tangled and muddy as before, in spite of my having spat them out *with style* in more than one character. To become a great writer does not mean to learn anything. After decades of self-murder in my characters, I have understood that I have not understood and the knowledge is of no help; ignorance has been greatly refined but not to the point of redeeming me.

A group of phoney primitive fishermen stop me on the beach, one of them shouts touching an arm: 'Cremona.' I explain that I am not called Cremona, that I am not an entire Italian town. Nothing doing. Since they have known someone from Cremona for whom they cooked fish and entertained, now all Italians are *Cremona* and very likely all searching for tribal delicacies in the huts of the interior. 'Fishing? Trip on cataraman? You friend, everything OK, no problem, me all prick.' Another jumps up, without energy, as if he were continuing an ideal door-to-door canvas uncovering three centimetres of puce gum like a minimal-ist paragraph: 'I explain. First fish out at sea, conches, then my house,' and looking round: 'All.'

It seems this person from Cremona had taken a trip beyond the coral reef – several times, in fact – everything included, every-thing with everyone. I pretend not to understand – when it doesn't suit me, when I don't make use of it, I don't feel like revealing the least thing, no one gets abstract declarations from me so as to have confirmation of my profound carnality. And yet

I would like to make a quick visit to their huts. There are giant flies like this and shortly they all become a buzzing fly. 'Boat trip price for friend?' he insists. 'How much?' I ask. 'Seventy dollars for two hours.' And in English I say to him seriously how do you manage to stay in it? Then they spell out the offer: there are nine of them? Right, they would take turns at swimming, in the bottom of the boat there's a goatskin as well, it doesn't hurt your back, and off we go one *inside* the other and for every fucked arse a conch of welcome. And then comes the fateful question: 'What the hell else do you need?' which means to say we'll see to it. Everything for sale. And even if it were not true that everything – the little there is – is for sale, seeing that I feel no attraction for these skinny negroes, I hang on to my prejudices and do not allow myself to be tempted for the benefit of some poor man who wants to put it into some place warm.

Not that I don't like blacks, let us be clear. I am not interested in black men domesticated from savagery but certainly in a black man rendered savager from being citizen of a metropolis, just as a big blond in Amsterdam is not sexually stimulating in the same way as the same big blond leaping on to you from a liana in the heart of the jungle. The eye for ambience also wants to play its part. Besides to let oneself be fucked by a black man, as distinct from a mulatto, I find is kitsch, lacking in erotic counterpoint; it is all written down. But to fuck one or a half-caste, what a dream! The true perversions aren't to be found already packaged – one spends a lifetime discovering them – that is to say, inventing them – and then if they are true and yearning they are not transmissible to anyone else. The perversions of my taste are born from the inventiveness of the perversions of my writing. I shall be categorical, indeed, contradictory: each time I discover, by writing about it, something rhetorically and linguistically arbitrary I am predisposed to transfer it into action in the reality of my corporeal existence as a chemico-social machine. In other words: *I do it*. It suffices for me to have a desire, because of the complex fact of having formulated it, to be disposed to do much in order to put it to the test of life. There is not a single word in my literature which has remained an oral or verbal *thought* of any kind, it is translated into *blood*, from which in turn it is translated. If I do not write it I do not know what I feel. I feel as if I were on the point of being born each time I write, to have been nothing previously, that there is nothing that I am not ready to refuse or to desire *for the first time*. And so when I experience a sudden emotion for a man who is sceptical about me I have no verbal tactic at my disposal: I throw out the words, but no one has ever understood that a writer has no other choice in life than to be brutal, but not because he has to make up for an embittered past of frustrations and repressions and love someone, but because he is simply opening his eyes for the first time like any other time. I really and truly adhere to the man of the moment for what lies in his immediacy *plus* what lies in my will to experiment, fed by desires unknown even to me; it is never a projection or a phantasm that I carried about inside me from before. You are all stupid not to have thought that I managed synchronously to reach the summit of a whole 'us' without the need to scale either of the two, that in a second ascent I was offering my life for an unthought-of form still in the making, that for an aesthetic whim I could knowingly muddy my sedimentations. I have never met anyone capable of understanding the cold rationality, the supreme style of my immediate and instinctive moments of abandon *here*, which is the only immortal space for living. I have to do with men who are what they are plus what they think they are, with opinions of themselves to act as a counterbalance to the vanity of love and who cannot procure for me – myself and one other – anything other than hysteria while, if I choose to love alone, I spin poetry. Because I have everything to gain and I fall upon a man with the power of a cyclone taking off, but I fight with the lightness of a breeze if they put my gentle stirrings on the market. In love I shall never renounce my lack of style. Rather renounce love.

And then it is fate that I fall in love only with fleeting olive-coloureds from who it would be difficult to squeeze out any other virtue than that of pleasing my sluggishness.

➤

An Afro-Garda amenity: The man who sells lemons at the entrance to Sirmione – quartered lemons and oranges but above all coconuts – 500 lire apiece – after dreaming about coming to Kenya had scarcely set foot in the garden of the Whitesands

215

Hotel, which is covered with huge slender palms, when he was knocked down by a coconut in its case, which split open his head. He is already on the waiting-list for the very next flight – the day after tomorrow – with a prognosis half withheld and the other half public knowledge. His mates are amused. It is probable that with this blow and his ear hanging down he won't even have time to change profession or to opt for a citrus orchard in Agrigento, let's say, full board, to be kept an eye on from his invalid chair. The most searing humiliation for those who are visionaries of memory arises from not being mutilated in the right place by the right cliché – what story is he telling now? That he was injured by a coconut? He will in fact never have the courage to tell the customers in the inn, anxious for African anecdotes, that the whole adventure consists in the revenge of the collective memory of the coconuts he had been disembowelling for a lifetime with a big knife shouting 'Coconuts, fine coconuts!' and putting money aside for big-game hunting.

~

Twilight. The phoney fishermen carry back to their huts not nets but little wooden statues, the tourists return from the beach.

In these days new loving couples have formed; I have watched them and followed them from the first meeting, from the dance in the open-air in the evening to the first embrace, the good-looking boy and the good-looking girl, with the parents accomplices, especially a mother who fears that her daughter is 'too serious for her age'. Since the good-looking, handsome Dane couldn't make up his mind to invite the girl to dance the quick-step or the slow waltz, the mother winked to her husband and invited him to dance herself – and then gave a little shove to her hard little maid with the severe look, sulkily devouring him with her eyes and observing him secretly with a mirror. The father sighed: 'What a greenhorn! What times these are!' Now the two young people will certainly be happy even if they are left alone not for an instant but for several whole, apparently forgetful hours by their parents, who are broad-minded and nostalgic. For the two young people it will be a memorable holiday – he will have lost his virginity because she, with a mother like that, by now could only lose her appetite and will go back languidly to school thinking of making love before and after meals, of the selfish harmony of the bodies of lovers in the water of the ocean, of him playing the merman round her and under the water, making her laugh and drink, they will both think back to the calls of 'Sven!' 'Liza!', blending with one voice into the shout that did not even seem to come from their own throats.

I learned that he will come to visit her in Italy and she will take him on a flight in a two-seater plane in skies over Madrid. Good, good, and I can't even fly a kite. Life is . . . add an adjective to cul-de-sac and go and take a dip, writer of gags – enough said.

Today on the beach the blacks addressed me with new nicknames (but how did I not think of it sooner! *Cremona* for them was not the place the lute-maker came from but he himself – literally 'the cream man'! 'Mussolini, Mafia!' 'You Mussolini buy elephant tiger monkey?' Then a big fat boy: 'You Mafia Italy want nice African mamma big tits?' He actually uses the word Roman dialect word for 'tits', the last buyer having been from Rome. High-grade whores work the front hall – but one knows that because of the retro-virus they are not coming up to the Third World tradition. Extremely elegant here, of mixed blood black/white, negro-Indian, negro/Arab, women I would take away for ever – and instead they are used a couple of times and immediately replaced, by the usual solitary men who rent them for twenty-four hours. Little plaits, accurate and serpentine, very light make-up, vivid glances – how well they must feed on the cock with those beautiful hoovering lips or women whom the provincial Casanovas have to rent so that at night, as they sleep happy and blessed on one side without pants, the women are awake with their pointed tongues going out and in up to the first vertebra, covering them with saliva and caressing them with circular movements; which is good for sciatica.

I try to understand what the maximum privilege enjoyed by money abroad is: it is to set oneself up in the amniotic dimension of Allyouneedislove: to have no more need of pleasure or the lack of it, please. It is oiled indifference, well fed, completely relaxed, casual, that comes from experiencing the pleasure of no longer being forced to live in order to get impressions from it. I would be unable to explain to myself in any other way the pleasure of these people on an adjustable deckchair under a palm-tree from eight in the morning to twelve-thirty and from two to half-past six. Day after day they are still living in the day before, enjoying the luxury of having treated themselves to hibernation in the sun or an inevitable return trip to the peace of an inexistent origin.

Not that things go any better for me – I sit here observing unworthiness but without arrogance; besides even in 1986, in spite of everything, man will win the palm as Jewel of the Cosmos.

I don't know for how many years more, because man is the real animal that is heading for physical extinction. Man who has invented everything for himself – from himself to God – unfortunately has never thought of developing that consciousness of the planetary collectivity which today would come in handy in order to deal with things bit by bit – why *unfortunately*? Cut it.

'No, come on – we're on holiday' – and I too shut my eyes but it's the other ones that don't want to hear of shutting. All the most intelligent things have already been written by Mallarmé and Verlaine and I cannot content myself with so little, I have to invent more perfect lies. I have the feeling of being surrounded by barbed wire and it makes no difference if it is to stop one from getting out or from coming in; it is there – that's how it is. And to think that forty is the ideal age for a man if thirty weren't more so!

There are two homosexual couples whom you would not suspect in the hotel and it would never enter anyone's mind except mine to connect their individual four-square virility with a deviation. I know they are so unequivocally and will say why – I shall keep myself company as I say it to myself. Both tall, dark blond, very beautiful, sportsmen, the first couple is English and windsurfing. The second couple is American – one blond, the milky complexion typical of redheads, his friend vaguely South American with a moustache but very gentlemanly and without the monstrous sinews of the machos who have frequented the *black rooms*.* The four, although they meet several times a day, never get to know each other nor do they recognize each other once as if, two by two, they were afraid of each other. Each pair releases energy only towards his own partner and one might

*In English in the original. (Tr.)

think it was self-protected under a glass cloche in which there is no air except for reciprocal breathing. The social class of both couples: middle to upper class. Their eight eyes never rest on anything by chance, curiosity, inadvertence, lust, desire for ethereal and silent gossip between human beings. What is the use of the surrounding world? they seem to cry out – immobile. The quartet swims in the vagueness of a mental horizon before which there is the void and beyond it the danger of a fullness – of a mine that is totally empty. Reciprocally hyperdependent, like Siamese twins, they have adopted that distance between themselves which does not awaken suspicions as to the cannibalistic nature of their bonds. Perhaps for years each of the four had been looking for a complement to provide a basis for a reason and to ignore the world and, having found it, the outstanding expenses of a capillary capitalization of the alter ego have raised an invisible, unscaleable, quite simply cordial barrier against others. No kind of affectation in any of them – but they have difficulty even in concentrating for a minute on the waiter who goes reciting the menu from table to table, and scarcely has he finished his refrain than they ask him please to repeat it. They eat unable to wait for the time to get back to eating each other and without paying any attention to the courses served – the windsurfer has dipped his fork in the thin broth *à l'anglaise*. Apart from the South American (tall, perhaps Argentinian, not beautiful but fiendishly beautiful, with an aristocratic air of the underworld, of dizzy sex-appeal, with a body that is used to saying everything and most of it with few words) it looks as if life had not had time to leave a wound or a passage, an open trace of bitterness endured, on the face of the other three. One would only need to see my swollen and repellent face on waking to realize what a life with such traces is like . . . Good: these three have put a plastic wrapping on everything, have delimited the pain and the anguish, the knife-edge surprises, the difficulties of the case; they have reached the stage, so long craved for, of mutual fusion, the sinister happiness of a feeling that is finally total with a man, in spite of the hostility of family, society, perhaps of their ex-wives and against the world so inexorably distant from them. They go on safari together, sleep together, take the sun together, give momentary attention to the girls they drive mad, but if one of them is in the water and a girl chats with the other, the latter says Yes with his chin, lights up his eyes out of chivalry but never loses sight of his friend until he comes out of the water and comes back to lie on the mattress alongside. Too refined to spread oil on each other's shoulders, they have become introverted and alien to themselves when they are *together*, sacrificing without effort any irredentist hint of their old personality as singles which will have been, like all the others I have known, hanging out of the windows on to the world for a good while to see whether even today something nice will not fall from on high to relieve the claustrophobia of the body grown rigid in its expectation. It did fall and, unlike what a woman thinks of her cunt, my envy has limits . . . They are here no differently from what they would be in an abandoned hermitage in the desert and a hundred and fifty guests around in the cloister of the hotel are not *people* but mirages of dust . . . To know what obscure effect this crowd, scorned by them one by one, has on the functioning of their Masonic little twosomes – if their *intimacy* takes its cue from being immersed but remote in the general crowd of heterosexuals, if their indifference is the most refined result of ferocious hate or a basic stupidity that has been brooded over since an infancy . . .

I would be something apart – if I were to enter into being a part of a process of loving couples, I would test our compactness by putting it at the disposal of anyone wishing to take a turn with one or the other . . . Such an approach would be rejected certainly both by my possible partner and by those unhappy persons who, instead of being content with something, prefer the Whole, which they will never have, simply so as not to give up the idea they have of it. The unhappy ones, in fact, not having anything, are never grateful for anything, and are not prepared to share it with anyone. Whereas I – when a lady after these four days of solitude said '*Oh*, good evening,' – but maybe that *Oh* is a weakness of mine to console myself – I instinctively replied with a joyful 'Thank you' to this unexpected gesture of courtesy, amazed that someone paired off should address me who am a stranger and unpaired. It seems to me that a stranger today is much – but very much – more a stranger than ten years ago, for example. And then a stranger, without even a dachshund – you can pass as a wife, a lover, a friend, but without even a dog! – strikes fear even in a luxury hotel after four days during which, in view of his continued solitude, which defies enlistment, he remains a stranger because *not together*. If he is not in a party, a *single man* today is like the threatening evocation of a dark age. And everywhere they manage to arrange an exodus, but a traveller who asks for a couchette – No. Impossible to describe the murmur of voices aroused by my *single* presence at the table reserved for me in the restaurant. And the struggles I have at each meal with the head waiter to get him to remove the place set opposite me. He keeps saying, 'Why? Why?', upset that a knife on one side, napkin in the centre and a fork on the other is not always better than no one. And these four carefree lovers who chew away on my right and left, proud and satisfied, oh if they would at least let me clean their bottoms!

And to think that I only wanted something and have had to be content with everything!

Goodness knows where Clementina Gnoccoli has stuck herself. Best not to think. If she turned up I could make a couple with her, she would drown my melancholy in murderous high spirits. Who knows. I could open doors for her – but there's only one here – or take out her chair at table, pour her wine, things like that. But then of course! she said there was something with her in the shadows and I am not sure I could have counted on her, apart from some appearance fleeting as light. And what if I aired my brain a little by walking, for example, the kilometre to Mombasa? It will be like here – a place never before seen, memorable for the memories of the thoughts of others which it awakes from the first moment to the last. But kilometre after kilometre, I hobble along under the mosquito net, seeking sleep or a little joy in living for tomorrow. I don't manage very well.

At midnight a pretty girl came down from her parents' room to the garden pond to watch the red goldfish. She was in pyjamas, enchanted on the low wall, forgetful of everything. Then, like a sleepwalker, she took the path to the servants' quarters and without knocking, entered a room. Of the second chef from the Nyerere tribe, who sleeps with the porter from the Niukuku tribe. At two in the morning a sleepy voice began to shout:

'Viola, Viola, *wo bist du*?' (Viola, Viola, where are you?) and the girl's father, probably turning towards his wife in the bed, grumbles:

'You know the girl wants to eat trifle at all hours of the day and night. She'll come back when she has stuffed herself.'

The pretty girl with the blond plaits – now a little loosened – reappeared calmly, slightly drowsy, smiling she made a gesture to me with her chin, her pyjamas were a bit dishevelled, and she was sniffing at a finger.

'*Wo warst du*?' said the mother on the balcony, putting her hands on her hips, and then catching sight of me 'Good evening' and going back in right away. 'You know that too many sweet things aren't good for you, look how fat you are!'

➤➤

The trade winds which blow from the ocean do nothing to moderate the unreal sultriness fired by all these honeymoon couples. In the morning they arrive in the buffet hand in hand, like ignorant children, glad not to know where they are going because, at their goal, there awaits them a flag, a flapjack, a handful of coriander. I must get out of here, go away with something that is not another taxi, get through the barrier of *everything organized for your comfort*. Now here comes the wives with children preceding their husbands, who have stayed behind to shave; then extras in the shape of housewives got up it's not clear whether for the beach or a gala evening. Ribbons and flowers in everyone's hair above summary make-up. And then the most horrendous vision: the little family from Bergamo beginning to play rummy in Kenya at 9 in the morning.

I take the bus at the stop in front of the road-block – it is supposed to be the entrance but with the barrier and the warders with helmets and truncheons in their belts . . . and am off through Mombasa, some district or other glimpsed on arriving, these bits of wood tied up in the midst of rubbish and crowned with a boiling pot and sad natives waiting for a ration or holding out a hub-cap or pressing together the palms of their hands. The people in the bus smile at me lurching about, I keep bumping my head because I am standing and keep bouncing. There is an energy here under the ashes which is released from looks half hostile, half curious, but I parry any glance with my irises, I challenge them, reinforce my decision not to consider ragged blacks as something special, something to do with folklore. As always I organize my own emotions and my desire for brotherhood. I am also asexually privileged because the great beauty of the black human being enchants but does not excite me. Much better to let myself be laughed at here because of the bumps on the head than there in the wide open spaces thwarted by a homely posture of happiness which has no surprises, apart from those included in the programme. Those tourists who come here for two weeks, maybe, they live ticked off between the timetable for meals and the timetable for the beach and when they get back say they have been in Kenya, what the devil do they mean? What would these safari hunters have missed or caught at some Adriatic resort?

In Mombasa I make for the railway station, following my nose, even if – given the time of day – I shall not see the mythical two-way train Mombasa/Nairobi which leaves every evening at 7 o'clock. I wander about among the various bus depots, each one also a goods depot for agricultural produce. It is that desire to go in one breath in every direction, to cut into a myriad of virgin pages without a ticket either way; I walk cautiously, each step reminds me of the sea-urchin needles, some of them are making themselves felt again. The district is a heap of beams and ruinous walls, broken glass, burst tyres, matting, where whoever lies underneath has some possession to keep safe from the thieves. Only sudden roars from doorless trucks lacerate the general sleep of the city, half-naked figures leap up from among the clouds of dust, which when they thin out, reveal nothing and no one. Has a guitar begun to twang? And where is the station? I walk and walk, pass through shouting crowds interspersed with crowds sleeping under trees and gutters. A strange sensation, not to be noticed, not to exist, not to be able to be included in their perception of the street. Together and simultaneously, they have decided not to make me exist. Unexpectedly a magic cloud – all pink and maroon – is rent open before me; the gleam of a lance behind a wall: three Masai warriors, very beautiful and feminine, brush past me speedily, authentic and slightly affected, lithe. They slip through a gap in the opposite side of the same wall, I follow them; beyond is the most silent market and most packed with people in the world. I am sure that that small boy leaning over the vegetables with his brusque gesture is signalling to me to disappear – totally . . . Living drains, local smells, half-new, cross, immobile goats, mounds of potatoes, bunches of tiny carrots of a lively orange, vibrate among baskets of chopped herbs and sacks of yellow spices. Stubbornly I continue on my walk – the same gesture as he made to me I now see being made by other peasants to long thin rats which come towards the millet. Perhaps I am wrong: they do not let me exist but no one has ill-will towards me. The rats are kept at a distance by bored threats. I like these mounds of shiny purple potatoes and the little milk-white cauliflowers and the little balls of bluey-white cabbages in front of the old women with their erect bodies and crossed legs. Observing the pyramids from the far end of the market, every article, including the old women, is arranged so as to form a little hillock with five units in the base then four placed on top, then three, two, then the best one on top. I turn into a lane divided down the middle by a rivulet which bears away rotten leaves, Coca-Cola tins, patches of engine oil. The twanging of a guitar appears: on a base of reinforced concrete a group is tuning its instruments and then the drummer begins a roll with a fast rhythm on his two drums, a copper plate, two big cow-bells, a big food tin, and the guitarist, having launched the first complete scale into the air with his powerful horn plectrum, casts an eye with a superior air over the heads of the people crowding below. He does not even beat time with his feet, perhaps so as not to rub his trousers which are like elephant feet, and is all dressed in white, from his jacket to the wide tie of gleaming Terylene knotted over a shirt without cuffs, something first-class second-hand available only to real artists. He must be bored by his own unstoppable social rise, he gives me the impression that he is looking at the people standing there listening as if he had to settle things with them one by one. Does he know that the person who can amuse most has also the power to humiliate most: I move on, always towards this station which cannot be found. I ask a down-and-out youth with his legs dangling who now cannot pretend not to see me.

'The station is here,' he says.

I look round.

'Where here?'

'Here – over there.'

And precisely what I had mistaken for a garage or a graveyard for cars is the Mombasa station. Deserted and spick and span, policemen in full dress move about among trucks laden with amazing suitcases. Ticket office, timetables, the tracks on the other side of the padlocked grille, I consult, I ask, I drum my fingers on my mouth, but I feel no desire arriving from my perplexity.

There are three classes: I would be tempted by a journey in third class, I have heard that people bleed themselves white for a seat and that the poor hide the money where life is regularly unsheathed. Apart from the third class, Kenya is a place where you can do nothing if you have not booked: everything has to have been previously calculated and arranged by the whites for the whites so that nothing is left for the blacks – except to remain motionless. Not a single decent pension administered by an Uncle Tom at suitable prices. Either the stars or the shacks and for the shacks you need their antibodies or at least a knife . . . I take a little turn among mothers the colour of clay suckling babies of a jaundiced black, yellow at the temples. I am bewitched by a black urchin with red hair who is following a hen that has come out of a basket of palm-leaves while his group is intent on settling accounts on a little pile of coins in the centre of a rag. Then out, taking care not to step on any of these men who are dozing here and there on the bare grass, on the ground – inside a dry fountain. A man raises his hand: '*Jambo!*' and he gives me a very broad smile, I could swear not a mercenary one like those I have put up with up to now on the beach. Not believing my eyes, I approach existence thanks to someone else: he is lacking his other hand, the little stump is abandoned on his lap, the wrist which is almost pointed, gleams. Alongside this dispenser of greetings a contorted and sooty and very old dwarf is apparently standing guard over a lead pot, from which nothing is reflected, old and so blackened in its turn, as if too sacred to have been polished even once since time immemorial. One feels it to be a pot which in its own way has been carefully tended, *loved*, perhaps venerated.

'He is my father,' he begins while his smile narrows, 'he spent all his life building the railway. He is a hundred.'

I look at him better, he too smiles at me in a cheeky way.

'He speaks English very well – better than me. He followed the track-laying from Mombasa,' and he points with his stump to the station opposite, 'to Nairobi. Then the railway stopped. Today we aren't selling anything – it's Sunday. But we stay here – so that the pot isn't left by itself. He doesn't want to leave it. When they got to Nairobi the English gave him the pot as a reward. Have you seen how big it is? And it will come to me one day.'

I am about to say to him – if they had got as far as Masai Mara with the choo-choo would they have given him a big spoon too? Every ten seconds the old man moves the still green bananas on the cluster in front of him. The son says:

'We serve them boiled but today is Sunday, day of rest. Today even the shit-machine rests,' and he rubs his stomach.

'And Miss Cathy too,' mutters the old man, caressing the cover and then the belly of the pot. 'She's mad about rain, the fucking bitch . . . She likes water on the outside, she is refreshed and the rain puts out the fire. Ah my lady Bitch.'

Then he bends his ebony head down between his arms and curls up, a motionless foetus, the same as he has been working himself back into for a hundred years.

Resuming my walk and resisting the temptation of the weak to put out a little money to provide evidence that I have already felt more consistent. I am perennially accompanied by this feeling of inferiority caused by the perfection of my sensibility, of sentimental inadequacy towards my feelings which are so civilized. I shall never be for anyone what that pot is for that man and my gratitude is out of all proportion to the causes of my emotions. I spill over and drown . . . I shall never know myself *apart* from myself, there is no one to go on to the end with me, where the mind explodes and perceives the marvellous nullity of a being that is human and in love. Now I understand that the only possible contact between my alienation and their life is that they should undo their sandals – twelve of them at least – and allow you to wash their feet or to go to the cross for them so as to savour, drunk with pain, their inability not to betray.

From afar a flutter of lengths of cloth in the wind under a long canopy of beams and corrugated iron. Now there opens before me an immense space with hundreds of blacks up against the houses with their eyes shut; Sunday, a day of rest, yes, but they seem to have been ordered to rest according to the letter without moving or blinking an eyelid or standing up. I turn off again and, pervaded by a strange happiness, wave my hand in the direction of the hand and the stump, which are raised in the air. If I kept on turning round he would continue to raise everything he has for me and to smile to me as best he can until infinity. He is a man like me and will pass his life peeling bananas with one hand.

Second-hand market – that is to say the Big Stores of these parts: European clothes of every kind and cut, all with that patina of starch which makes them seem to crackle in the air, rigid coloured corpses piled up in the hanging grave which is the European concept of help to the Third World. How many wedding dresses dangling rigid under the eaves while some girls stand and look at them with their heads tilted up more than is necessary. I walk lightly among my shadows, I try to catch their glance but the girls pretend not to notice. No one can harm me; I am invisible, perhaps I do not exist. And if one doesn't buy anything and if one doesn't even have an order to give, for a black person one is not even a white man: one doesn't exist and that's that. I feel myself furtively with a lump in my throat; yes, I am there, and it is a dream.

An open gate – I enter. I don't wish to be moved any more by the big damp eyes of the blacks nor to have my stomach turned by the whites of these parts: two kinds of the same ignominy. The complicity between exploited and exploiters exhausts my brain, leaves me worn out, as if only that part of the brain which neither I nor others have ever used, or still use, concealed the ineffable explanation of the pleasure there is in making some people suffer because of others and to put up with it without rebelling. What sense is there in giving a caress to someone who has known only whiplashes? He does not understand and tears at your hand – and instinctively I put my right hand to my mouth.

A burly, tall old man – I could swear Indian from his beard and turban – is coming in my direction in a state of alarm, he is trying in an extreme agitation to tie up his trousers quickly with a piece of string with lots of bobbins.

'You will excuse me,' he says immediately in perfect English as he finishes the knot, 'but I ran in here because I had stomach-ache and didn't want to dirty myself. Do you think it will rain?'

'You owe me no apology – I do it too wherever I happen to be.'

What place is this? There are some low buildings, shut, with greenish paint and great hanging strips like fowls about to lift off. A goat passes, matronly, and stares at me sceptically and smugly. Some guinea-fowl are scratching about near an old man who, with a tin of Campbell's tied to the end of a bamboo cane, is collecting water from a circular ditch to pour it round dwarf plants.

'Is it a public garden or what?' I ask my old man, whose stare I deliberately try to ignore. His white and red beard is carefully tended, otherwise he is all one rag, bare feet. Then I too look hard at him, I am not sure what kind of challenge he is proposing to me, bending slightly forward as if he were awaiting a word or gesture from me: his blue eyes make a dangerous depth pirouette in mine, an abyss in which he is making room for me *for ever*. He is weighing me up as if I were a belonging of his, I feel, something he was the first to have found in the street and which he will not give back.

'Give me a kiss,' he says in a peremptory fashion, catching hold of me. 'On the lips.'

'No.'

'On the cheek.'

'No.'

'Wherever you like.'

'Then nowhere. You haven't answered my question – is it a public garden or what?'

'It is a cemetery,' the man, who is perhaps not so old and certainly not very wise, tells me feeling put down. 'My father is here, my son and my two daughters.'

I think that now he will tell me that he couldn't make up his mind on which of the four tombs to deposit it but he doesn't look like someone indecisive even if he had diarrhoea in a bus.

'Are you a Catholic? Protestant?' I ask, very interested in this business of shit and the dear departed. And then I am caught by surprise by this statement: he is the first person with whom I have exchanged another word except on the weather or else where I have to submit to certain standard black themes about wooden animals and embarrassed polite remarks in order to refuse a ridiculous commodity. I look at him again – old or not, he is a monument to male beauty, his eyes from being dangerous have become merely curious, his superb figure slightly bent forward because of the belly, toe-nails like the horns of pre-historic animals. I decide to inveigle him into my fairytale, slipping into his mind along with him. He is perhaps a man of high caste wounded in his historical and family dignity by the circumstances of being an emigrant, and now much more so by my sudden, elegant appearance. We must have the same size of shoe but I don't have a second pair with me. I could bring him one tomorrow.

'No, Muslim. Do you want to see the tombs?'

'Yes please.'

'Do you have enough trust?'

'Excuse me, trust in what?'

'To go off alone with me.'

'Why shouldn't I? If you insist I can go off by myself and not trust you. But please – no kisses.'

'Have you been sent by God?' he asks in a faint voice. So I did not hear him properly.

'No, my travel agency is Rhino Safari, I don't know whether you know it,' I say and wonder how the conversation would have gone on if I had given the only answer that came to my lips: 'Yes.' Every time before falling asleep I have an exchange of this kind, I do, my enraged melancholy leads me to think up these trifles because they amuse me and I have a great fear of giving in to them. Besides it is the only reason why I have never asked for a gun-licence – because I would never be quick enough to use it on someone else.

'Look, this is a recent burial,' he bends down, begins to trace a rectangle with his finger in the extremely fine sand which is humid in the heat. 'They dig a grave, the corpse is lowered into it and it is covered over with a fence of loose wooden planks without nails or metal; then the planks are covered with earth. In its grave the corpse breathes with all its body, freely. It is naked and absolute in a sheet of natural cotton – coarse stuff. And without any jewel. Have you ever thought of the splendour of the dark?'

'Sometimes . . . There's no name on the stone.'

'This is a perfect Muslim burial – a wooden tombstone and no name, no date, no "last words" epitaph. And what do you say to the light? Look at the light up there – isn't it splendid?'

How many thousands of years old can he be, this old man with his heavy, hard lumps of flesh, his amber-coloured skin, his eyes which now have a fire that consumes him? What is the nature of the attraction in my bearing that overcomes him, that lies respectfully in ambush, with its strange sensuality, from another world? Why do his nostrils come so close to my neck and armpits and seem to breathe in the memory of a perfume which I do not have? For years I no longer smell of liquorice as the lovers of my youth used to say, or of mimosa, but I smell of boiled meat in a kitchen where the meal has been eaten without remembering to empty the ashtray with the cigarette-ends. I have the smell I deserve – of an onanist terrified of falling prey once more to that hunger for a man which impels one to set off at once and to be a confusion of painful and unsatisfied muscles in the compartment of a train, on an aeroplane, running along a street coughing because of the sudden effort or escaping across the fields from a gang of assailants with the baying of the dogs behind.

'They rest very well with us.'

'. . . and without sex,' I am about to say but I keep this poetic exploit to myself. No tombstone, no date, no name, no gender. Dead is dead – male or female. Death a female animal with a variegated sex, oviparous of its own worms.

'Whereas do you see the ones with the stones? They interfere with the liquefaction of the Primary Oil of matter.'

'Sorry, what did you say? What kind of oil? Tell me, what size of shoe do you take?'

'I don't wear shoes. Don't you know the pleasure of adhering to the earth, of being a plant that never detaches itself and moves from place to place only by dragging its roots behind it? But tell me – do you think it will rain?'

'But this is a fixation! What difference does it make?'

'Rain is like a drug to me. My feet get lively. Then everything goes to my head. This stone, one with all the useless information and even a quotation, disturbs God who created the angels. Do you see these white clouds?'

'I don't see any.'

'They're too white for you – you can't see them. Well they are God's angels called out on parade. The angels of God, when they form a good squad, fall on the plants and drip into the oil of the earth and the corpse slowly melts into it. Oh I have been in your Catholic cemeteries with little stone cells shut in on four sides . . . I heard dead humanity howling in desperation, they had no peace there, walled in. I can never stay long in your cemeteries – the plastic flowers . . . And the angry noise you make when you are dead is deafening . . . My father was Indian and my mother was an Arab, oh my father was from Kathiawar, don't worry. But I feel I am part of the land of Israel. The root of roots is Jewish. Man's sacred texts are five, five as is written in God's hand. Genesis, Exodus, Leviticus are in England on Queen Victoria's bedside table . . .'

'Sorry?'

'It's a way of saying the British Museum . . . The Aryans, for example, are descended from my Mother India. From one region in particular, the Punjab. We talk about a motor with so many horse-power, we should talk instead about so many angels because they are the origin of all the Oil. The other two sacred texts are . . . But are you all right?'

'Fine, thank you. Low blood-pressure. Very pleased to have had this chat. Goodbye. Let's hope it rains.'

'You really weren't sent by God?'

'No more than anyone else, believe me. Thanks for your hospitality. May I . . .'

'For goodness sake put away that filthy money.'

He holds on to my right hand. If now he plays the trick on me of raising it to his lips I'll give him a push with the other. Embarrassed, I don't even want to be confronted by these ardent eyes, I look away towards the way out where the same ragged old man is still using the tin and the bamboo cane on the mud-coloured plants. I take a better look – it isn't water it is liquid sewage. Human oil, perhaps. My mother always did the same with the horses' *apples* – that is to say, the angels which went by pulling lorries and carts.

'Listen to me a moment more,' implores the old man with the immense energy in his knuckles, holding my hand in a vice and pulling me towards him, to his greasy and buttonless shirt, to his canary-yellow trousers with urine stains on the thighs. I resist, I do not want either to offend him or to see myself swallowed up. This time I stare at him too.

'All right.'

'I am only in part Indian, as I told you, and in any case am not from the Punjab, otherwise I'd have stabbed you in the back by now. All my life I have been dreaming of being able to do something like that, but I have never done it and will never do it. Have you never felt an urge like that? – to kill – the enduring of an insurmountable inability of which only you are not capable and everyone else is?'

'Yes. No. I kill them all myself and myself with them without doing too much harm to anyone. I put up with it. Like most people.'

'Me – some days I wake up and say to myself: Ah, another day without belonging to the Punjab. They are the dregs of humanity, those for whom everything is possible – pimps, thieves, procurers, blackmailers, committers of incest, traitors, cowards, assassins, *spreaders of the plague*. By means of the Oil. Here – as everywhere – they have taken root, they have in their hands the prostitution of young girls and the business of homosexuality. Don't go into the Old Town, the men and women are absolutely the most beautiful in Kenya. They are brought there for the pleasure of the Belgians and the Scots, who thus take their pleasure now with the penis and now with the arse. God created the race of the Punjab to give a different dimension to all the others who use them. The angels recompense the Punjabis for their vices by giving them enormous wealth and no political power and by making them take upon themselves all the hatred of which the blacks are capable, so that when there is a revolt the blacks never take it out on the whites but tear to pieces all those who look like Indians. And each time I have to bury myself for weeks, me and my family, otherwise they kill us too, who are not

232

immigrants from the Punjab and don't have distilleries for the Oil and don't have a petrol pump concession.'

'Very interesting but I have to go. Do you feel the first drops?'

'Life by itself, without people from the Punjab, would not go on; life is too fragile to find a motive in itself. The violence and the oppression, the cruelty and the trade in the young bodies helps it to stay alive. Like a young woman of the people, a girl of rare beauty, who enters into marriage with a dirty, powerful old man, disgusting but rich, urged on by her family and by the price of the sale: the young woman makes a face but in the end a son is born nevertheless, another forced life which will be able to make a choice however because the father is rich. Life is the marriage of freshness and purulence, and it is the repudiated Indians of the Punjab who provided the purulence. They disseminate death, the destruction of hearts, but behind them they leave the belly of a pregnant woman and a *better* unborn babe. An heir to this life, someone else to prey upon in his time, giving him in the meantime his own fertility, so that everything can continue and at the same time ministering to his most base needs, guessing them, stimulating them to make them *the slaves* of their mediation . . . You don't happen to have a visiting card or better a photograph? I'd like to show my daughters and grandchildren whom I spoke to today. Otherwise no one will believe me.'

'I don't have anything like that.'

'Don't you even have a watch – not even a ring or a chain? You are already a perfect corpse – ready.'

There is a drop of rain, I start to move off dragging behind me the hand, which is now clutching my wrist.

'I too would like this kind of burial,' I say just to see if he lets me go. I know *vice* by heart, its organization is the same everywhere and the only desire that comes to me is that of founding a worldwide orphanage and of dishing out rations and good examples till I get the cramps.

'I studied for ten years in the colonial schools. From '26 to '36. As language, English and Nduru. Now Nduru is a dead language for everyone. The oilfields are born from the dead tongues of the departed who talked them. Do you have oilfields in Italy?'

'No – I'm very sorry but . . .' and I think instinctively of

Etruscan. To advise Agip to try at Volterra. He's very animistic this character.

'One has to be patient until a tongue – a language – is really dead,' and he lets go. I hasten my step, am at the door, through the gate. The tulle of the wedding-dresses is fluttering and the same girls as before are still there with their necks bent back, ecstatic. It begins to drizzle or perhaps it is a spray of crow's piss.

'Wait,' the old man calls behind me, running after me again.

'What is it now?' I ask impatiently.

'Wait, please,' he shouts, 'Your photograph.'

'But I told you I don't have one.'

'Please.'

'I'm sorry – really.'

He looks at me from head to foot as if he had lost me again.

'There's no splendour in you.'

'I know. But don't be unpleasant.'

'Oh, what a pity! I'm afraid you will never be able to have that kind of burial even if you have no jewels, even if you are robed in cotton.'

'Oh yes, and why not?'

He passes his tongue over his teeth, completely shutting off his glance.

'It is not said that they will find your body.'

And it begins to rain angels.

~~

Chaste Kenya – three times chaste. My glans: caper-coloured through excessive hotel inactivity. Here the passions do not explode at all, they first go through the bank. Every so often a dancing delegation of Masai arrives to the joy of the Bavarian housewives. The superb and vain *warriors* who jump straight up in the air from morning to evening – and not even to get taller – who drink the blood of cows from drinking flasks and are filmed by the usual person with the camcorder, make me sad: they are not men profoundly reduced to cretins by civilization but, like women in general, by the compulsion to what they consider 'cunning'.

Here one gets bored with everything – even the female American savages fishing for trout in Lake Turkana with curlers on their heads. Only Paris can really cope with mass tourism, Kenya is too small and fragile to tolerate these funguses of obese people who begin to dine immediately after the lunchtime dessert, or those charming girls of good family who continually put their hair right because they think it is more feminine, instead of getting it cut; which would be more practical. And what is one to say of these Tarzanized rangers, with wild beards, prepared for any jungle contretemps, who descend on the great hotels as if onto a set and in their fabulous stories of a whole life spent in Africa never get further than an antelope grill and a *real life* recording. They can stick up their arses all the miserable rhetoric of the hunters, of the missionaries, of the explorers, of the archaeologists, who repeat that this is 'the cradle' and 'they would never go back.' This voracious recourse to *authenticity* is killing Kenya while Paris goes on unnoticed by the centuries. Here in Kenya there live 20,000 Italians – *live*? Apart from the understandable reasons for flight from Italy for fraudulent bankruptcy, sentences passed in their absence, terrorism on organized holiday, shady affairs with hot stuff for nostrils and veins, and white-slave trading, how can an Italian really give up for ever the neighbourhood where there must once have been a kind soul who, grasping his wrist, said to him in his dialect: 'Don't take on so, it will pass, you'll see.' I do not believe that a decent European can stay here in Kenya; the company is what it is and that is to say presupposes a mentality so racist (and if is not so yet must by force become so) and so typical of the superman that one might as well have stayed in Birmingham or Padua or Dortmund where no one would have noticed or made much of it. Here in Kenya the basic vices of an individual leap out, eating the whole personality of a person, highlighting the worst aspects because the person who comes here is looking to make his fortune; the person who comes here is not one who can take life as it comes. In Europe one's defects remain more in the shadow and are more blurred, because for every little outburst of megalomania, of narcissism, of the mythology of sexuality, of the culture of violence, there is the address of the right shop: you go in, pay and give vent to your feelings without exposing yourself or others too much. For instance the European entrepreneurs have decreed the death of the Foreign Legion by creating in its place training camps, reachable even by bus, for any pocket and any impulse to take instant flight and a subsequent return to *take revenge* on a grand scale. We are still at the same spot: anyone who has feeling remains where he is and how he is, anyone who has an idea goes elsewhere to infect the world with his sentimentalism.

As for tourism, one should come to Kenya in fours (to enjoy the discounts and economic advantages), with an international driving-licence (to rent a jeep), with a pair of old high-heeled shoes (to barter with the natives for their bloody awful necklaces of plexiglass), with condoms as at home (so as not to catch diseases which, were they defined as venereal, would make Mercury give Masai-like jumps for joy). If you are alone, come to Kenya only if some eccentric African airline puts down at Nairobi in order to land at Marrakesh or, if you prefer, find on the pavement at home the authentic big black women who are on the job from Syracuse to Merano.

Consider that *the development of the country*, which has been taking place now for more than thirty years, thanks to tourism and zoological business on an industrial scale, does not touch (not to say *skim over*) more than 15 per cent of the population. To come here and bring one's own holiday money means to make the poor poorer with no way out. Go to Italy, Italians, where – however badly things are going – you will make the rich richer and no poor man will ever manage to be poorer than he is . . . Stretched out in the sun I think in full neon-lights: 'a real piss-off: there is nothing special about going fishing for cod and coming back with a whale on your hook. But try going whale-fishing and . . .'

'I came to Kenya' and Clementina Gnoccoli with a powerful tug pulls a mattress next to mine on the beach, 'not so much to get over Faustino's death or to rest . . . oh, that business of the murder, I'll tell you about the hammer-blows to the head another time . . . as because my doctor advised the Indian Ocean for my recurring verruca on my right big toe. Look at it. Ten years, nine operations, and it is still there, grinning at me in there and hurting but how it hurts . . . Of course! Do you know how I got it? By trying on the samples of underwear when I stood for hours and hours with bare feet and wherever it might be . . . At night I use a mysterious little cream which a herbalist in Lower Bergamo gave me after I had been putting a thick oil on it from a herbalist in Upper Bergamo; in the instructions for the cream there is also the instruction to bathe the feet in the Indian Ocean. You see, for me herbalists, health service doctors and the Kenyan embassies are all a pack of robbers. All that was left for me was to take the advice literally – the cream I had already bought.'

Around other Lilos with faces glimpsed on the plane – it is inevitable to meet again sooner or later in the same hotels, if only to be able to pay a visit. I am looking for one face in particular but it looks as if I had to shape it first to be able to say that is it.

'When the police – the police, the Carabinieri! because to all intents and purposes I am an all-purpose aunt, even for gaffes – summoned me because of the way my husband's cerebral tissues had been reduced to pulp . . . I mean what he was doing there in the shop at that time, half-past nine at night, God alone knows, and when our accountant telephones, we were all at his house and tells us . . . and that he has already informed the police, the first thing I thought was "they'll blame me, I always wanted to do away with him" but I thought it out loud and it was embarrassing for my Loredana too, who was there as well – we had both been invited to supper by the accountant's family and Gnoccoli should have got there before us but instead there was no sign of him and we were waiting for him to sit down at table and then the accountant says with the receiver in his hand "no one is answering not even in the office, I'll go and have a look" and in fact we were all taken by surprise to learn that he was in the office, even if dead, because Faustino wasn't mad about extra hours, I mean that he pretended to leave his office materially at six or seven, like everyone else, in that way he could carry on *at home* and me and my Loredana with him till midnight – doing the books, agents, clients, programmes, he said it was better than the television and we were mum, oh he kept our noses to it . . . and so, just look how little one knows oneself, when the accountant arrives as pale as a communion wafer and mumbles on about what he saw, the pool of blood, the hammer nearby, I began to laugh, yes, in front of everyone, but not because of a nervous collapse, no, because I have too hot a temperament to give sighs of relief and nothing more. In short, in spite of the fact, believe me, that I was not involved, Gnoccoli's death made me feel happy – and gave me an appetite. Maybe that is why – out of consideration for the accountant's mother, the cook, neither I nor the little girl – little girl but let me tell you, twenty-four years old but carrying them so badly she looks like, what shall I say, an infant just Gnoccolied not by a mother but by a cement works – we withdrew and insisted that the meal should be served before any visit to the scene of the crime. There were boletus mushrooms fried in oil with garlic and grilled, just think, a real mortal sin not to do them injustice! And of course I was tense, nervous, but I swear that while I put mushroom after mushroom into my mouth and my Loredana too, who is usually so choosy but a hearty eater if there's something she likes at last, and I was thinking: can a woman nurse such hatred, contempt, ill-feeling and not even know it or discover it only when faced by a misfortune there's no going back on? Mystery of the human psyche or perhaps only of women, I don't know what my little girl was feeling – oh poor thing, in every way like her father, just to give you an idea – at fourteen she was already as bald as this hand and we had to buy her a wig with a pony-tail because she was mad about horses and would have liked to be a jockey, just so, like all the girls with huge bottoms, oh, Loredana really was born with her father's bottom and with Faustino's lively eyes too, the same build, the curve of the spine a little monkey-like, but she wasn't bad. In short, that evening at supper over the dessert while the sergeant was taking a drop of grappa and waiting for us to finish the pudding with pine-kernels, in these moments I understood *who* I was, that I was a different person even to myself, a new, unknown woman, and I have to thank you and your novels because, Busi, whether it's in the Canaries or shut up in the toilet I read. You know one has so little time and books cost so much . . . Oh, you have this immense talent to dig right down like that to the nothingness in each of us! It certainly is quite an undertaking – I had always to carry a dictionary to consult about with me, I put it on the corner of the wash-hand-basin, I remember one word 'meconism' – oh what excitement when I went to look it up! but I couldn't find 'prostomy', I couldn't find anywhere 'conical prostomy' – oh, by instinct I'd be inclined to say 'knob on a prick', did I guess right? Where were we ah yes, there, at the accountant's with the sergeant who, impatiently – because my Loredana chews very slowly, it's the only thing she was good at – the sergeant who was doing honour to the little glasses of grappa and the Carabinieri at the door, I thought at first I had left a dangerous clue – a burst of laughter. Can you imagine? They tell me this that and the other, a whole lake of blood, and there I am, bursting out laughing! And in the end, at the interrogation sessions it was the laughter that saved me. In short, they thought that someone who has a cast-iron alibi for some hours before the time determined for the murder – and even afterwards because the murderer came at about 3 in the morning to finish him off, just a whim because there was no need – and bursts out laughing holding her belly cannot have given the job to a killer if, when she laughs, she also puts a hand in front of her mouth – too shy basically. But I wasn't laughing about the matter in general – I was laughing because Gnoccoli, ha ha! him, with his little sheep's tits, his bandy legs, all so ugly, Gnoccoli put such store by the three hairs he had on his head which you see is the same way of doing his hair as Loredana when she is in *déshabillé* and I imagined to myself that bald head arranged with such care dodging the blow from the hammer, which according to the investigations was delivered from in front, not from behind as one might imagine, and it wasn't as if Gnoccoli had dodged it because he panicked, not simply because it would have upset his hair-style. Oh him – even in intimate moments always said "take care you're rumpling my hair", a tic, you know, not as if it were a whole permanent wave . . . Whereas my daughter – oh, I'm sure you are tolerant with lesbians as well, that's easy for you, but to have them in the house – whereas Loredana started to cry, her crying and me laughing, and the accountant, his wife, his white-faced mother-in-law, with the Carabinieri who had started on the cognac now because the grappa was finished, all worried and amazed, and the mother-in-law who plucks up courage and says "Excuse me, Amelia" she says to her daughter-in-law, "What do people put on the table in cases like this? Candles?" and I'm off laughing again, getting the hatred in me for my husband off my chest and I felt as if I was going down to new depths within me in spite of the thirty-year-long torment of the knickers, pulling them up and

239

down at all hours of the day and night – I told you Gnoccoli, yes, he brought work home to me and thanks to this extraordinary fact we sometimes had routine sex but never with enthusiasm – I felt a kind of posthumous sympathy for Gnoccoli and was so pissed off at not having killed him myself with my own hands . . . What are you making that face for, Busi? Why don't you put something on your head instead, take my Florentine straw hat, I'll give you it, you know.'

If she thinks I'll begin to look around me she's mistaken.

'I was saying that after all I didn't hate my husband – I had killed him off inside me while he was *alive*, perhaps to survive the humiliation of the knickers, to become a clothes-horse is not flattering for a woman and perhaps not sufficiently degrading either. A woman hates things done by halves – she has enough of that already by nature. But I hadn't realized before my atavistic – I'd call it – hatred for him, for all men, all the Gnoccolis on earth. My Loredana, on the other hand, has other reasons, but her – you know – her and her skinny little blonde girl-friends, pale, with good-for-nothing rings under their eyes, using their tongues all the time – don't make me talk about them . . . The point is my Loredana had . . . has the same virile and non-existent charm of her father, they had the same character, so you can imagine the fights! The unpleasantnesses! The way I see it they all ended up in the little girl's palate so she became – oh, with a father like that it had to be – lesbian! And of course she too was suspected for a little, a cast-iron alibi hers too – and then by her constitution she is so much stronger than me, she's all iron that depr...essed girl and the day after – no one had shut an eye that night – at the Carabinieri barracks I who hadn't lost a moment to look back over all my past as wife and mother in a new way, and first I sort of turned myself outside in and then turned myself inside out again and felt FREE! And I started laughing again almost at once like the evening before, laughing and stamping my feet because I was saying to myself, Clementina a little restraint, what is there to laugh at so much after all it's only a husband who has died. But THAT WAS IT and off again laughing and everything that came into my mind to make me stop giggling set me off again even more . . . After the first quarter of an hour like this amid the tears brought on by laughing the sergeant says to me "But *Signora*, you're laughing!", shocked, at least he tried to be that, and I say "I feel I'm in the wrong, Sergeant." "Then confess, you're guilty, do you confess?" he says crudely – he was in a bit of a hurry because he had lots of other things to do and was giving a hand with the referendum on hunting as well. "I don't know who to curse, I mean, to thank!" and I went on laughing even in front of the public prosecutor, the court attendants, I burst out when I didn't expect to, I couldn't do anything about it, my jaws were all sore and . . . not once did they ask me who the fu…heck really killed him. Even during the trial me being the accused naturally when the prosecution tried for the last time to catch me out thinking this is just someone from the backwoods I fell victim to the usual fit of the giggles and the lawyer roars at me "Clementina Gnoccoli, confess! It was you who killed Faustino Gnoccoli with premeditation! Say the name of his assassin! Let's get it over with because it's time for an aperitif," I burst out saying: "I wish it were, I wish it were, I could really do with a little white vermouth with a dash of soda." They couldn't make head or tail of things. They discharged me out of desperation, I think, not because I am – really am – innocent. The trial was postponed three or four times, inquisitive people behind the barriers, poor dears, unemployed, romantic women who came to find out how to do it, if they don't laugh a little when they get a great chance . . . And here I am. But can a woman carry about inside her for thirty years such a repressed desire to laugh till it hurts, to laugh for some reason at last? . . . And don't worry about my bathing-costume and its frills – even if it is purple it's not a sign of mourning. I bought it, what do you expect, in the Canaries ten years ago, along with that apartment in the beach-bunker. It's a little Spanish costume, you know, if they don't stick a little extra piece on they're not happy, they have to shout "*olé*" even when they are having a steam-bath. But let's take things one by one – in order . . . Oh dear – perhaps there isn't one . . . Oh they've come to fetch me! Goodbye, my dear Busi, they're taking me beyond the coral barrier-reef, will we see each other one of these days? I never know, I make up my mind where to go from minute to minute. They say that it is very exciting – the sight of a whale and that it's good for the cholesterol. They keep a couple out there on the surface. One has to have seen everything, don't you think? I know – Busi, you can't even find words in this life to reply to my up yours to the whale. I'll say hello to myself from you.'

And the disturbing Signora Gnoccoli sets forth on her trip to the whales; someone else gets up from the Lilos to follow her on to the same absurd catamaran – with a motor and deckchairs, you might as well talk about a raft with shower and cabins.

I know the terrible thoughts that furrow these oiled foreheads in the sun, these impassible faces, the thoughts which few of them ever know they have and which they forget each time, the terrifying thoughts of men and women with their eyes half-shut without sleeping.

The mind wanders to and fro freeing itself from its own chemical substance. It connects and disconnects every memory of itself and of others, in an epidemic of phosphenes. The impotent brains under the linen hats and the scarves watch themselves dream, powerless to stop themselves, terrified. Nothing leaks out – the brain will not know anything of the brain alongside. Today, too, everything will remain shut up in the misty solitude of the psyche by the sea. Nothing will ever be silent, not even today, in the mind, none of us will go and change, retaining an image in the retina of what we witness at this moment. Because we all of us here think that, although our nervous system is incapable of giving us satisfaction, it will only require a single moment's pause and it will be death. If not why would one after another start up like that from the mattresses, why would they seek the bottle of oil with such immense terror? To think of something else for as long as possible – the sun-tan, the postcard, the DDT for tonight, or not to think at all, annointing with excessive love this body which is still ours for a little. Lord, a title!

'Bard's Black Box'

Then God too will withdraw along with the high tide and we will all break ranks for grub.

~~

The usual hotel non-existence, marked by the three sittings in the restaurant, by the two tides lazy at coming in and lazy at going out, by the tugs-of-war with the hucksters of trinkets which are always the same and which I end by buying with nephews and nieces as an alibi ('In despair the Marquise went to bed and sent for a bottle of champagne' because there was nothing else left to affirm the ill-advised privilege of the arbitrariness of her gestures once she had been detained by whoever had chased her to bed – detained by *love*? And the *champagne* she sent for, does the Marquise succeed in making it come on foot?).

I invite a black youth to accompany me for a reward to a bare reserve not far away, I pay a fortune to say 'shoo' to three giant tortoises and to the clutch of guinea-fowl belonging to the warden – when, having put a snake to flight, I am about to take my cock out for the youth he tells me he is a Muslim and asked whether I am not interested in ivory bracelets. It already costs me an equatorial effort to feel curiosity about sex with people who are already too commercialized, if then – over and above the customs barrier – I have to leap over whimsical altars I decide, with a sigh of relief, to forget about it. In any case I had already bought from the garrulous youth (who for the occasion has put on his finest suit two sizes too small so that everything from the nipples to the rest, which I suppose must be at its indispensable minimum, is spilt out) everything that could be bought, neck-laces and earrings for 'Italian *mamma*' – can you imagine to yourself, proud Maria, with these two big bone rings in her ears going out of door to knit away under the streetlamps so as to scrounge light from the council? I can't go on paying for all these perfidies in order to keep them sweet for another ten minutes – and now ivory into the bargain! Not for a bit of a rub between the thighs in front of the pond with two crocodiles in their dotage as voyeurs, never! I stick my nose here and there into flowers as big as church-bells and there isn't one of them that has a perfume. Profusion dries out the essence. I return humiliated by this guide, who clung to the idea he had formed of my wallet, exceedingly polite to him, and a big tip, even if he doesn't deserve it; certainly he has no idea of the gift I was prepared to make and the risk I was prepared to take to feel I was a tourist at least and in Kenya at least, as they say.

～

The only *happy* rich people I have known were happy to be so as such, they paid no attention to the plebeian convertibility of wealth into goods of second or third or fourth degrees of necessity but to the power of money as such *safely put away*. *Celestino Lometto* spends less than *Angelo Bazarovi*, has an extremely low living standard, is a thousand and one times richer and *happier* than Bazarovi. He possesses things to such a degree that he is never touched by the *quality* of life as an aesthetic of commodities which mirrors the quantity of one's *possessions*. For him to have is already to be, indeed is all the more so because it is multiplied by the certainty of *being* in the Perspective of all Perspectives; and that intoxicates him even when he squats on the second-hand pan in the lavatory. It is the happiness of Donald Duck's Uncle Scrooge – the possibility of using the money with both hands if the wish, the desire, the whim should present itself, in fact never makes you spend a penny more than is strictly necessary – in itself the function of the second-hand pan in the lavatory is not *inferior* to the function of a first-hand pan and if everything corresponds to and is linked with the second-hand lavatory pan, in all we still have a *style*, the style of a person who *could* by magic sit on a gold pan smothered in rubies if he wanted to. It is the rejection of prospects *in advance* by those who own nothing which corroborates the marvellous happiness of those who *have* and who permit themselves still less than the have-nots who are also can't-haves. Lometto, having immersed himself in the incommensurable consumerist ecstasy *à rebours* of 'I can – so what's the point?', in this way immobilizes the energy of his competitors who, not understanding the subtle game of power, will end up by convincing themselves that there is no point *in having more* – just look at the way Lometto lives. And Celestino Lometto can with rather more calm refrain from wasting his own energies and concentrate on a single horizon of *pleasure*: the contemplation of himself contemplating his own inalienable wealth. At this point Celestino can also decide to shit wherever he likes – even outside the pan so long as it is there. Because his happiness is total, secure, fruitful and ethereal, thanks precisely to the vulgarity of the reasons and of the ultimate ends by which it is sustained. But this *is* what happiness is: a perfect stuffed animal looking alive in death. Only pedants insist in seeing the negligible difference in quality and take pride in the poverty of their views where nuances are concerned.

➤➤

Have been to a disco here on the coast, taken along by a little group of Italian boys and girls with orchids and sprigs of wisteria in their hair. Since the youths are all German or Danish I was the translator-pimp: 'Tell her I like her.' 'Say to him that I have to go back soon.' 'Tell his girlfriend that my brother is arriving from Stockholm tomorrow and has blue eyes.' 'Ask him if it is *Drakkar* or *Pour lui* – it's nice.' 'How long are you staying here?' 'Tell her I give tennis lessons at the hotel next to yours', etc.

I danced for a few minutes just to get them stuck together on the floor and then hid myself away in the farthest away of the divans at the end of the world in the most total darkness with my eyes hurting from moving about in all directions – one just mustn't think – but happy for them, they are really beautiful children not yet messed up by life, they come from families which still protect them, and daddies and mummies who exhorted me – me, as if I were headmistress of a kindergarten– to look after them.

From here I see the night life of heterosexuals in the Third World take its course – all along the semicircular bar there are single middle-aged men, some already in company, others who turn their backs to the dance-floor scornfully, leaning over their glasses. There isn't much to be happy about: it is exactly like being in one of our discothèques at home waiting for the great event – The Radiant Lady who will come down from Paradise and will change your life because '*she isn't like the others*' . . . but it is clear that each one of them will allow himself to get his hand on her thighs in exchange for the second vermouth. And next day they will be there again in their places as bored and disgusted males, while the women 'are all etc.' So once more I am in a museum. Which has nothing to do with me.

At midnight, ballet: five not very liberated and rather rickety girls mime a sexy cotton harvest and at each tuft, since they bend over, they shake their little bottoms to the joy of the boss. Then another number, a solo ballerina this time, with a somewhat plump belly and without any direction, announced as 'She who comes and goes from the Nile', a redhead of about fifty, her hair falling loosely over a snake – a boa – which surrounds her neck and thighs and the rest – she has to keep her legs very wide apart, poor woman, within her eyes the look of an erotic figure that merely calls to mind an old folk's home or a State pension. The boa does what it can, by its allusive quality it contributes a sense of the vagina to her well-meaning elderly flaccidity and everyone is happy. She goes back to the Nile. I was dozing, hoping that the little troop to whom I was acting as mother-hen wanted to go back to the hotel. About half-past midnight there arrived a group of African adventurers, slender creatures of all the sub-races, and imposing owners of German sausage factories who were kissing the prostitutes' lips as fast as they could while the latter went straight for the cock to get things over faster. They openly took it by hand and began tossing it up and down – for a moment – from outside the trousers and then inside them, sitting comfortably here and there. A few hand-jobs on the stools with the door continually thrown open – it looked as if all the white tourists had suddenly escaped from their rooms to make an appointment here. A lot of movement in the toilets; I presume – for blow-jobs there. I have never seen women so nimble with their hands and everything else with men: a miracle, a gymkhana, all perfectly concerted, next please. Suddenly other doors, big and little, opened here and there, but it was with difficulty that they stayed still for more than ten minutes. A whole frou-frou like black wings in the neon-light, inside and out, the men pulled along by tie or sleeves. There wasn't one of the women who was shy – they came out counting the banknotes of the last client and caught hold of the first one within range by the cock while the more refined ones put a hand on his bottom and gave a pinch of the kind that really goes deep. Suddenly, perhaps because I was the only man a little apart and seemingly horrified and delighted by such an open mart and with no more of my schoolchildren (all down on the dance-floor), a splendid Watusi comes threateningly towards me, sits beside me, rubs her cheek against mine, crosses her legs, sticking a knee into my thigh, I have scarcely time to bring my legs, which had been open, tightly together but she was quicker than me in fact and gives me a squeeze in the balls which automatically makes me part my legs like a catapult.

'When I saw you, darling, my heart missed a beat,' my dark lady begins to recite.

'I'm sorry – I ate so many of those onions this evening,' and I give her a chaste caress to get her claws off my fly but it seems she always has something up her sleeve.

'Oh, you've only got indigestion. Come into my arms, love, and I'll make you feel better. I'm called Jennifer.'

'I'm Milan Kundera – pleased to meet you . . . I'm here with my girl friend', and I point her out. 'She's dancing with friends because I'm tired.'

'Ah, Milan, Italy – you're not American! But when can I see you without her?'

'I'm very much in love with her, Jennifer.'

'To me you only look sad.'

'Take this – buy yourself a drink,' my God, what a great line from 'Farewell to Arms and the change'. 'Goodnight, darling. Don't waste your time with me. Business is business.'

She looks at the money, I have got one banknote mixed up with another and she finds herself for nothing with the equivalent of what she would ask for using her mouth – splendid square teeth – on three stupid old salesmen of stolen Mercedes – and I smack a kiss on her forehead. Jennifer too gives me a kiss on the cheek, then she takes me gently by the hand, I take it away from her, she looks at me in a way that is no longer banal. I take advantage of this to humiliate her thoroughly (rage at not being able to go into reverse over that money given to her in error) and I bring hers to *my* lips, I kiss her hand respectfully and definitively. Jennifer, on the brink of a hysterical crisis, gets up, murmurs something, 'You're not like all the rest.' 'Unfortunately not,' I reply, she turns away, searches the dance-floor, swallows looking at me again, disappears among the clinging sequins of her colleagues, slips into the toilets where my frustrated Don Giovannism hopes she will burst into tears and will recover faith in the snow-white life of a black woman for hire. There's nothing like treating a whore as a lady to make her feel herself to be an inferior being through and through – that is to say an ordinary woman. But I shall long remember the dazzled look from Jennifer who is now reduced to unexpected sincerity even if it is an item from the repertory. Scratch a little at comedy and out comes tragedy and vice versa. Everything, it seems, lies in knowing how to stop in time.

One must know how to go in either direction according to the moment: truth if long-drawn-out is not in itself preferable to the onethousandeighthundredandseventythird repeat performance of *The Mousetrap* by that poor Christie, Agatha.

〰

Where certain places are concerned, however, 'mass tourism' is merely a formula to be nice to the real mass, which has stayed at home.

Here in the hotel, full of well-off and respectable Italians, no one – apart from Gnoccoli – has ever heard of me or has ever set eyes on the title of one of my novels and I take good care not to reveal an aspect so insignificant to them all. Since clearly my readers are not part of any mass, they are hidden and are the guardians of secrets ineffable for most people. The favourite topic of these nice, educated, in short completely illiterate Italians is 'the beauties of nature in the wild' which according to them is a poetic way of saying 'Jesus, this is the life!' The tourists are real because they do not read – if they read many of them would stay at home or would stop playing at vingt-et-un in order to rest from the beauties of nature which is wild but demanding as well. A pareo with little yellow and red flowers mixed with shells flutters for an instant in the mind, it is tea-time and from the queue *She* detaches herself and makes for me like a rocket.

'Oh, Busi, I was just looking for you! You see my husband came from a family of grocers,' says Signora Clementina Gnoccoli in a volley, slowly stirring her cup of tea with a drop of rum. 'True-blue Bergamo people, to get things straight, the kind who sold everything with water in it, wine, sugar, salt. And then elastic by the metre, bleach, castor-oil and some basic iron-mongery – stove-pipes, copper gutters, scissors, cutlery, nails, hen-coops. Then, knickers, people made them at home if they suddenly decided to wear them and then you know how country ones are made, only the tummy and nothing in between, in that way they straddled their legs and pissed on their feet. Faustino was an only son and not very well endowed . . . sentimentally or . . . But listen, to me the size of the penis never mattered much or at all until a month ago – I only knew Faustino's and obviously to a simple soul like me all men have the same kind, isn't that right? And what a surprise for me at my age to learn it really isn't so. You see a month ago I . . . Faustino who was determined to expand the grocer's shop and turn it into a hypermarket can't ever have been a person who made women go mad but he certainly went mad about them – in words at least – or out of vanity like people of his kind. He had one peculiarity, Gnoccoli, he was a bit like *you* with men – queers, excuse me, don't they always look at all men at the level of the crotch? It is a tic which naturally conditions them to look down all the time . . . Well, Gnoccoli looked at women at the level of the pussy – which is to say he looked at the material and that was that because we don't have it imprinted on our skirts like you, do we? What he saw or rather imagined I don't know. But believe me thoughts like that never came into my head till I read your novels, Busi, and they have – since we are talking about materials – broken the veil of consciousness for me. Believe me . . . Really! . . . It doesn't matter. When Faustino asked for my hand he already had under him two sub-agents (intimate clothing department and every-thing for bed in general, two pigs like himself, all talk and nothing concrete, the kind who pay court to the boss's wife for years and then pull back at the wrong – I mean the right moment – and he was building the first wing behind the late Gnoccoli's grocer's-ironmonger's-tobacconist's-ice-cream-parlour. He could have gone in for any other branch but instead he had decided to specialize in ladies' knickers almost by instinct. And to think that Gnoccoli never even went to the cinema because he said nothing upset him as much as close-ups and head-and-shoulders shots of actresses. He would have wanted actresses only to play parts in which they appeared as torsos . . . Fortunately along with knickers go bras and because of business he became a little more tolerant at least up to the neck. In his own way, I repeat, but he liked women so much he had a fit if one appeared even on television in a dressing-gown with lots on underneath. With me, for example, to get himself worked up, he always made me put on those granny knickers one on top of the other – not exactly striptease. He liked laces, buttons much less, whale-bone stays, body-belts. As far as I was concerned it was an excuse to put off as long as possible getting down to business and when he did get there he finished it off in three minutes. Business grew, you bet, with these bees he had in his bonnet. It seemed to grow before your eyes, he only had to look at a woman to get her size for her to put on flesh at the hips – because the price depended on the size and the bigger they were the more fat they had here in their tyres . . . Oh he had a way of looking a woman up and down as if they had their features all in their heels or – at the very most – between one knee-cap and the other, he went over the essentials, tights, slip, vest and if there was one, the antirheumatic corset now on sale too in the pharmacy. But do you know how Gnoccoli and I got to know each other? Like I told you I was working in the canning-factory, oh backwards and forwards on my man's bike, good calves, good thighs, even if a bit skinny elsewhere – since the section head was one of the pigs who went about with Faustino, Ginetto to his friends (in fact no one – I never heard anyone call him Ginetto and so we may as well forget his pet name) and then the boss accepted Faustino's suggestion to give up the panettone and for Christmas to present each of the women workers with a nice pair of knickers, brand-new – yes, because if not Faustino was capable of giving them second-hand, American. And Faustino arrives in the business to take the measurements. Because to begin with he ran up the knickers *à façon* in his basement – at that time they were made with the Singer – there weren't any factories for readywears like today. So he arrives, goes round the factory and since it was to be a surprise for the women, says to the foreman, looking at me so that I was shaking like a piece of calf's-head brawn: "Ask her to come and try on a pair, she's the right medium size, I'll do a bigger and an extra big size and we're there." They called me into the office, Signor Gnoccoli extremely nice, really slimy, with his two little unhappy ferret's eyes, he puts them in my hand and says "Try them on – mum's the word – it's a perk." . . . I had no idea what a perk was and thought it was some sort of animal from the North Pole. I shivered; I put them on there in front of all three of them, they were fine and I was fine too. From then on I didn't stop being fine for him, an ideal thing to put knickers on, the body-belt of his dreams, not a woman, not a wife either – someone who worked away taking on and taking off, up and down, till I got cramp in my joints. But if I think back the first real present he gave me was one evening when he turns up there with his station-wagon and waits for me outside the factory and ties my bike on the roof, he hands me a pair of knickers with transparent lace in front and a bra just as transparent on condition . . . but no he was too cunning to impose a condition on me, with the character I have; he said: "Like that you can see if they suit you, if I have an eye, otherwise we'll change the *set*" and on the spot I thought – what else? – Lollobrigida, De Sica, Cinecittà, of a screen test, because he really did say *set* and I'm an ordinary girl of humble origins like her and I already knew a couple of words of English when working with potted head and corned beef . . . What were we saying?'

I'd like to say that only she was talking but I haven't time to get some saliva on my tongue before:

'Ah yes, on condition that I tried them on in front of him "because he had something in mind, a business for two". We can imagine what sort of business it might be, I thought. But instead it wasn't *that* at all. What a disappointment for me. By business he meant commerce and that was all. And I was stupid to get ideas in my head but in any case that time had to come because I was still a virgin and it seemed funny to me that such an ugly thing in between the legs was only there to pee with. Yes, dear Busi, I was a virgin in bad faith not from chastity or *pruderie*. Oh, you don't believe me, but not only was I a false innocent – I was forewarned. But instead with Ginetto – but he never allowed me to call him that always with his surname and that was all – nothing happened at all. He looked at me, oh he looked at me he did while I slipped off the Christmas ones to put on this luxury pair – I was very expert and very embarrassed and it was him who said, without looking at me, not at my face of course, I think that if I was Polyphemus he wouldn't even have noticed, "Now try this other *set*. It's a marketing ploy," which I thought was the name of the firm and I say "But Signor Gnoccoli, these ones suit me very well" but he, for the first time, I think, looked me straight in the eyes in such a way that I understood right away that if I didn't make him look at me again I would have everything to gain and instinctively I corrected myself "Let's try on all the set." "Sets," he corrected me. He had the very devil of an S.

With his worried and professional little eye he followed me in my clumsy movements there, in the middle of the countryside, me putting on these knickers and bras, trying not to get them muddled up and his station-wagon that didn't even have a heater. I stood up to the cold well too and we got married . . . Oh, but I'm late!'

And she disappeared in her cloud of gaudy silk.

➤➤

A person's degree of sexual potency is directly proportional to the degree of autosuggestion of which he is victim – and of which he is capable. This is the fruit of the marriage of the thing-in-itself and the thing-in-us, that is to say the power of psychic refraction which the myth has over each of us, one by one. There are sexual autosuggestions which diminish with age, like any other *property*, others which remain intact, and the longer they last without being seriously damaged by the years, the more sex retains its sense – even if it loses freshness and charge – at any moment in the life of a specific individual. That the machine of the body should be jammed has never been important for any potent ninety-year-old – almost always through stupidity or from the superficiality of the passions, almost never for the opposite reasons – in the sense that if the mind wants to go on running it doesn't give a damn even for the body in a wheelchair. The mind thinks the sexual intensity of the body in order to make it fade better towards death. For grand passions, grand clichés. In order to stay perfect lovers, it is inevitable that we should remain mediocre researchers and experimental nonentities. Therefore only those who have never had the need to understand something different from the traditional datum can preserve unchanged this potency of sex with its absolute symbolic value: desire will break out in old age and in illness no less than in youth and health. The seventy-year-old, for instance, with the erection who is after me at the evening dance is still a vital man – that is to say a perfect little idiot who has come intact through every collapse of the myth, of fashions, of political systems. He is so idiotic and vital he will certainly have an unconscious where he stores all his ignoble certainties, which now permit him to exhibit an erection – and to adhere to it, presumably, with a true desire to live, the fool. Everything is degraded by living – if even the *thing-in-itself* of sex remains the same, it's refraction dies out in us. To die out is the guarantee that one has been set alight, like volcanoes – and what is more boring than an old volcano which floods us with its lava day after day for seventy years on end? A man, in fact, who instead of being devout, is still there being vital. A nervous system is precarious because it lives and ought to pull along with itself in its own precarious state all *things eternal*, including beauty, which seem timeless to us – like the myths . . . Anyone who lives intensely has no time for eternity; by involuntary chemical power he desexualizes the world around him day after day just as he devitalizes it, he destroys its palate, destroys its tactile powers, carries down with him that piece of history the world presents to each individual. Living *comme il faut* there cannot be fixed points, desirable desires, unbreakable symbolizations, everything moves – towards death, the act of turning back on oneself, so that even the idea of death finally ceases to be overvalued.

The prick is a great anatomical-symbolical invention: pleasing, evaginated in form, with these natural-unnatural rhythms of high and low tide at its command (called *instinct* according to the moons and the influences of the stars but still always at its command), it is also the part of the body, *the only one*, which allows the male to link up with the space outside of himself and to pierce, to violate the dark, to lose for a second the memory of the intolerable solitude of being a man in order to fill the Hole, until he is one with it, and to defeat the obsession with death within himself, in this his own hard-soft part of himself, torn from the placid oblivion of the cosmos of which the cunt is merely a corner-shop. Woman, it is said, is there to give energy to the male, not to take from him what he does not have, by nature. A woman, weak and *alone*, is a nonsense: a puzzle reduced to a piece to be fitted into another puzzle, which does not exist unless the woman has decided it does, which is either strong and *together* – the whole puzzle without the one piece of the male – or it does not exist. In short, there is dependence because he and she have got along well together like this since the night of times. The prick in the arse – of another male – is unlikely to be anything other than a prick and an arse which are very distinct, of which the one is never truly cosmic space and the other never a segment/spacecraft: the mythical symbolization is very weak – oh for any Greek amphora, a little Etruscan in style, but all of the earth earthy, or rather clayey – and never upsets figures of a certain nobleness like love/death, desire for perpetuation through conjunction with the other half of the primitive prototype. Between two males the Figures are coarse in kind and hysterically disciplined by the question as to who wears the trousers or the skirt even when both ought by now to be naked. In fact male couples who are in perfect good faith about the concept of happiness (in terms of valentines) are composed of the one who always fucks and of the other who lets himself be fucked. If the rigour of this active/passive, male/female/ *do-ut-des* is broken everything else is broken; if this symbolization of sex between males fails, every possibility of *happiness* fails. Because the homosexual and, like him, the heterosexual, are both today as they were ten thousand years ago: every emancipation is false and their oneiric models are the same old ones: who will make me ride sidesaddle on the white horse this evening? With whom shall I live happily and contented for ever? And, with this symbolization of a *superior* penetration between their teeth, almost all of them give up the ghost without ever having experienced the intoxication of being content to ride on an ass. All of them also stands for all women, the male never goes astray in this: he does not see, he does not speak, he does not feel. He is male. He is exonerated from any other responsibility of the senses.

Moral not humoral: anyone who lives intensely, desymbolizes intensely – the dream is reduced, instant by instant, to an extinct species of reality. One can live by dying long before as a revenge on one's self and one's own intensity which, by neutralizing the symbols and myths of others, does not have time to affirm the *vitality* of its own lack of definite chimeras. Today the great idealist is the person who is prepared for any compromise with the realities available in the delusion of not deluding oneself, once and for all, about any idea of *one self*. The infinity of human worlds and the human finiteness of each person who pursues my tenderness, demands that moral integrity should be the fruit of promiscuity that is at once persecuted, sentimental and political.

Every need must be subject to a double dream: mine and yours. Otherwise try another need. If they all come to nothing never mind; dream by yourself without importuning the reality of others. Don't lose Time on the road, you'll lose the way as well . . .

'Ah widowhood, widowhood!' cries Clementina Gnoccoli, diving into the swimming-pool down the slide and missing me by a hair's-breadth. 'What a great invention, dear Busi! Adopt it for a little too, we'll keep each other company and talk about the weather and men because whatever way you look at it the little they say if we didn't put the words in their mouths . . . All the more since, as you inform me, one still can't make babies through the arse. So give over with your hysterical maternities and your wedding-marches, which are no good even before the organ has been pumped. Oh, I have read Loredana's diary on the sly, I know your tunes about I want to but can't do it in public. Eh, girls' diaries aren't reading for mothers any more. My poor big boy-girl was a thorn in the heart of Ginetto, she was as like him as two peas, so it's logical that she likes women too, almost a rival in the house, and one of his own blood, who stole entire stocks to put lace on her crushes! But me, listen, she's still my daughter, for heaven's sake, but now that I'm a widow I also want to take advantage of it to be a mother incognito. Not that I am ashamed, a mother is a mother, but certainly it is embarrassing to have to deal with a daughter who is from the other side. And then she is abnormal but at least she can write. But Loredana! what an indiscretion to fill pages and pages of diary about the taste-buds! Till this evening, dear Busi, see you at the tango at nine o'clock . . . Don't say a word. I beg you – not a word.'

And she disappears until she touches the other side.

➤➤

There are a number of dead periods in a journey and one has to remain dead to be able to live through them adventurously. So I am completely stuck with the funereal atmosphere of a family hotel without liveliness, without culture, without sensuality, with kids who were not lively but very conscious of *having been in Kenya*. Some thirty-year-olds of Scandinavian origin – very beautiful, dark-blond, beautiful muscular legs, the kind from a commercial for macho cigarettes – who have moved to Kenya to get a slice of organized capital. They speak five languages plus Swahili, they can bring down a running gazelle at a hundred metres, they are very properly without soul and stand in guard over the favours of their own bodies. They have *business* printed on their brows and are very nice, they are not disposed to give anything for nothing – not even a little flattery to a short-sighted lost-looking little French women, they laugh well, they seem to carry about with them a mirage within the reach of any purse.

Don't you feel like touching them to say Hey! I exist too? And yet I will not make use of any of them, and then I think I have had my bellyful of animals from the lobby and on the beach. But down there at the desk is Fatima delivering her packet of leaflets – it is she who is trying to organize the most routine safari in the world at my express wish. The usual difficulty – she doesn't know where to fit in a single.

'Mamma,' says a child coming running up, 'what are lesbians?'

'Lesbians are not educative,' I catch in full flight as I pass between the divans; but it is Clementina Gnoccoli who comments on her own at the top of her voice in the direction of the tousled pair who are dancing like singles with all the grace of two broomsticks! 'Look, Busi, don't pretend not to have seen me – you owe me a tango. Sit down, I'll order you a tonic and listen to me. I . . .'

'But what kind of question is that? Forgive him, please, children . . .' says the mother sitting there alongside Gnoccoli.

'But I *want* to know! I never saw them at the zoo!'

'Animals for export which disturb the ozone in the stratospheric layers of the globe,' says Signora Gnoccoli in a peremptory way.

The child and its mother hang their heads intimidated.

'I told you, Giordano, not to ask questions you don't understand,' the young mother rebukes him again.

'Look, Giordano,' Clementina Gnoccoli resumes, 'to put it very simply, they're worse than the Concordes. Is that clear now? But Busi, where are you off to? Hey Busi!'

I give her a vague hint of a greeting as if to say 'Later', I take refuge in my room, from there I shall call Fatima, I won't allow the Gnoccoli woman to put one of these *idées fixes* into my head which then keep me awake all night and have the effect of making you want nothing but a repeat dose as soon as possible. Am I mistaken or was she definitely with someone? I believe I have drawn from the pack *the person* who follows her everywhere at a certain distance. A young man, obviously, with black sunglasses, even at night, and not even particularly attractive – a sedentary person, I would say. The killer of Faustino Gnoccoli on a prize-holiday. But I shall have to go down in any case to that dinner which I never manage to miss and if Clementina Gnoccoli has come to stay here it is better to be able to confront her or to ask her to give me a cut, since I have enough novels to write, in fact, if she knows someone who wants a few . . .

There she is at table in the restaurant – alone but opposite someone, the usual ugly man, mysterious and with a khaki vest. This evening Signora Gnoccoli is resplendent in a leopard confection – my God, it's real – with this heat! – and is extraordinarily attractive, so tall when she is seated, so slim when she rises and with two strides devours the space between her and the buffet where she begins to pick away without deciding to put anything on her plate. I pretend not to notice – maybe she might leave me the time and chance to be the first to do some pretending. My table is behind hers, she has her back to me, she hasn't noticed me – she has moved about as if none of these hundreds of guests existed and the restaurant and waiters were solely at her disposal. Perhaps I am wrong or the killer in khaki is moving his mouth – oh what a pear-shaped head, swollen, with an enormous bump for dreadful deeds – is giving a grinning good evening? Signora Gnoccoli is the only person to have the bucket with the champagne bottle next to her.

I dine stealthily, quickly, go back to bed and after a little, in desperation, excited, run down to the foyer, to her.

'I was waiting for you. Oh, what a relief – among so many ugly men and women. Boy, a glass please.' She has had the bucket brought and put on the little table in the foyer. 'So when they took me to the scene of the crime, I thought right away: "Golly, what a great piece of work."' The murderer must have waited for Ginetto, oh excuse me, Faustino, for a good while or else they must actually have had an appointment. I don't know – my

257

husband didn't seem like a man of mysteries, and he was too mean, too lazy to get involved in problems with a lover. Shady deals? Maybe. Gambling? The Mafia? Can't be excluded – everything is possible except having anything to do with a cultural officer from the council. With me he only talked about the models he dreamt of putting on the market – a bit freakish latterly – maybe he was getting a bit odd in the head. He wanted to build into the crotch a battery-driven propeller. Just imagine, with a video screen with waterfalls and gusts of wind for ventilation. As if there were eyes down there! The prototype I tried on gave me a third-degree abrasion on the left outer lip and when I protested he cut me short saying that the right one I still had was more than sufficient for intimate femininity. A hellish life? I really couldn't say. I only knew this one and how is one to judge? Perhaps, I thought, they did him in for one of these horrendous patents. According to him nothing was impossible and he used to say to me: With the propeller women would save on deodorants and the natural flora wouldn't be destroyed, and then with the film little by little a sixth sense of sight would develop for the irrigations induced and it wouldn't be necessary to go to the bathroom to powder one's nose with that stupid complex about the smell, and all these advantages would justify the extra thousand lire a pair. I always said yes with my head and no with the first finger of my free hand. I am ambidextrous, ambi-sinister . . . As you can conclude I got married in one piece and Faustino didn't insist very much – a little bit on the wedding night then that was that – my God, what patience he had with his tongue and when I had my . . . oh, tremendous! Deep down there must surely have been something that sanctified this marriage, don't you think? With him licking away and repeating "Oh, my lovely dummy, ah my lovely dummy", you understand? He had his living clothes-hanger which he adored in his own way; standing up like I did I thought he was a little bit of a fetishist and that in this way we'd never have an heir, but I pleased myself – that's why I am so thin, because I took my pleasure for hours and hours. Not just a little rub! But I have always thought that our Loredana – ah! she was more likely born from a spermatozoon caught in the gum of some label because you must know, dear Busi, that once upon a time the labels they stuck them on in the crotch and who knows what kind of universal sticky stuff the little firms under Faustino used. Oh, he was capable of anything! He never threw anything away – I mean not even other people's stuff – he brainwashed them, talked about divine providence, of the sense of thrift – and he got in among the choirs and the boy-scouts, put up the money for some little competitions for adolescents and showed them that mastur-bation is good for you, all you had to do was use the proper little receptacles and then empty the sack at places where the women made the labels. . . . I don't remember any of the teams he sponsored ever winning anything. . . . they looked a bit worn out to me . . . but they were a kind of adhesive, if you like, between the product and its marketing . . . Ginetto, pardon me, Faustino – oh since he died I feel so close to him – was full of plans, he had extended the sales network, he had got as far as Val Sugana, in the mountains, he had got a grip on them with his way of going about things, never mind the style, and all on a grand scale, oh he had a genius for business that had to do with women's skins. He so much wanted – seeing Loredana was such a mess – a *real* boy to give him all his experience, to hand on his inheritance to his descendants. Once I dared to tell him that it was too easy to put women's underwear under his trousers, he ought to go to a psychiatrist or have himself sprayed with holy water since we both had so little time for analysis and do you know what he answered, darting his usual look at me: "And what if I am cured?" As far as religion went – fervent both of us – the moment we had five minutes we were Catholics too. I still remember that ill-mannered priest who asked from behind the grating: "How often, Passera?" and I say with a sigh "Not even once" from my earliest childhood, because in our parts frankly one knew all about sex right away and even more than was necessary, but to me it seemed an idiotic pastime whether there was passion or not. I don't know, maybe a wife is always shaped by her husband, but it feels to me as if sex in my day was only something to keep the wheels turning and to give the priests something to do, nothing autonomous for a woman and nothing dependent for a man . . . Women only interested Gnoccoli, as I have told you, in the sense that he asked himself out loud and in front of me "I wonder what brand she's wearing?" for him to give them his *sets*, at least a pair of knickers, a bra. Still Gnoccoli he owed his fortune, his boom, to me who had nothing in my name before he died, while now I have everything and Loredana, poor thing, only what is due to her, at least she's being sensible and behaving. The jewels he bought, for instance, he put them on me when we had to go to the mayor's but when we came home he'd take them off me and put them back in the safe and at that time I didn't even know the combination – whereas now I've actually had it changed and only I know it. Me, well, for an easy life, by an oversight, I'd turned into a robot without noticing it and do you know what my speciality is? And I discovered it thanks to you, dear Busi – it is that I can do any number of things at the same time and do them all well. Look here, for example – give me that biro and stop taking notes so frantically because then you give a wrong picture of me as a person! You see? I can stir the champagne bubbles with my right hand and write proper thoughts with my left and I'm not left-handed. Oh, I used to send Ginetto into a rage! With one hand I could hold the telephone receiver and answer any question or give orders, give instructions to the accountant with my eyes to take a particular file from shelves and with my left go on reckoning pay slips, VAT, or work the computer. Do you know I can type three hundred characters without a single error? Do you know that when I type I never look at the keyboard but only the text at the side? And between one thing and another I managed to try on a pair of knickers. In short – a real wonder – it was like having five employees plus a model without having to pay even one. Obviously a man, an average sort of businessman, falls in love with a woman like that and ends up by confusing the two-legged shop with passion. Because Gnoccoli with me it was terrible – he never left me short of a mink, diamonds, shoes and real crocodile handbags, but I had to ask him for the thousand lire to buy sanitary towels. Wasn't it a hell of a life? Not at all – it wasn't anything. I'll explain – we were happy without knowing it – too happy for me – it's only now I feel it. Damn, but this is African champagne! Oh, excuse me. I'm going to the reception desk for a moment my daily telex must have come with the day's stock. What do you expect – work never ends. I told you a little lie too – I haven't closed down entirely . . . You know, the show must go on and then isn't it exciting to keep the theatre open, to make the public pay even when you're not on stage? Goodbye, I really like you a lot! Goodnight, give your head a bit of a rest or it will get addled.'

And Clementina Gnoccoli rushes off. Someone else whom I seem to have seen in the restaurant already but with a different hairstyle, only the glasses are the same, gets up from a divan next to ours and follows her.

I wait for a quarter of an hour. Clementina Gnoccoli does not come back, I get up and go to the toilet where the noise of the ocean is dampened. In front of a mirror no one has a life of their own any more. On my tomb I should like this final epitaph to that humanity which is still there for a little: 'Never put down moquette but tiles or parqueting. Because of the dust.'

The palms are devastated by the wind and a thin dusting of green light breaks away from the branches and falls on to the ocean. The guards walk in the night wrapped in their hooded sacks. Three o'clock. Four o'clock. No – it is only two. The clock has stopped – rather *keeps on stopping*. A ring of the telephone. And yet I haven't gone out of the room to call myself.

'Oh, I knew you aren't sleeping either with the cold here! Where were we? Ah yes, well, there was model after model for which I was guinea-pig! I and Ginet . . . Faustino broke off any . . . what shall I say . . . sexual relationship when my organ was made unusable because of a deep abrasion caused by a cooling installation also woven into the crotch – tropical model – for women who didn't want to give up either comfort or elegance even if they naturally exuded a lot. Oh, a new material, linen and plutonium with a little heart that came in front in light asbestos. Maybe then I began to understand that I was being used away beyond the common decency of shameless women. And when I saw him there – in the storeroom – in his fine pool of blood I had the first feminist thought of my life: Gnoccoli you bastard, some woman has avenged us all. Because I immediately thought of my Loredana even though she was at supper at the accountant's along with me. Because the girl was the second victim of Gnoccoli's grab-all tactics – from her adolescence he forced her to play the little man for men's underpants, and who would have thought Gnoccoli would have got into that sort of line too.

Loredana never dared to rebel, in fact she seemed to be very content because in this way she had an excuse to hand for hating her father with all her heart because it was his fault if she brought her girl-friends home to do their homework . . . you know what I mean. You see I had to read up about it, try to understand, to put her back on the straight and narrow which, if you ask me, is to take a husband so as to have a nice quiet time without men for the rest of your life: nothing doing. And meantime with the excuse that she wasn't normal, Loredana put on the underpants and the men's button-up singlets in everyday life, when she stopped playing the mannequin she played the dyke, such a pain for a mother, and people, you know what it's like in the village and beyond as well . . . an only daughter with the big wind-cheater, dirty jeans, her hands in her pockets, a cheroot always in her mouth, and the false pony-tail she threw away in less than a week . . . She displayed her baldness like a trophy, she said it was just like the head of a . . . Oh, such a disgrace for us two parents! But to come back to the homicide she couldn't come into it either even if she had bags of reasons for doing away with him, poor thing, always there going up and down to show the samples to the clients with those man's tits and those legs like Turkish wrestlers' . . . There's no question of Loredana, she had a cast-iron alibi too. My thorn-in-the-flesh is, as they say nowadays, a bit of a *mutant* of a girl – you know, with all that slave-driver Gin . . . Faustino made her put on and take off! A strong-willed girl, in words only, a bit odd but quick to take offence, the ideal type of daughter to suspect of a contract murder with a father like that who with her had only one answer to anything she asked for "No" and when he made an effort "No and again no." No to everything, No to going out, and No to not going out – Gnoccoli didn't think much of sexual handicaps different from his own. Gnoccoli was like that in the family – I think he was even jealous of the little girl's penis – I mean that she was more endowed than him as far as things sticking out went . . . Just imagine – I used to buy women's dresses for Loredana secretly or altered mine for her even though I'm taller and slimmer and everything oh, it was almost always because she had to go to some fancy-dress ball not for anything else – because her father insisted that she wore his old jackets and his old trousers – that way you save money. Because with her he didn't beat about the bush, "hippopotamus" "big white whale" "where on earth did you come from, eh?" he kept on at her just as if he were speaking to a mirror because they were identical even in the voice . . . And just to tell all about his meanness – do you think either of us ever wore a pair of knickers in our lives that weren't defective either with the elastic that needed adjusting or else things that had been returned because of complaint? Gnoccoli was made like that. He loved us in his own way. And either myself or my Loredana always there at the disposal of the stockists, reps, suppliers, and even private persons, having to drop everything, the books and the shop, and run up to the salon with the catwalk . . . And him getting fun out of calling down the stairs: "Passera senior, to the catwalk! Passera junior, to the catwalk!" Oh the shame of the first ten seconds trying everything on there in front of everybody! . . . Perhaps the girl who is very moody and humourless was a bit shaken by it – I mean, for ever . . . She turned out badly for me, that's a fact, and yet I don't understand her, if someone treats you like a monkey for twenty years do you have to end up swinging in the creepers? Yes, unfortunately, but never mind, this is not a very nice subject. And then, after all, to comfort myself, to comfort him over the turn our only daughter had taken I used to say to him, never mind Faustino, she may be a bit twisted but at least she has her sexuality, hasn't she? Why do we get upset so much about so much? Of course for a normal and healthy mother it is difficult – so just imagine for a macho papa, to know that in theoretical terms he has a rival in his bosom. Then I at least read something and resigned myself, thanks to you too, dear Busi, with all these Byzantine women mutinying on the roofs and . . . the moment I get back I swear I'll buy her the Kawasaki but it isn't easy, believe me, for a widowed mother to have a daughter and to have a daughter-in-law as son-in-law when the time comes . . . And yet the suspicions – oh what time is it? Only half-past four in the morning? Have you seen what a wonderful light is coming up today again? Ah, the world – what it really is is a wonderful Central Electricity Board without pylons! The suspicions, as I was telling you, *nevertheless* were concentrated on my Loredana, but nothing was proved on her account either. And then of one thing I am sure – like me, not even she would have had the good sense to hire a killer, if at all just the pleasure of smashing that pear-shaped head of his we would have taken on ourselves, each one for herself, never together, because there isn't much trust between us . . . And they discharged us quickly, we gave a big dinner to all the staff to celebrate the new management and left . . . And yes – now you know as well who I am here with . . . My companion in the shadows is a woman companion but maybe at this hour Loredana is capable of having hidden away with some black woman . . . But let's look at the menu for today. Would you like me to read it to you? "*African Night* from early morning on: macaroni with three cheese dressing, tortellini alla bolognese, spaghetti puttanesca" and read this, read here "In the evening dancing with the Four Mulattos from the Danube – *Waltzing through the night*". And to end the midnight show: "Ballet *Heart of Darkness*, costumes by Gerta Wirsleviniecz, choreography . . ." Ah, the famous lady from Warsaw who toured all provincial theatres in Italy! A time of migratory ferments, ours is. Since the Red Sea opened for the first time in such a divisive way everyone comes here and Africa empties.'

▲▲

Safari! Seen at Tsavo East: a herd of horned cows, three rats with extremely long tails, five obviously English people (those with whom I shall have to share the sensational quality of the wilderness and four days of my one and only life). Having arrived at the Safari Lodges – 2,050 metres above sea-level (I don't know if it is a measurement valid for both the Indian Ocean and the Mediterranean). View of the savannah and related waterholes with zebras, the usual buffaloes, elephants, while I have a desire only for felines, the non-existent ones. A great clicking of cameras. A group of Cypriots who, even though whispering so as not to scare the invisible animals, would have the power to waken lethargic moles. The head of the group approaches me: the double of Celestino Lometto, laughing, hearty, nice, one of the kind whom you haven't even time to notice and they have already stuck it up your arse, he tells me that in Cyprus he runs an insurance company and that he is here with all his colleagues and why don't I come to Cyprus to visit him and that he lives alone with his maids and is always up to all hours with Greek cognac and Turkish women, the warmonger. The nicest thing is that, while he is adjusting the belt under his enormous belly, he issues the invitation surrounded by three smiling female employees with hooked noses and a washed-out look, his favourite aides in dealing with Cypriot sexual matters, I imagine. My God, how amusing life can be if you know how to take it for what it is – a game played outside one's own skin – but none of the four is really appetizing, and one doesn't come to one of Africa's many hearts to bang mangy anti-Turkish sexes.

I have not, I repeat, any predisposition for *nature* – all those gazelles driven mad by the clicking, by elliptical comments like 'Gazelle on the right'. We have seen it all *before* in the cinema, on TV, in the magazines, when we want to make a journey it is someone else we send in our place, since in person reality is disappointing. There they are now all in Indian file going on to the terrace to search the night with latest-model binoculars. Even if they were to see Noah's ark on parade where would the novelty be? What is the sense of photographing a baboon? On the contrary at the sight of a human animal popping up from the bush all my senses leap to their feet, reverent, languid. How moving the human figure is! How wonderful it would be to go some way with one of these stupefyingly beautiful women and one of those red warriors who direct their gaze to the infinite and are solitary, carrying from village to village inconsistent messages about a magic spell on which a life depends. To me what goes on in the head of a monkey is of absolutely no importance: if I photograph it once I shall again have a kind of monkey that looks like reality, that is to say I shall have two monkeys which are profoundly dissimilar because the one that looks at me (from the photo) is precisely the one that has nothing to say to me in its reality as monkey in itself. And so why be the cause of useless scissions where before there was a magnificent unity? Why take possession in a false entity of a beauty which consists in its being *different* from us and which cannot be caught in the necessity of its existence which does not concern us? Why can man not refrain from cheating the monkey of its right not to be the toy monkey of his image? Has seeing it leap from one creeper to another in a beam of sunlight not been an immeasurable joy? No, they have to put into the roll of film what they haven't even room to allow to enter their heads.

Leaving the Lodges again. The English companions on safari after a few hours together look at me askance and all at the same time as if following a secret understanding: perhaps they are annoyed by the fact that instead of watching the animals outside the minibus I watch the ones inside – I watch the human animals watching the beast-animals. But now we stop at a Masai village and our guide begins to bargain with the tribal chief to let us go in. But I smell a perfume in the air – Verrucaria No. 10, which I have already smelt somewhere, penetrating, proud and . . . Yes, there she is, Celestina Gnoccoli!

'Bloody Masai', but it really is her who is come out of the village in a rage followed by a dusty cloud of shouting women who put bracelets on her, hang chains and trinkets all over her, and she says 'Shoo' as if they were hens and shouts louder than any of them. 'Hands off, Burundi! Oh Busi, here too, you too in this hell of a supermarket! Get away while you still have time – don't go into the shit – it's literally shit. Take off right away with your friends, they are all possessed, my daughter and my companions are still trapped in the Duty-Free Hut Number Three on the right – they won't get away with less than two lances and a shield each on their backs! Oh these damned flies! Have you seen them? As big as beetles! And do you know what a young single parent Masai said to me when I gave a caress to a baby that looked like a bit of fly-paper and whom I felt sorry for just to pass the time? "A hundred shillings, please," and that it was a hundred to caress one of them and a hundred and fifty for two. And they don't even wear knickers and my Faustino . . . Oh he would have had a stroke – a brain-wave and he would have seen to it that he got into negotiations with President Moi but look, look, the men in minis with their cleft all in the open saying come and get it! But just think at my age having to see so many there all dangling – apart from the one a month ago! Because a month ago . . . it wasn't *true* . . . you see, three packets of cornflakes and they gave the batteries, five packets and the vibrator as well . . . I couldn't resist, I wanted to see how someone who wasn't Faustino was made! I could have waited instead, but tell me if . . . my God, what big long things! And down with these

266

daggers, you, or you'll dagger me in the head, no and I mean no, I won't buy a shield, and I won't buy the Yves des Masai scarf, no and I mean no, where is my Loredana since now we're here I'd better introduce her to you . . . Africa loves a horn of Paphlagonia, they mean Africa shakes the collecting-box! But they could at least make them of natural fibres, the knickers, I don't know, of palm or raffia or coconut hair, like their baskets, but no – naked as hell made them. Poor Gnoccoli – please take the pieces of straw and dried dung off my dress – a pure linen two-piece – whenever we stopped! He had seen that film with Marilyn Monroe, you see, taking her knickers out of the fridge oh! as I've told you he had one idea after another about cover-ups and don't you know what he was up to with the Fontana sisters? Knickers with a Thermos built in for winter with lots of coffee, a whole cup, for shift workers who have to stand in the cold and frost waiting for the public transport that never comes and obviously he makes me try them on and . . . My God, what a shock, all those ovulations with palpitations, you know, the caffeine . . . ever since then I have been frigid with some breaks. With all these traumas I really had motives for getting rid of him . . .oh, here's my Loredana and the others . . . my guide is telling me to get in again, who knows whether we'll see each other again. The magistrates thought I had been lucky, that there is such a thing as a perfect crime, they're not really convinced. Oh it's a shame I feel that the perfect crime only exists when one isn't in the least guilty! Oh, Loredana, come and say hello to Signor Busi.'

The one I had thought was the thick-set teenage-companion-killer comes up to the minibus: the usual dark glasses, white helmet, dumpy person.

'Pleased to meet you.'

'Goodbye, Busi,' and while Clementina moves off Loredana quickly whispers at my little window:

'Don't believe a word of what the old cunt told you. It wasn't me. I . . .'

'Loredana, hurry up, don't bore Signor Busi, he knows, he knows it wasn't you.' Clementina retraces her steps and seizes her daughter by the arm. 'And I beg you, use condoms here, even to masturbate, you never know, you are a writer at risk as a man . . . It would have needed five of them, five of Gnoccoli, to

267

make one of these!' she cries furiously, tugging at her daughter more than was needed. 'And to think he kept me in the dark saying his was the biggest! Ah, Lord, poor savages, what a terrible hard life! And many thanks, Busi, for having recommended Genette's *Figures II*, frankly there isn't a better guide to the Dark Continent.'

➤➤

One can calmly assert that where a middle class with middle-class services does not exist socially nothing yet exists. In Kenya there are the blacks and the very rich, apart from Nairobi where it might perhaps be possible to identify a small bourgeois social group of emergent blacks (thanks to tourism) – highly racist, it goes without saying. In all Hemingway, for example, I do not remember the existence of a black who is not the caricature of a black looked at from the usual white point of view – that is by someone who has every interest in seeing him as little as possible. Hemingway and Blixen must have been wonderful at enchanting the local authorities in order to obtain every possible permit and provision of facilities in the savage jungle: caravans of bearers, rifles, mosquito nets, servants etc. They understood how to use human beings and did everything for their good: they permitted them to serve them. I (even if I pay a pittance) after a few hundred yards begin to ask myself what right I have to have my baggage carried and have to start all over again. Because I worked for ten years in hotels and you need to have been like me, a waiter in the years when one was flesh at the beck and call of the clients, in order to understand and justify the profound hatred which develops in a man who has to clean the shoes of others and into the bargain is despised or sees himself forbidden to bathe on the same stretch of beach as the hotel's clients – as happened to me at the age of fourteen on the Lago di Garda. Thus my observant nature is instructively concentrated on the black servants and not on their white masters and the black servants obviously do not understand my thirst for solidarity and complicity and distrust me like anyone who uses them and that is all. It is terribly impossible to talk to them as man to man – there are racial dimensions so deeply inculcated into the blacks that, if you observe them among themselves and then in the presence of a white, you would say that they carry about a double phreno-pathy. With a white person they are one thing, with one of their own, what is left over by the white – that is, what is left of a man. Blacks are schizophrenic exactly like whites, emotionally unreli-able: they change mood, attitude, morality, according to the notion of wealth and power they form of the white man of the moment. I get angry to think that an individual, because of the grave fate of being born into a family of servants or blacks, should be moulded from infancy to consider himself, even when looking ahead, a black – that is, a servant. I see him in the lodges taken by white couples of Danes, English, Scandinavians who here, in Kenya, decide the fate of high-class tourism (high-class or none at all). The little black girl of five smiles at me exactly like her mother of thirty, a smile which is not hers, the smile directed at her mother's masters. Such a scene ruins the day for me – I hate the atavistic smiles of a congenital *role*, I prefer the terrible grin of a contrary identity, bloodthirsty but rebellious. But today the problem for me is – in what way is the little black girl to blame?

This morning we began at dawn a pre-safari around the lodge – the minibus chased a few, tired, neurotic animals kept in the open spaces much worse than in any zoo. Then there is the view of Kilimanjaro, with a little spray of snow at the summit and the usual lower slopes. Everything that has already been described by Hemingway disturbs me. So I shall be brief: Kenya is not for me, you get rid of that portentous *mal d'Afrique* only by staying at home. And these hotel arrangements, conceived of for two per room as a minimum, and alone everything is 50 per cent dearer. When I say that I am single my problems begin, as do those of the organization which seizes the opportunity I offer to impart a lesson. Here *single* travellers are so rare and annoying that they would willingly use them to embalm their heads and hang them in the hall. Nothing here makes sense in itself, everything has a sense in terms of tourism: every stranger capable of buying anything here suddenly becomes a *friend*. And who on earth will the true friend be? How can they still use the same word to define more complex relationships than the desire to fasten on one a necklace of a rhinoceros horn? Without the word the thing does not exist, just as it is true that we only see the colours we can name: a *friend* who can no longer be designated as such is not a friend. If you prostitute the word *friend* (because of commercial problems and with the aim of a generalized overture between strangers) that brings with it some very precise semantic-existential consequences: that you don't know what a friend is, that no one has been your friend and that you have never been anyone's friend, that you have excluded from your individual history the possibility of ever having one and that, as with all the words a black uses to a white person, he does not designate anything of his own and therefore does not give up anything, he is prostituting a word that belongs to *others*. Not many linguistic studies are needed to prove from life the sad reality of this statement: Anyone who prostitutes words ends up by burning the relative referents – things no less than persons. Thus every time in Italy I hear or read expressions like 'to fight the Mafia' I feel like going over to the side of the Mafia; if I hear the word 'fatherland', which unfortunately is coming back in many other Western countries, I feel like going over to the first foreign enemy that comes to hand; 'the pro-life movement' arouses in me desires for a violent pro-abortion policy etc. 'I love you' is all right on one's death-bed – provided you don't then presume to recover: the word is no longer valid. What need is there to bring into the limelight feelings which, if they exist, it is in their nature to be inward, discreet, constant or not to exist at all? When a man says 'I love you' it is because he has substituted the full word for the feeling, which is becoming empty. Anyone who distorts the nature of words distorts the nature of reality – degrades any possible naturalness of the feelings. One must be intransigent in the use of words and very acquiescent with everything which can take place better in silence. The word is an exacting phenomenon, usually the costs are greater than the profits if one tries to force it. I have noticed that if you talk too loosely about your 'most sincere' feelings you finish up with not having any, and the fact of not feeling any longer will lead you to increase the dimension of the void shouted out by the words in order to mask it. Obviously this is something I notice in others, not in myself – I never pretend without knowing that I am doing it; if I instrumentalize the word for the purposes of *falsity*, I am creating something that was not there before, I am not playing games – I am not deceiving anyone, not even myself. The word is the official stamp embossed on the free paper of the mind which up to the moment before has been immersed in the tyranny of silence which is radical, primitive and right – 'there is nothing better than to remain silent', apart from naming things by their name and not in vain. To dissent, one speaks. To speak to assent is a superfluous function of language. Anyone who expresses himself – and, best of all, who writes words – should from time to time represent the final expressive synthesis of a given sentiment from the moment it came to light in a man's nervous system till it reached him, here and now, and that in its expressive evolutionary – and evolving – shade of meaning. A smile is the synthesis of all the smiles of all men past and present: to be conscious of this is not bad, this does not mean that the *smile* is debased in its aesthetic need for rapport. Anyone who smiles thoughtlessly offends the human effort to transform – across the millennia – a hole for putting food into into a mouth for communicating a signal of sympathy between predatory animals in the process of perfecting a social convention with their lips. Instincts are not improvised as the naïve – the diplomats and the churchmen and the party men – believe. For those who can afford it, naturally, it is better to refuse a business deal than one's own instincts. There is more that is humanly holy – and therefore linguistic – in someone who errs with his own head than in one who gets things right with the heads of others. If *yea* had remained *yea* and *nay nay* we would not have had the moon but at least we would still have had the earth. And now man is losing all that little because he has not been a man of his word . . :

It is odd how these lovers of primitive nature come here loaded with cartridges and dream that some Kenya ranger will take them poaching – just across the frontier, let's say, in Tanzania. But I who – apart from running water – like nothing in nature leave it alone in every sense of the word – I have never even taken a photograph in all my life so as not to dazzle the midges, it would never enter my mind to catch a butterfly, and I am even perplexed when confronted with the fat plants on my terrace full of little bugs that must be killed. I mean *nature*, after having revealed itself to man for what it is, what else is it supposed to do to be *alive* in you and me? Allow itself to be transfixed with a pin,

271

to be crucified first so that man may consider himself satisfied in his desire for representation beyond what is in the state of nature? A lion roars for a second in my eardrum and my brain is grateful to it for existing for that roar and that is all; the whole life of the lion is concerned only with the lion and its surroundings, not man's brute desire to consider *his* any component even at the price of having it dead, stuffed and exhibited. For man a dead lion is more alive than a live one, prey to others, or even than the lion itself, living for itself, an entity which is not granted to any living being.

And all these savannahs photographed in volleys, animals no less than the natives of the place: millions of photographs have stripped them, their colours in real life have been degraded, the skies polluted by desire for the negative, for life fixed once and for all, that is by models of death. And those Masai who make contracts with the guides (most of them ex-Masai as well) for everything: a photo five thousand lire, dance, twenty-two thousand, song, thirty thousand, fifty-three thousand circumcision of a newborn child, the change they don't give you. Couldn't they instead be given 110 thousand lire not to let themselves be photographed or sing or dance or make the little tots whimper because of the white zombies' joy in death?

Kilimanjaro Lodges. Animals seen arriving: curried chicken, beef stew, Portuguese sardines in oil, a liberal American lady in the flesh, two wizened dykes from Liechtenstein, three Koreans dressed in Made in Italy. The natives, not having that sense of the future typical of the hegemonic entrepreneurs (who forbid the natives to kill the animals but are not however prepared to share with them the high profits of tourism, which is threatened season after season by the disappearance of the primary material: Kenya in fact), offer, but with the required circumspection, bracelets of giraffe tail, rhinoceros horns – very precious because of the aphrodisiac which is extracted from them in the Phillippines – masks of the shells of giant tortoises, ivory necklaces (you only have to put your lighter under them to see if it is plastic and it is never plastic), lion's teeth, tiger's teeth etc. A massacre there is no way of arresting between one order to halt it and the next.

In the hotel, late in the evening, at the sight of a leopard – or, given the unusual sighting, of *the* leopard, perhaps the only one left within a radius of thousands of kilometres – all my fellow guests leapt to their feet and stood at attention. But not to pay homage to a species which is being extinguished but to immortalize a photoflash.

In the morning we resume the journey back to Mombasa. Seen – a little shepherd with a cock which came halfway down his thigh bouncing in pursuit of the sheep which broke ranks. Last night the bats, the crickets, the snoring guests in the adjacent rooms: noises. A herd of buffaloes in the dark night formed constellations of slowly moving masses on the silent clearing. I was awake on the balcony standing with head high as if in front of an altar. In two years there will be nothing to see here any more, only photographs of animals on the walls of the bar. End of the safari: the young and very nice Irish couple (they are on honeymoon) will send me the following negatives: myself with a background of hippopotamus backs, myself in a Papal outburst lifting up a black child, myself in the missionary position squatting with black children strewn with sweets, I couldn't say no, particularly since, so as not to be fussy, I insisted that they take some photos for my nieces and for *Voices of the Railroad* – an *underground* magazine of the State Railways. Sorry not to have seen the rhinoceros – currently on tour in the north-west – nor the lynx (already wrapped in fur), we go back to our respective hotels. Our guide, father of four, with wife and mother to keep, earns 800 shillings a month and if he falls ill or has an accident so much the worse for him, he should have been more careful – he is replaced at once and immediately afterwards sacked without notice. I, for three days, had to pay out the lowest figure – 4,650 shillings. Outside the hotels where we stop to be put down, the blacks are squatting like hens laying an egg that doesn't come: dressed in their best rags they are waiting for some other black to be kicked out so as to take his place, even if only for one day. A stonemason working with hammer and chisel in the rock gets – earns, as the gentlemen say – two shillings for each stone dislodged, a stone costs two days' work. And yet here and in almost all the *recent* African nations the good governments are the *white* ones since the greatest savageries – after those of colonialism – have always come from black dictators against their own people – see Amin and Bokassa. What to do? First and foremost a nice shower, then a nice sleep, and then we shall see. I wonder what it is like in Prague.

⌖

A little plane, nine seats plus the pilot, and off for Lamu! From on high the salt-marshes recall areas of the human body, velvety cells magnified by geometric patterns – purple, green and blue – intersected by black veins. We fly over the first little islands of mangroves and land. The group travelling with me consists of eight chapped Americans in their fififties who did not know each other before this trip, which has been organized by their leader through announcements in the papers. They keep together, quarrel, pay court to each other, are no longer *single*. At table, during dinner, I am overcome by sadness over being at the critical moment of return, I eat listlessly, I think that the water in the bay is maroon and I have found all the blues of height muddied here below.

For writing – which I take in exactly like the cow which swallows down grass and hay to chew the cud at leisure – I have done everything, I have even been reduced to living. I move about, I give myself a life that is more and more tiring and squeezed out, journey after journey – and I no longer like to travel but I have to make the effort. I capture new nations of words, waves of verbal suggestions which, if I stayed in one place, I would find in no library because what has already been written is *past* for a writer – fortunately not for a reader and for a woman reader it has still to come . . . My books I have first to winkle out of a mind that is more and more obtuse and indifferent, always more reluctant to relinquish its secrets to me and conservative, diffident towards any Busian novelty (it already possesses *His Own Casanova*, my fourth and penultimate novel, and is thinking about the final one, and anything that does not belong to them does not belong to that mind and even this organic diary it considers an unprogrammed exploit because it isn't at all partisan in its views).

In a dhow at the first light of dawn – following my suggestion – I and part of the American group leave for the ruins of Tawa: baobab, elephant dung, the poor traces of Arab culture transplanted to regions not of its choice. In the civic museum the two *siwas* – ceremonial horns with fingerholds on the side – are suitable for triumphs and the circumcision of sultans' sons. And, walking through the little rooms, a breathtaking discovery on a caption: 'The ink for Islamic writing on wood or parchment is composed of coal and milk' . . . And the fascination of a similar product follows me right on to the aeroplane going back to Bergamo. 'Coal and milk, coal and milk . . .' I continue to repeat to myself: that someone else has gone and mined for me, that someone else has milked for me, that someone else has blended for me . . . How easy is any non-democratic intellectual greatness, how stupid it is if it is not applied to the memory of the person who made himself small to go down into the dark of a mine or who bent over to milk an udder . . . The aeroplane begins to go through the routines for landing, only now it comes to my mind that Clementina and Loredana Gnoccoli should be on the same flight as me. In fact Clementina is there and can be seen, even if she has remained for hours in the crew's cabin, undoubtedly telling the same horrendous stories, and between one parade up and down and another she has given a little present to each of the black hostesses, a small package in Cellophane with a ribbon. I can imagine what is in it . . . But lo and behold Clementina Gnoccoli, after having so hogged my attention on the way there and on arrival, now passes in front of me in the cockpit on the runway without even a sign of recognition, not a greeting, going off as if she had never seen me, never spoken to me, never *read* me . . . From behind up comes Loredana Gnoccoli, even more horribly masculine, the lowest form of punk, a big gorilla of a woman. Having come up alongside me, she grips my wrist hard, I move away in astonishment and see a little male wig fly from her head, from beneath it a tangle of chestnut hair spreads out with a pony-tail, Loredana takes off her glasses and then snatches away the second wig as well.

'You know, Busi, I and my wife hated that terrible dyke of a daughter with Clementina always saying "just like her father" and so we made her up like me – oh it didn't take much – and did for her in disguise. Of course for me it is a pain because for a good while I shall have to pretend to be my daughter but soon we'll make *her* disappear too and I'll be able to go back under a false name to be with my Clementina again – oh a new life, oh a new honeymoon! I have promised her after the business with the present from the cereal packet, to have a transplant for our golden wedding . . . I don't know whether my wife ever spoke to you about my patents for ladies' underwear you wouldn't have a moment while they get our baggage . . . ? Well, yes, men go for bottoms, how do they imagine ideal knickers? What the hell can we build into them? Obviously I wouldn't worry about royalties if they take on . . . Nice to have met you – Faustino Gnoccoli, Ginetto to my friends.'

And the three creatures of my travels explode and de-gnoccolate into bubbles of air before the Customs and so I did not have to declare anyone to anything. The only thing to do is to leave for Prague, maybe for Lisbon. I start up my car which has stayed outside in the car park of this very nice little airport. Am I here already? Kenya, country of rapine, Deep-South of Africa. But all the earth – and the sky too – are raped day after day, stripped for ever of their most precious qualities which can never be made pristine again. But it has always been like this – the difference is that now the inevitable nature of the degenerative process of the human species is so much more disgusting. Yes, the human species must perforce disappear. But it will not be because of natural catastrophes – provided that the death-drive we all harbour is also neither a natural fruit nor a cultural one nor the arbitrary expression of our destiny nor our last act of will – to die, to be no more by choice. Perhaps all humanity has grown so much *with profit* to the ultimate limits of psychic consciousness only so as the better to turn together towards a total, self-induced mortality.

God is a word which belongs to me as much as to anyone else and I use as I see fit, out loud and on the autostrada and without a tear:

'God, you are mine, see that I am always inside *this* instant so full of its fleeting truths, so poorly intense, so oasis blue.'

~~

For the purpose of art the homosexual writer is no less diverse than the heterosexual writer and, if they aim to be writers, their linguistic route – which is a deviation from the norm and which makes them similarly particular – is spectacular and eccentric. Their common diversity consists not in having this or that sexual inclination but in being writers, certainly in their chemistry things are staged through a psychic dynamism which pre-supposes a self-directed violence superior to the violence suf-fered socially and a further arbitration between the opposing violences. To live and also not to live is an accident that is easier than to pursue an aesthetic tension, which can only be gratui-tous, in order to safeguard the terrible game of liberty and the search for the truth which *does not concern us*. The presence of a propellant of this kind – one extraneous to any human and social economy – in itself undermines every received rhetoric of the blood, of life, of happiness, of the feelings, of the conventions, of the *convenances* and of sex – of public decency, of being human and not artists *against* (and if sublime *against and alongside*) a humanity which, being incapable of aesthetic tension, proposes a single end in order to escape from its own infamies: to reproduce for itself ovaries and spermatozoa like itself with the only means it has and recognizes. With a concert of slavish violence against those who attack its state of neutral and undying reproductive bestiality, it is capable of defending itself by forming a ring round its one *cultural* patrimony: the exaltation of the Prick and the Cunt – that is to say, the cult of the nice couple *which has always existed and always will exist*. You only need to officiate there and everything is in order – you can, if you are homosexual, perform well by yourself only if you feel you are in the wrong and therefore recognize the Model and pass your life confronting yourself with what you think ought to concern you because it excludes you, and when things are going well for you, you will develop yet another stupid skill in Eternal Justification; there is quite simply no use discussing the matter if you are heterosexual.

In fact they are legion, the thurifers of this St Valentine's Day wrapped in ribbons by the subculture of political sexism, which is both automatic and normative (and hence gratifying to the boastful cowards – the hangers-on of *art*) and I shall not concern myself here with the infinite number of scribblers who, by being homosexual and heterosexual in manner (without any notion of this oblique way of being *against and alongside* which includes being against oneself), carry on a trade with their sexual bags and baggage under the demographic sign of good organs. No, I desire to enucleate – coming up with a great deal from my own writer's anthropology – those elements which I might call physiological and which, by exclusion, give rise to (or are a condition of) that rare bird (cock) – the writer, who is unique and unrepeatable, the one who tails along behind an epoch because of having (almost) determined rather than described it, bent it more to his own aesthetic will than supported it in its natural placental sloth.

One could begin by stating – without too many demonstrations being required – that the received idiocy is not a presupposition of art, although it may be so for good artisanal work – and so we shall have the artisans of sex in escapist literature against the writers *tout court* in literature *tout court*; the ones continually reproduce the same series of phallic/vaginal novels, the others create a single work of sensual manysidedness which is not further reproducible. Let us determine, therefore, who is an imbecile and therefore denied to the aesthetic *anastasis* from the very root of his sexual assimilation: the guilty homosexual who gives some sort of primitive or personal justification for his own sexuality is an imbecile and an imbecile is the cheerful heterosexual who does not feel guilty and does not provide at least a couple of them. The homosexual who stoops to a justification instead of rising up in aesthetic assertion is an *artist* lost for ever (Pasolini, Genet, Gide); thus he is an artist lost for ever – the heterosexual who confuses his own firefly with the sexual beacon *par excellence* and does not feel himself sufficiently guilty to be impelled to *perversely* conduct an investigation into his own *normality*, conceiving of it as a pre-text for a text that is all yet to come and never yet written, once and for all, by ordinary heterosexuals and their passive collective memory of being in themselves exemplary (no point in naming names as examples, it would be very difficult to name anyone who is not crushed inside this *vicious* circle). Humanity, made up for the greater part of *guilty* homosexuals and cheerful heterosexuals, is inartistic by the nature of its constitution and therefore profoundly composed of imbeciles devoted to good artisanship and denied to art – and, unfortunately, almost always to the art of living. It is evident that

the pseudo-artistic market is invaded by gays who, as a profession, play the penitent gays (or the proud gays, which is the
most underhand form of penitence) and by heteros who, as a
profession, play the hetero (the caricature of machismo and
feminism pushed to their limits), so by simple human beings
anxious to sell a product in the artisanal immediacy of the
demand/supply of the moment (which has lasted for thousands
of years) while true artists are rare, fortunately for everybody
and, in particular, for the artists themselves.

To sum up, the artist cannot and must not load himself with
the *clichés* (of whatever nature) of society and its commercial–
consolatory horizon except to stigmatize and mock them in their
shameless claim to absolutism. Otherwise he will produce the
umpteenth pink, black, yellow, ballet-green clone – to confine
ourselves to the literary genres most in vogue. Besi. , it is
biologically fair that this aesthetic mutation, which is intrinsic to
being a writer, should be in itself very rare in nature (and,
moreover, does not in itself suffice to produce art) because man
manages to give up much but not the *hereditary*, comfortable
ability to enjoy a sexuality which is contemporaneous to himself
and others, whether it recognizes or promotes or denies itself is
not important – the victim role of the homosexuals is a patrimony
forming part of this comfortable state of affairs which is thrown
as a dowry to the black sheep. In its various forms as precept,
sexuality responds fully, without being conscious of having
subscribed to them, to the canons of the taboos, of the sentimen-
talistic madonnas, of the chimerical frustrations, prone to secu-
larization by the only way of being sexual laid down by collective
caution which, in order to include the gene, excludes the genius.

The artistic genius dramatically and frivolously soars above
this prison of sexual being and for arcane reasons, which would
deserve separate treatment, decides to dismantle the barriers
which are invisible to the prisoners themselves but not to him –
thus violating the *sexual* sense of time and space to which the
given society has conformed and which has an immense struc-
tural effect on the conception of the work of art of the genius
(Beuys no less than Warhol, Flaubert no less than Proust, Dante
than Wilde, creators whose primitive sexual matrix has, in my
view, lost what one might call any *biographical* pre-eminence in

order to further a critical-aesthetic examination of their work – and of their existence as men).

Another conviction of a hermeneutic nature which I confide with a grain of salt – but not so much either, since it concerns no less than myself and my existence as a writer – is that the genius (the product of the social urge to create one rather than of the individual urge to become one) does not perform any castratory sacrifice in this process: he does not castrate or sublimate his own pleasure but the gangrenous genitals of Pleasure as the Truth of the world. Woe betide the butterfly that refuses or removes the grub, of which it is the perfect superstructure, in order to try blandishments on the concupiscence of a *net*: it is transfixed on a pin and immediately framed under glass – it is given a monument *while still alive*. The work of art trans-sexualizes the world without therefore remaking it less realistic than it is: it is not entirely assimilable nor entirely digestible by the particular society in which it has been conceived and received, otherwise it would be cannibalized and expelled. What the cannibals do not manage to finish off is called *hope*. And hope is a chameleon which must constantly and unimaginably change sex if it wishes to find safety. So one must disembarrass oneself of every mystifying mystique of the sexual-self and of any Carmelite rhetoric about the *gift of oneself*: the writer is the total wardrobe of the little theatre of his time and does not, because of this capacity for superior osmosis with the costumes of his likes, renounce his own particular fig-leaf for what it is.

There is such a thing as the voluntary holocaust in the various public careers which, because of hysterias of manner, have to espouse a *better* vision of sex to the point of misreading *exemplary* sex (all the more reactionary the more of a façade it is); in the career of a genius, no. The genius is the one who does not belong to himself and does not belong; he takes the truth from the hands of the few who give it out and distributes to the fingernails of the many who have scarcely met with it, setting in train the reciprocal esteem of ephemeral and most tender humanity in each one of us. For him sex, like the State in Marx, finishes by vanishing as a form of control, remaining a games convention between equals, an exchange non-value – and from here it is only a step to the City of the Sun . . .

The moral of the fable of the writer is all the more *his* the more it is everyone's and no one's, and yet inalienable, pregnant, alive – anciently new. This attrition between art and society, between the emotively revolutionary autonomy of the writer (who more than many conservatives often has in his head the liberating value of tradition) and the sentimentalizing tameness which society would like from him so as to phagocytize him in its own inaesthetic animalistic instincts of *let's get on with things then*, is not without pain in the life of the man who is writer and often makes impossible his social and emotional life in the sense that society and individuals never stop flattering him to capture him (to reduce him to nothing). They put him to the proof to test his basic seriousness (his effective eccentricity), they tempt him to see if, in the end, his aesthetic destructiveness is not merely a passing disguise with a view to a nomination by a salon, a parliament, the secretariat of a party or company, and if the writer does not play along (he is in fact far-sighted on society's behalf and is doing it the favour of his own planned marginalization), it creates a scandal, absolute evidence of the popular consensus to dissent and therefore to proclaim the authenticity of the writer who is both envied and necessary, partly integrated in, partly integrating of that same society that persists, silly thing that it is, in pushing him to the margin – normal people, that is to say *normal* homosexuals and heterosexuals, are so badly educated in its own millenary abominations that they are scandalized by trifles.

If the writer is healthy he will not have sudden recognitions of this or that person and, continually making new enemies where the others only find relatives, will create in isolation what is closest to his heart – a new work of art which mutates in time and along with time, with the history of man, with the infinite aesthetic process of which it is the anticipated precursor. This is, by and large, the fixed physiology of a writer – what does it matter or matter to him to be sexual in one way or another? If anything the argument to be made would be different – that is to say, how is it that there are more *real* writers with a homosexual neurological system than a heterosexual one and does this aesthetic ascesis not perhaps find more fertile ground in the nature of the former rather than of the latter? But these are commonplace

281

synecdoches – the writer can very well change his part according to the way the script works. In art sexuality is in the prompter's box – it is positive that there should be at least one of these but the theatre is something else – it is just as well that the performance of this momentary tragedy does not contain stammers or gaps of memory *ex arte*. The great tragedian of writing knows that there is this prompter's box and does not complain of it, but woe betide if he should forget who he is and begin to look around elsewhere than in himself – someone will stop his mouth with *his* words or *his* sex . . .

'Look at him – he's here' I exclaim exultantly in front of the little figure who is slouching in the night among the pathways in this so bitterly dear parking lot.

'Well.'

It is Demetrio, that is M., one of the minor characters in *Standard Life* who I am seeing again after so many years. Always in an undershirt, always shivering, always never having thought to put on a pullover, always incapable of knowing whether he feels hot or cold. Always tiny, smiling crookedly and in astonishment, already with nothing more to say. Astonishing. M. became Demetrio in everything and for all purposes and now M. too will become M.

'Me – this year I was in Russia – and you?'

'Me – in Kenya and I was bored. I was thinking of going to Lisbon on Monday but there are no seats on the plane till the thirteenth.'

'Portugal doesn't mean anything to me. It would be a nice idea. Why Lisbon?'

'It's the only European capital I haven't seen yet. But I don't have much time either – I can't wait till the thirteenth.'

'I'm on holiday at home,' he says. 'We could go by car.'

'I can't be away for a whole week and get to Lisbon in one go . . . Suppose we went to visit Ludwig's castles? With all the times we were in Germany we never . . .'

'Excellent idea. We'll do it in four days. But me – I don't have much money.'

'Splendid! We leave tomorrow. Do you remember Czechoslovakia – we'd just got to Brno and the car broke down and you got conjunctivitis? But this time we'll really get to Prague. We were at the gates.'

'Let's go to Prague. The Czechs are . . . I remember,' says M. thoughtfully.

'I remember that in Brno we saw nothing but blacks and a native of Japan and a Peace Garden full of tanks and guns.'

'But in Budapest they weren't bad – that's the kind they are.'

'Ah, do you remember that Hungarian boy in the Turkish bath with that huge red knob who trembled and didn't know which prick to begin with? They're sure to look like them. And how was Russia? What impression did it make on you? Leningrad gave me one of these fits of sadness . . .'

'First I was in Basilicata with my bachelor brother – I went with him – he has married someone from there.'

'Ah, one of the ones that the agencies send a photograph of and then they introduce them, bringing them up by bus and then marry them in two ticks.'

'Yes, one of these. How she will manage to get into the same bed I don't know. But he likes her – she's like someone from the Middle Ages, does what he wants and has some hairs as well. And I took him down there by car. Then to Russia.'

'And what sort of a time did you have in Russia? Did you score or not?'

'In Russia I had the same human relationships as in Basilicata. None. And it was even colder than in Matera.'

'So we leave at midday. Tomorrow we'll go to the bank.'

'I still have all the small change of the trips we made together.'

'But that was at least five years ago.'

'Ciao, till tomorrow.'

'*Demetrio*, I beg you – don't forget either your driving licence or your passport, eh.'

'The car goes on methane gas *and* petrol – it doesn't use much. I had it fitted out – even if you take in the VAT it didn't . . .'

'But what's this about you not having much money? You've been working all your life, have a steady job, you don't spend a lira except on petrol and you have no money? You got taken to the cleaner's by that woman in the advertisement.'

'Yes, watch out. No, my other brother. Everything I had I gave it him. Twenty million. He was being ruined by his workshop – it was to plug the biggest holes. Well . . .'

'And the business would have gone to hell just the same and you kept your mouth shut, eh?'

'Exactly. My sister-in-law's mania for power. And now we find it difficult even to say hello when we see each other on the stairs.'

'Oh but you're such a masochist I'm sure that for you this is like repayment with interest. Return to the bosom of the Little Mother and the Big Needy Brother . . .'

'My mother still hasn't stopped hating you. When she sees you on television . . .'

'Because I kept taking away her baby boy, because I took him off the straight and narrow path, because he wouldn't be *cured* and it was my fault. That she had been your ruin never entered her head. You were saying – how did it end up with the woman from the advertisement – separated – with two grown-up daughters?'

'It lasted a few months. I had got quite fond of her but . . .'

'But did you manage to fuck her at least?'

'A little, then one time she didn't . . .'

'Only you could get certain ideas. To marry a human being and at your age with your arsehole that is mad about lorry-drivers' jacks. What will madam not do to get mad normally! Ciao then, I'll expect you at my house.'

'My mother will be struck all of a heap.'

'She'd do better to stay a heap of shit. When she dies you must light a candle to the Madonna . . . He's not bad that guy, ciao M. I'm going after him.'

＊

And it is off by way of Austria. M. has brought with him a briefcase because in any case he never changes. He continues to scratch himself, it seems to me, specially his hairy bottom. We talk about this and that and then less and less. When he is driving he gets big-headed. But his legs are too short for the clutch pedal and the gears get worn down before being properly changed. M. is such an introvert but so scatterbrained that even when he whistles he does it mentally.

'Did you take a look at the engine, have you got the green card, did you see that the tyres are all right, do you have the spare tyre and the sticker with I for Italy . . .

'Everything's OK. Did you think I'd leave like that . . .'

At Affi we stop short in an emergency area – steam from the engine. The water is evaporating and the thermostat can't cope. Another couple of kilometres and we would have been on foot.

'Oh, it's nothing. It always does it. With the methane gas we're all right. Get in!'

He would like to arrive in Prague that same evening. We don't even have visas.

'Maybe now they've made tourism a little easier and do them right away at the frontier. We'll get them after Linz. Shall we try?'

Then we stop at the Mondsee and sleep in the Mondseehotel a little beyond Salzburg. M. is all excited by the way I play up to make us laugh – he works in the Post Office and I call him 'the postman who always rings twice'. He is amused and happy, finally, he has in me a shadow to which to make his little body conform – a body which is ravaged by bouts of exhaustion, by resignation, by the weakness of not being strong. If I drink he drinks, if I stop he stops, if I piss he pisses, if I eat he eats. If I go to bed he jumps into bed too.

'But look M., you can go wherever you like – take a turn by the lakeside, you're not obliged to do what I do.'

'No, I'm tired. I'm going to sleep.'

He continues to scratch himself in his sleep, curled up on himself, and always with the smile of a little newly born corpse. When we went with men in the first years of our strange and laconic friendship, at night he ground his teeth and did not scratch himself. Now he scratches himself and doesn't grind his teeth any more because he has gum disease and the teeth he has left are too few in number. The skin of his face is patched with sudden purple spots which under his little beard change him into a pitiful elf. Now he shivers in his sleep, tries to snuggle down even further, is cold but it is as if he did not know he only needs another blanket. I get up, open the wardrobes, find it, throw it on to him. A type like this is well worth four days of enforced company – he is a perfect idiot, a little funeral monument to failure. And I have noticed that he is no longer up to driving and has lost the only quality left to him and which I valued when I still did not have a driving licence – the psycho-motor one when he had a steering-wheel in his hands. He accelerates and slows down needlessly, following an untidy internal dodecaphony of his own rather than the demands of the road, and he is also no longer distracted by the men on cycles or on foot in the landscape but by himself – one feels that he is contemplating himself internally as if he found himself interesting and nothing else existed outside, including possible road accidents. He drives as if he were alone, as if life were worth nothing – or at least not as much as his own, to which he is attached with all the inane ferocity of the coward and the loser – not to remake himself, no, but to enjoy the passive interests of a rather cunning pain. There is only one thing I do that M. doesn't do – wash and brush my teeth. On the other hand he does something I have never done – he combs himself. Continually. But he does not comb the hair up top, he combs the hair down below, and when my eye fell on the comb he had left in the bathroom the teeth had traces of dandruffy blood. He sleeps scratching his neck convulsively; fortunately he has no nails – he constantly eats them. He could have agreed to this trip to hurl me down into a ravine, to kill me even at the cost of killing himself. We haven't said a word how I depicted him in *Standard Life* but he told me he had read some passages just last night, those about Jürgen and about Celestino Lometto; he asked me whether I had seen them again *afterwards* as *living people*. Jürgen – who dies in the novel – no; but *Lometto* I see every so often because he came to see me, we go and eat a pizza and each time we meet a feeling of festival is set loose in us. And his wife *Edda Napaglia*? Like her husband B., I. is admired – she more than he. It was she who read the novel out loud to her husband – horror followed by consternation. After some months of 'shame', of 'now I'll deal with you', they no longer thought of doing away with me and now she does the honours of the novel to as many people as possible. Both of them are proud of it. B. has told me that I could even give him 50 per cent of the author's rights because now he gets a kick out of pretending to himself that he is really Celestino Lometto. Those who took it worse are 1) J.W., the German lady who is discussed paradoxically at the beginning and who is indignant, not so much at how I treated her but at the scant space reserved for her and 2) those excluded who, in their unquestionable judgement of themselves as persons excluded (?), no longer recognize me. Reveal crimes *with style* and you will have done a signal social honour to the *guilty*, the murderer becomes a hero, and one forgives a *paper* murderer everything including the reality. Moral: the crimes of reality become the feats of the human condition. M. never says anything about himself as *Demetrio*, he does not ask for explanations of the *self* whom I saw in perspective and who, fictionalized, was excessive compared to the real M. It seems to me however that M. has now definitely become Demetrio, that the person has conformed to the character created by me, thus acquiring an inauspicious bodily shape. M., perhaps not knowing how to be nor who to be, seized on *Demetrio* and what in the novel could be considered a warning, a sad self a week from now, has been taken instead as a present model. And how grateful he is to me – grateful to the point of not wishing to know anything about himself or about Demetrio *and* himself.

M. drives and laughs into his moustache without a common reason – he has already taken the wrong road, perhaps he does it on purpose so that I have to scold him, shout at him, he goes through red lights, brakes hard at green ones, wants to make me angry, to arouse my most unpleasant attention, he knows that nothing infuriates me more than to make a mistake and not learn or to make a mistake on purpose and without reason so as not to be forced to behave himself as a result. An artist of the tic.

At the frontier at Hoffbrunn, without visas, they obviously send us back as foreseen. Apart from a few curses, I don't lose the chance to joke with the Czech customs official about the way the times change but never in the countries of the East where one has to go through such a performance to spend one's own money . . . Destination – Vienna, as we always knew. But it allowed M. to stay at the wheel for three hours more than necessary, I have invented a false target for him so as to extend his target, I have diminished the goal which neither of us is interested in reaching, he still less than me – all M. wants is to see the road run past under the wheels. We stop for a moment to stretch our legs, we look round, we pluck two little apples from a tree on the bank, we laugh – he goes to piss but has to find a blackberry or a bush to hide himself. He shakes his little head like a turtle in an aquarium, making it go right and left and at every third beat pulls the neck down between his shoulders and starts again at once, faking happiness, and jumps about and exclaims in his dialect 'Oh God!' I talk to him about sex in a comradely way to amuse him, distracting him a little so that he won't totally distract himself with himself, but I know by now and so does he that sex and tobacco are the drug of the propertyless, the smoke of the poor, the plain fare of someone who'd like something special once in a while.

In Vienna we look for a pension behind the Czech consulate to be ready tomorrow morning. Afterwards, seeing that we are in a city of art, I take him to a sauna. The sauna is broken and the internal television is overloaded with porno movies. I realize how many little films I have missed in recent years. The porno-stars are the authentic Saint Francises of our times – they must be very good, have a great spirit of adaptation, love for animals and the arrogance of photogenicity in the ecstasies of simple people who take things as they come. It isn't easy, I believe, to move one's bottom about on cue, nor to have an erection with someone in front of you with a clapper-board who goes *clack – take two, fucking*. I fall asleep at once but I am worried about M. – I open an eye; M. is beside me and is sleeping too and scratching his legs. I shake my head – in his sleep he seems to shake his too. Here is someone who tears your heart out to do nothing with it because the little you can give him he uses against himself and against you, opening his arms with a resigned air. Poor, dear friend with the adolescent's body and now coming up to fifty. Many people asked me, when we were going steady, what pleasure I found in keeping M. close to me, what sense there was in my constantly talking to someone who was always silent and moreover never listened to a word; I would say to them today what I said then: M. is in no way freakish, a happy victim he is lively and loyal. I trust him: I mean that the slight distaste he can cause me is only a consequence of the harm he cannot help doing to himself and that he loves me.

Having left the sauna the Vienna twilight merits that we go to beddy-byes right away; at 8 we are in the Pension Gloria, I cutting away at my verruca, him flaying himself for the thousandth time. Does he have scabies? No, he says, it is to give the sawdust some air . . . I have no better friends than M. close by, I have them far away and therefore do not consider them better – those who are absolutely better are those who are close to us for what I am and what we are. I suggest to him that he takes a walk, that it is me who keeps impossible hours, and that for me life after 8 o'clock has no longer any sense unless I pass it with eyes shut and that I can't wait to shut them at the first darkness just as I open them at first light. Nothing doing – he asks if I am mad; after quarter of an hour he, who is used to keeping it up till 2 playing cards with his mother or going about looking for truck-drivers, is sleeping like a Cupid on a saint's tomb. We are two elderly men in isolation, the room reflects the yellow light of the streetlamps below, our persons are pi-pi coloured, but placated, excrementiciously in order. The only negative thing in my sleep, for some time now, is that there are too many dreams of which I remember every detail, indeed I often wake up to take stock of them and then resume them exactly at the point where I left off. There is not, I mean, a great gap between one state and the other, apart from the horizontal and vertical positions. I also dream the dreams of the characters I am metabolizing – last night's dream was not my own but Anastasia Cofani's, I know, which means that I shall pass all this Monday putting the final touches to it in the test-tube within me, keeping hold into the bargain of the thread of *her* dream grafted in me as if in a stranger's belly. In any case with M. there's no need for me to speak and for him not to listen – but it is nice to have him with one, the pleasurable sillinesses of our paradoxical and slightly stale little theatre keep us company, acting the part of a gay is a great invention for sending up straight drama and after every time we know as much as before, but we wouldn't know to who else's attention we should submit, we have no one, and no abyss is ever filled between us who are resigned to a distance which has always been defined since the first approaches.

And we arrive in Prague. After a couple of busy hours I meet a Jugoslav of about thirty, there for a technological convention; he seems to me to be slightly stoned, he has a brisk way of behaving, jerkily, but he's nice, he is like a hare because of the syncopated swiftness of his gait and gestures. I met him down in the lavatories of the underground there in Wenceslas Square, it is amazing the number of men who look at their cocks as they handle them, policemen and soldiers included, all with hard cocks such as I have never seen anywhere. It looks as if they had organized an Eastern olympiad of wanking. The Jugoslav was the only one to keep on changing places, undoubtedly the better to humiliate and get closer up to anyone who deluded himself that he had one bigger and finer than his. In fact, the size of his weapon (and the memories it evokes: a little friend of my youth had one exactly like that, he too being Serbo-Croat in origin: a *macédoine* for connoisseurs) gives me food for thought and when he signals to me to follow him out I follow him more from geophysical curiosity than for the menhir. In the Hotel Europa he presents a document to the porter casually and we go up to my room. He doesn't waste time: he kisses out of politeness without opening his lips and goes straight for the arse with his hands as happens only in films about eighteenth-century hussars. He stares at me fixedly with a cordially interrogatory look, murmuring things unheard of in English like 'C'est bon?' which he thinks is English. My cock subsides at once, the gentleman demands very precise and well-performed services; while I am resigning myself to procuring him that relief which will set me free as quickly as possible from the disagreeable situation, he complains of the fact that I am not taking it all right into my mouth, as if it had ever been possible for anyone else, I wouldn't have needed to have dental bridges nor an oesophagus, I'd have needed to have an empty tube in place of a neck in order to comply without suffocating. He presses on my head, I begin to retch – sauerkraut and *Wiener Spiessl*: he tells me with the same delicacy 'Come on, the balls now!', he emits short sputters of consonants in his own language and then, as if asking 'may I' at a door with the bolt drawn, he turns me round suddenly and hoop-la! I give a shout which ought to let him know nicely that there are limits to my well-bred willingness to put up with things. No use – he is horny, doesn't give a damn, smiling (he smiles horizontally, in a slightly sinister way, like a weasel, and his little almond-shaped eyes, black and sparkling, I don't quite know what it is they threaten – I don't want scenes here, usually in such cases one always manages to find a middle way when it is too late). And he continues to ignore my attempts at resistance with 'C'est bon?' in

English and as he takes it out puts it back in again covering it anew with saliva to the base and begins to tell me about his three brothers who have as big a one as him – apart from his big brother who has the biggest one of all – so much so that after a couple of weeks of marriage his wife was in hospital with haemorrhages and now is divorcing him because the gypsy is one of those modern women who are afraid to open their legs up a little and in any case never more than so much, which for his brother is always too little. It is incredible how he manages to tell me all this saga with drawing-room manners as if to distract me, while he does not stop and continues his brutal and tranquil excavation in spite of my fists pushing at his stomach, which is as hard as stone even if there seems to be the beginnings of a sedentary paunch. And then I start laughing because, undeterred, every so often he asks me things which seem very mysterious because they do not contemplate a reply and he answers for me 'yesyesyes' accompanying them with jerks of the chin and opening wide his little hare's eyes. Giving me the final stroke, which makes me curse the day when I found that it pleased me, he tells me with the air of a historian that his wife too has problems, unlike his wife's brother, the little brother-in-law, who is young and elastic, and that it was the little brother-in-law who initiated him into these practices when they were both studying Basic I, oh, now he wouldn't be able to give them up, nor would he renounce them for all the information technology in the world. Now I am letting him do what he likes going down a road which is so open as to seem to me to be almost a stretch outside of me, but I feel the pressure of the floods of sperm because his prick gets bigger, swells for some interminable seconds. I say nothing, it has been more than anything else an unfortunate experiment good for retelling and that's all. Then he, who describes himself as engineer, tells me that now I am too old for his tastes, I am an interesting man and now, please, will I stand him a whisky and that as a youngster I must have been the end of the world. We go down into the hotel saloon and he goes on telling me about his hearty appetite, he points out to me this and that boy and says I'm not to be offended but certainly one of these little bunnies would be something else, he'd spend a whole night there, one has to understand, they are fresh, they don't make as much fuss as me, perhaps they are simply more elastic. I tell him that I fully understand him and meantime he takes the liberty of calling the waiter and ordering another whisky, he swallows it down, gives me his hand and a pitying look and disappears through the swing-door which showers me with all the reflections from the Liberty lamps in the ceiling.

M. has gone round the square, looking for me in vain; I tell him the story, urge him to go down into the lavatory and the procedure for going up into a room is very simple. He doesn't dare, he says, when he has gone up to his room with someone no one has ever lost the opportunity to attack him, beat him up and take away watch, chain and wallet – these things don't excite him any more. There is a pretty blond boy sitting alone at a little table, one who a little earlier was down there handling himself but shyly like any toy-boy. I smile to him after asking M. if he likes him and M. says yes that he has been looking at him for a lifetime and that he winked to him outside as well. I go to the round table, strike up a stupid Arthurian conversation and signal to M. to come and sit there; M. shakes his head, he's afraid to be a nuisance. I go back to our table, tell him I intend only to serve up an hors-d'oeuvre and that they should go upstairs. Nothing doing. M. is afraid – he is too attracted, awkward and embarrassed now. Then I say to the boy can he act as our guide tomorrow, in that way he will accompany us to the castle – and meantime M. can stay with him and melt into sexual trust. But one thing is clear: the more I try to throw someone into the arms of a friend the more he would like to throw himself into mine. Perhaps I do it on purpose.

～

Visited the Castle of Prague – the little blond had never been there, he doesn't know anything about his native city, he was the only one to be astonished at how many things there were to see in Prague. M. and this Edward are both short and my step is exactly twice theirs. I drop them off as arranged. A nook, a cranny, who knows. I go off and come back again, every so often I track them down to give them the tickets to get into the various rooms and museums and to tell them where to go and where not. Edward – to whom I have promised a large tip for his precious guidance (he doesn't even know the streets because he has no driving licence and I think he lives on baroque gays, indigenous and foreign – he said he has a friend with whom he is on bad terms who acts the woman while he plays the man . . .) – he follows M. who follows me. But what a disappointment – apart from a picture entitled *Santa Katerina, Santa Magdalena, Santa Marketa* a possible cover for *Byzantine Dolphin*, I do not find anything because the interesting things are being restored.

From the castle we go to a sports and recreational centre, because there is action there in the Turkish steam. They perform very badly, but sportsmen from various national squads arrive – very beautiful slim bodies with incredibly small penises; for twenty minutes I stay there enchanted, admiring them and then off, I want to see the nearby synagogue and cemetery – a forest of marble tombstones piled one on the other and then up to the museum which stands over it with the drawings and poems of the children deported to the concentration camps. It is like at Dachau – the emotion that seizes me so intense that my eyes blur over. The point is that I feel them all as if they were my greatly adored children, so many little Aldos killed for a whim of a theory about normality. All my greatest loves have always been already dead. To lower the dramatic feeling, since M. is lost in the clouds, and so as not to hold it against him that he doesn't feel the same emotions as myself, I touch Edward's bottom as he passes in front of me, indifferent, uncultured, with the lost air of his stupid youth. Edward seems to have been waiting just that, he protects himself coquettishly. Then I tell him to take us to all the places where there is some action. I know them very well, these places. We set off for a sumptuous public toilet which, as we go down, reveals the severe majesty of a catacomb. You could get at least forty little tables into it and a platform for a hundred-piece orchestra. I toy with a couple of youngsters, one with glasses and red hair, the other curly – he does not wish to have anything to do with me and whispers to me in English: 'You're too young for me, change places.' It has to be admitted that Czech mammas make their sons in large sizes. And then we are off again, up to gardens where I immediately see hundreds of men making love hastily from the first moments of sunset till dawn, going about in herds among the bushes and rosebeds. To the first journalist to ask me what homosexuality is for me I reply: a reality, my dear, a reality.

Here I and Edward drop M. – and Edward takes me behind a big wall, I kiss him intensely and then push him down. I am dripping from intense excitement – and I notice that meantime we have two inert spectators leaning over the wall. Edward stops, I make a sign to the couple not to stay there transfixed, they join us but Edward doesn't want to. I am seized by terror that he may not want to go on, then I politely ask the two new arrivals to go off for a minute and Edward bends down again, he sucks me with passion, my prick must tickle him to death, and now I forget – do not notice – that meantime behind us there is a youth with an extremely white prick and an apprehensive face, I ejaculate my soul, which is an expression to be used only in rare circumstances. Where for all these years I have found these interminable ejaculations, only that part of my innermost heart which has always rebelled against the literary use I intended to make of them must know.

M. kept wandering about – we found him watching children on the slide and smiling to their respective fathers. Since it is already late, quarter to eight, I propose to the two of them that I intend to go back to the hotel and sleep while things are just getting going here.

'But you're mad,' says M. as usual.

'Tell me, do you want to stay with Edward or not? Notice that he hasn't had an ejaculation.'

'No – it's better like this. I want to sleep too. At our age.'

'At yours, please.'

I give Edward a hundred crowns for his trouble and go up to our room. M. is already happily under the blankets.

'I haven't slept so well for years.'

'At least it does you some good,' I say.

Prague is extremely beautiful. We are going home.

'Let's go by Munich so that I can drop in on Jürgen. If he's still there.'

'Why?' says M. at the wheel, making for the gates of Prague.

'His friend was taking the Definitive Slimming Cure.'

I shout, 'Look out,' to M. He brakes a centimetre from a certain accident. His head is always elsewhere.

'Christ, can't you look where you're going? At least you used to know how to drive – now you've lost that skill too. Can we know what you were thinking about? We'd have lost at least four hours here in Pilsen if there weren't two of us to drive and put on the brakes . . . And don't keep so close to the other cars because you make me seasick with the way you brake in waves.'

'I was thinking there's no reason to do what you advise me with my teeth – I'll go to Amsterdam – they put two electric wires in your mouth and by a simple contact they all fall out at once, painlessly. A million lire. The important thing is not to feel anything – then they'll put them all back in at once – in any case all I ever take is minestra – even if I don't chew much . . .'

'Yes, but by not feeling anything and being afraid of pain one becomes completely cretinous like you. Forgive me if I still haven't told you clearly but your prospects are a home for the mentally ill. You'll shit yourself and will have to have someone to wipe you while you cackle like the half-wit you are now – with your beautiful Dutch ceramics added.'

'I'll think about it when it's time. Why worry now?'

'For some things the stage has either not come or is past. In your case you're at the second already. It is from today that one needs to construct one's own past – not to speak of the future – if not one runs the risk of making time into a phenomenology for managers. Signorina Scontrino . . . Oh, never mind. She's got nothing to do with it.'

'And who is she?'

'Someone. But she doesn't feel like talking to you. Someone from the *Dolphin*.'

'And I'm supposed to be the mad one.'

The frontier passed we are now in Germany, after having had him tank up with all the Czech crowns left to us, which wasn't too many, M. wants to do things in his own way; his road maps are ten or twenty years old and we make a whole circular trip and find ourselves at the previous spot. At last, autobahn. The only thing he can still do is to go straight on. The methane gas is finished too and there are no pumps for a hundred kilometres. We pass one and I say: 'Stop.' 'No – there's still some left!' and seventeen kilometres short of Regensburg it gives out.

'The petrol's finished too.'

And he begins to chuckle.

I say nothing, light a cigarette. No use saying to him, 'You could have thought about it sooner', in his brain everything that comes *sooner* fills him with terror. Little ironic laughs on his part, while he turns the engine off and on and jumps out and gives the bodywork the kind of shake you wouldn't even give a tin 'to squeeze out the last drop'. I don't move from the seat – I haven't the slightest intention of moving. I smoke and leave him to his efforts, for he has to rock me as well as the petrol tank. I think I ought to get out, hitch a ride, let him get on with his little bit of money and his imprudence, just for once. I am his helmsman, tell him when he has to wash and shave, if he is hungry or thirsty, I have to watch what speed he drives at and at what speed he brakes or skids, check the oil, the water, I have to be his interpreter, change money for him on the black market, find him men, now I am not going to push his car – and then; where to? This is a secondary road, this one, neither cars not lorries pass. And now M. begins to push the car with all his might and then jumps in behind the wheel. Fortunately we are on a hill and I am still sitting inside furious; the car slides slowly down the access road, I continue to smoke, indifferent to his puffing, he pushes the car with me inside it and jumps in and out and pushes and straightens the wheel, it is the minimum punishment.

'You aren't even angry,' he says cheerfully.

'No, I have learned by now. And I'm not even sitting here and insulting you. You enjoy it too much.'

'But these are little annoyances – that's something new! If it happened with my brother he'd beat me to death.'

'That's why you drive him down into Basilicata – to give him an excuse. But I tell you one doesn't kill a little dead man.'

'Then they wind you up a little .'

'Come on, turn off on to the side of the road and pull up here. Someone is bound to pass.'

He gets out, opens the boot (my God, how he enjoys seeing me repressing my choler), takes out a plastic petrol can and starts trying to get a hitch. To annoy me surely, he goes to the side that indicates 17 kilometres to the first inhabited area, not to the opposite side where the first is 2 kilometres away. I get out of the cab and tell him a thing or two, he goes and stands on the opposite side of the road. But two cars pass and he turns right round and laughs and doesn't stick out his thumb. I take in a big breath and myself stop a car from a motoring-school which was coming slowly down from the corner, I explain what has happened and M. climbs in.

If he doesn't come back in half-an-hour I shall go off with his bag, I can't stand his coarse loyal presence any longer.

After an hour at least M. comes back with the can. I am still there walking up and down by the ditch.

'My doctor once told me that in me there is a lack of stimuli towards external reality.'

'Flatterer – that must have been at least ten years ago – who knows what he'd say now if you went back? By the way, maybe your brain is screwed up because of syphilis. Have you had any check-ups?'

'Yes – no – I don't remember. Perhaps.'

'Ah, we're doing well.'

'In any case now there's AIDS –'

'Yes, but it's not as if they put syphilis in the archives, the Reaganite Syndrome is just another shiver down the spine, Nancy Thatcher isn't the cure-all for all the other venereal diseases. Have you had HTLV3? But they change the names so much every day that maybe you know it under another label.'

'Well, I did have tests. Wassermann.'

'Idiot, and I suppose you took an antibiotic first to be dead certain that it was negative, isn't that right? You can't fool me even if you're depressed. Depressed but not to the point of looking reality in the face. It's cunning your depression; convenient – your madness. That's how you used to go on – don't bother about an illness and it won't bother you. You kick the bucket with a heart at peace.'

'At least in the meantime you don't think about it.'

'And you use your brain to play at rummy and sevens with your night-owl of a mother. But when are you going to pack your things and live by yourself?'

'You know my mother won't give me a flat for myself till I'm married and settle down.'

'Then she'll never give you it.'

'Meantime my brother has had an exhibition of American curtains in it.'

'Does he pay you rent?'

'No – you know he has a family,' he says, biting his lip, waiting for me to decide to give him a slap in the face to make him see stars.

'Great. That looks right to me. Go on, accelerate, I want to get to Munich quickly. You go to the sauna, I have to look for Jürgen. If I find him, fine – if not, Amen.'

Jürgen is nowhere to be found, either in his cubbyhole or in his friend's luxury 'attic'. I leave a card at each one with an appointment at 9 at the *Ochsengarten* and a prayer to be punctual because I am sleepy already. And at 9 exactly Jürgen arrives in a black leather coat, more beautiful and icy then ever. He doesn't greet me out loud, kisses me and coming close to the other cheek whispers to me:

'A bad man once revealed to the king of his country that he was father to a girl who spun straw, changing it into gold. The king said: "I'll marry her but woe betide if by tomorrow she hasn't spun all the straw in the hayloft" and the girl, desperate because she foresaw certain death, was desperate and weeping in front of a mountain of straw when a dwarf appeared who says to her "I'll help you to spin all this straw into gold but on one condition . . ."'

The fairytale lasts for the first twenty minutes of our meeting and, as always, has no moral – neither for me nor for him; he has told me a fairytale and that's all. He looked as if he might be about to start another – or the very same one – but I stop him and pass, unwillingly on his part, to the modest '*So*' for which I wanted to see him. He immediately holds up his hands: first and foremost his life is no longer what it was – as if it ever had been! He has given notice, is moving from his one-roomed flat, he hasn't paid the last bills for the gas, the electricity, the telephone, he has given away all the records, the wooden toys, the Meccano parts, and his great-aunt's funerary angel (which I had always wanted him to give me one day) finished up in the rubbish; now only one *essence* counts in his life apart from his friend – Chinese meditation. Chinese meditation fights any deficient immunological system and even clears up Kaposi's sarcomas – his adored friend is all bejewelled with black peach blossom, he doesn't say the word 'sarcoma', but either peach or cherry blossom; black. Love is blind, he says, when you have that you have everything. I tell him he is the most decadent man I have ever known and an exploiter of fashion. That he is another of my many friends sucked in by the undertow of the West towards inwardness and sentimentality. He draws back, offended, how dare I judge him? I answer that it is the only alternative he leaves me: a verdict against Chinese meditation. A meditation has no adjectives or else I cannot see the difference between a Chinaman and a Bavarian. We're back where we started – it's the fashion. And does he, Jürgen, have it? On the telephone he had told me that he complained of the first symptoms. Never had it, he says. What do you mean, I insist, I can't have made it up. I came on purpose to find you. You're wrong, he says, never felt better than now. So much the better that you had thrown me into such a state. You misunderstood, you understood what you wanted to under-stand, he adds, for your novels, isn't that right? Not to this point, say I. But with your friend, he too – I suppose I misunderstood – he . . . Jürgen asks for an orange juice with milk and vodka. Then I change my way of putting the question, he has become wrapped up in himself and diffident in recent months, he who had made of the lie the most light and direct art. But with your sick friend . . . My friend isn't sick, you're wrong, you see things completely wrong, I didn't expect it of you, he adds, disap-pointedly. And I say: Do you still make love with your *sick* friend or not? But first of all sickness is a subjective point of view and, secondly, certainly we make love – as always. And do you take precautions? I want to tell him: I have your life at heart, can't you do something to expose it a little less *for me?* But I am silent, what right do I have, it's not as if I were so important to him. You're not infected – sero-positive? I ask him again. I wouldn't know, he says.

'There's only one way to know, Jürgen – to have a blood test.'

'I don't do them – I don't see the use.'

'My God, you're all the same. It's as if we had gone back to the Flower Children. It's great for agriculture too.'

'One mustn't confuse India with China. The orgasm with Chinese meditation, for instance . . .'

'Ah, so it involves an erotic technique!'

'Of course. In every possible way it's the same as the Italo-German orgasm with the difference that, when we reach it, the sperm doesn't come out and all the orgasmic flood goes back up through the body and goes right into the brain, it spills itself out . . .'

'Into the top of the skull, I imagine.'

'. . . and it's all the same. Twice a week, the course lasts a year, my master is called Ahi-Lai.'

'Ah, in short you don't ejaculate.'

'No.'

'And you needed to have a Chinese master? But when did you ever ejaculate?'

'Yes, you're right – but now it's the end of the world.'

'Indeed in every sense, you have my word for it. And doubtless you go to fortune-tellers.'

'Go? They're the ones that come to have their sessions at our place . . . and the girl, having married the king, is blackmailed all the time by the dwarf who demands in return for his services the first child the queen bears otherwise he won't spin the third room of straw which the king wants to find the next day full of gold or he'll cut off her head . . . It's the first time I've given you a short version of a fairytale.'

'Yes, it's a pity. But the years go past, at least for me. You wouldn't think so with you. Or maybe the opposite is true.'

'. . . the girl queen gives in to the blackmail but when the first heir is born . . .'

'She refuses to give it to him.'

'That's right and she weeps desperately and the dwarf arrives and claims the child and she begs him to leave it with her. The dwarf says he will give her three days and three nights to find out what his name is after which if she has found out his name he'll cut off both their heads at one blow.'

'The one blow is the rule in each case.'

'You've changed. Aldo, you're gloomy.'

'I'm supposed to be gloomy? I am pure blotting paper, my dearest love.'

'. . . and at last one of the messengers sent across hill and dale to find out the name of the dwarf sees a gnome hopping about shouting happily "I am Rumpelstiltskin! *Ich bin Rumpelstiltskin*" and, sure that the queen will not have been able to find out what he is called, he turns up to cut off the heads of her and the baby but the queen says to him "You're called Rumpelstiltskin!" and the dwarf takes the dagger, rips himself open and dies.'

'I'm going to take a look at the toilets. If we don't see each other again, ciao!'

The toilets are in a bad state. Blinding neon light – as opposed to the veiled red of a few years ago. No one pissing, no one beating his prick against the head of someone bent over geisha-like, no one taking poppers. Bad times. I hang about for a while, smoke a cigarette, hoping not to bump into Jürgen again when I come out of here.

For years I have been following his shadow games (were they Chinese then too?), watching over his student's record book and his health, urging him – in vain – to work from time to time at least instead of touching his mother for money – his mother whom I telephoned to comfort her or to keep her informed like an apprehensive busybody of an aunt (not to mention the times when he and his mother got into contact with me because of daughter or sister robbed in Brindisi or fallen into the clutches of a Piedmontese count or lost in the Piazza San Marco, each time madly in love because all it needed was a compliment in the street for her to follow the Italian of the moment, enchanted, forgetful of everything, passionately in love and ready for a thousand and one abortions for a mirage of love – and, being as beautiful as she was, she did not remain a tourist for long in some Italian city or other, if seated at a table in a bar she drank her coffee in haste and had already become the lover of the waiter, of the drug-addict, of the playboy, of the *paparazzo*, of the street hawker behind Santa Maria Novella, and for me it was not even easy to let her know that in case of need she should turn to me – in fact she never did so; only once she came to my house and fascinated my family, my nieces, all Montichiari, so much so that my mother hoped this was it this time, as if it had anything to do with me). But Jürgen, that is to say J., is still leaning on the balcony, my laconic farewell is not enough for him.

'*Gut*?' he asks.

'*Gut*,' I reply. 'I wanted to tell you that – you're not bound to love your friend to the point of dying with him.'

'You talk like a peasant with his money in his shoe.'

'It is the only wisdom that has allowed me to survive until triumph arrived. Because I, unlike you, am a triumph both to myself and to a lot of other people, all right? You have exploited yours for years without taking an exam and now, but for the American millions, you wouldn't even have a job at the bottom of the pile. You who built models of academies and museums! Here you are – the genius of architecture on paper. Going to die of a death which you aren't obliged to allow to concern you – you with your need for a luxury caress in a luxury "attic"! Your friend, when he was healthy, didn't put a room at your disposal, you dedicate yourself to terminal nursing, he is a very cunning person and a disgusting egoist.'

'He can't do without me now. We're both the same.'

'You have reached the parity of death. Your total love is funereally kitsch. Jürgen, I can't take it that you should die because of yet another fad, that of Chinese or absolute fidelity – whichever. If you are still healthy forget it, stay close to him and look after him but stop there. You're not bound, you're not morally bound. If you get ill too how will you manage still to be indispensable? But why on earth do I take on so?'

'Because you are a father *manqué* – it's all there. On the other hand you are an extremely successful mother. Oh, I have done a new project for Dachau, did I tell you? I have turned an isosceles triangle of land where there used to be a pond full of mud – an area away from the lager properly speaking – into a little lake with a trout-farm and dwarf Chinese trees, that way it is much less depressing, you know, specially for the veteran American officers, the moment they come in they're given a line and all go off to fish after doing the tour.'

'And the huts, haven't they asked you yet to turn them into a mega-disco with lasers, barbed wire with neon lighting, swastikas for door handles?'

'I water geraniums from morning to evening, I like it very much – living with Z.'

'Geraniums! One of the most cultured men in this country waters geraniums and meditates in the Chinese way and gets himself up like Count Dracula and he is thirty . . . *Aufwieder-sehen*, Jürgen, I'm dropping with sleep by now.'

He finds it difficult to convince himself that I am capable of such a parting, without pain or joy, he opens wide his ash-grey eyes, orders another orange-juice (?) and shakes my hand.

As I see it, J. has never been in love with his friend who is so well off, so opaquely opaque, so theatrical in sex, but with the luxury in which he lived and the role he occupied socially and, above all, with the airy structure of his flat which takes up the top two floors of a neo-classical house; J. fell in love with the parquet of light-coloured wood – and not in herringbone pattern which he abhors – and with all the restored antique beams which, here and there, cut across the sudden spaces filled by balustrades of wrought iron and by the immense crystal windows, with the few but highly refined pieces of furniture on which he liked to run his finger to feel the history of the great houses tremble. Stupid but that is how it is. Once I told him that if he kept on with LSD, coke and poppers, if he had got through the years put at his disposal by the State to get a degree, if his mother had closed the bank-account, if, in short, he had had to stand on his own two feet . . . he might have been able to be a waiter or a butler. He replied drily that he would rather have killed himself. And why on earth? I asked him, I was a waiter for ten years and worse still. From shame, he said. I think I stopped loving him at that precise moment but then I didn't want to admit it, I tried for years to understand his reasons, to manage to convince myself that perhaps to be a waiter, to serve instead of being served, is an ignominy that merits suicide: but I never succeeded and I have had to make J. commit suicide inside me. And yet, since I am superficial and in the end put up with what there is, I had come to Munich to implore him 'to take care' so that he would live for his own sake, seeing that for me for a long time he had no longer been living. I owed it to him for all the great memories of our peripatetic philosophizing on the banks of the Isar.

And what makes me, idiot that I am, want to be loved for *myself*?

M. is already in his bed, he was only waiting for me to shut his eyes. My only desire is to crash on my back as quickly as possible and to set off again at first light for three kisses, towards another

Gethsemane with candyfloss, eight roundabouts and at least one shooting-gallery. M. pretends to wake up, turns round and says:

'Did you meet him?'

'No.'

'Lots of greetings from Willy . . . he was in the sauna.'

'I'm not surprised. Is he still very beautiful?'

'He's a miracle, he's still the most beautiful of them all.'

'He'll be getting on for sixty now . . . just short of it but very close. He goes to the sauna every day, what a life he has too. White waiter's jacket and towels round his hips, waiter's jacket and off to beddy-byes. Every single day. He practically doesn't see the light of the sun.'

'He's very worried about his son, he told me, he's become one of these uppish kids. And he forks out and forks out and forks out. He feels guilty.'

'Listen who's talking. Ah, Willy's son! member of the neo-Nazi Party! And him, the father, so nice and good . . . I have a good memory of Willy, very good. And do you know he gave a hand too to people I used to send him looking for work. He put them up, fed them without even asking their names, and to him sex out of gratitude was ridiculous. What a man! The more they are needed to emerge, to dedicate themselves, I don't know, to politics and high finance the more they stick themselves away in restaurants . . . The more beautiful, honest, loyal, democratic they are the more they end up hiding themselves as if they were afraid of themselves, of their power . . . wasted power . . . they no longer ask for anything for themselves, they serve the spaghetti alla bella Napoli and then fade away in the steam of a sauna day after day . . . That's how they all end up, and I'll end up like that too . . . I don't really mean it, I feel a bit like crying. But now, bye-byes. Sleep well, make a nice nest on your pea, dear princess, and golden pricks.'

'Golden pricks, Oh Gawd!'

'Golden or ashen – so long as they're pricks.'

~

'But didn't you want to go to Lisbon?' says my sister. 'You're always going down that way these days.'

Because I'm fed up I answer:

304

'I go to get rid of my cold. In Lisbon it's as cold as here now.'

What's more, Africa is the only place nearby where one can do good while enjoying oneself. So here I am in Sousse, Tunisia. In another hotel with full pension where you can't take men to your room. Unable to shake off the thought of Jamael, the rampant Tunisian technician met on the plane. And alone, watching these processions of cats with their Venetian allure, stuffing myself with food, buying ashtrays with my name inscribed on them in Arabic, walking and walking, blisters everywhere, tired, and yet going arm-in-arm with daily courtesy in order to say *No* oftener than *Yes* to men, disgusted by the *tric-trac* that goes along with my laborious whims. Zealous the young masseur in the *hammam*: 'Sport or sexual massage?' he asks me with a breath of complicity, looking to see if anyone is coming and putting his lips stealthily on mine.

'Sexual.'

It is a case, to be brief, of a proper massage of the cock with both hands as if he were making thin dough for pasta, not even pretending to make it fly like a supersonic plane or something not all that different from a wrist or ankle. I shall never stop marvelling at the taurine quantities of sperm I manage to produce in the dark enclosed space of the Platonic factory which is my spirit of adaptability. But I have written about this before; I am writing it again because yesterday's marvel was less marvellous than today's.

And, the massage finished, I went on with my ablutions and a little while ago was spying on a man, alone in his nook in the shade, who was masturbating with gritted teeth, he did not even notice me – cautious, touched and inexorable. The emotion I experience is as intense as that time when, at a traffic-light, I looked round and in the car next to me there was someone weeping shamelessly, he looked at me and went on weeping and did nothing to hide himself, he threw his weeping at me – anonymous to anonymous – as if I were equally responsible for it or it were odd that I did not weep with him. I almost have heart-failure, then fortunately it turned to green, he slipped away and I drew up, got out of the car and went into the first bar to splash my face with icy water. The Tunisian who was settling accounts with himself in the nook was a handsome squat man, not too tall,

305

middle-aged, with a sharp glance, superior to all in his solitude; stupendous circumcision, the glans of a uniform and glazed coffee-colour. These scenes do not have the power to excite me, I get a knot in my throat, I am assailed by all the phantasms of all humanity at the same moment, if I were to draw breath wrongly all at once I would die. And the fundamental rejection of sex; instead of uniting two bodies which desire in vain and are unhappy, it comes down to the reproduction of a ghost of a body for the sake of an assured singularity. Love beats only in one's own temples.

When I leave at dusk there are two watchmen on a building under construction, talkative, reasonably ugly, one also a little retarded mentally – how much do I give them pour l'amour? What would they say to a shirt each for not doing anything? The one who is retarded – but not much really – says: right – the shirt *and* love. I go into their lair down in the unlit basement, one is holding a candle, while the other one, whoever he is, has remained outside at my request – I said: 'One and that's all – there are too many buildings under construction between here and the hotel' and then one said to the other to go on, seeing he isn't married and will need it. From the dark the candle outlines a camp-bed, piles of rope on the ground, and I turn round and let him fuck me awkwardly – oh, just time to lower my underpants and we are back in the open air again. The tenderness I feel for him and for myself is such that I begin to laugh at the top of my voice and say to him come on, let's go to the hotel, you were so quick I'll double the shirts. Halfway there he complains, he's not used to walking so much, couldn't I give him some garment *here*? Then from the street I go over to the beach – evening has come, not a single fisherman's lamp in the shimmering sluice of those shades of black which the sea has if you are a prey to a mad joy – and I take off my shirt, trousers and shoes and give them to him so that he is spared the remaining kilometre. I go back to the hotel in my underpants with my wallet stuck in the elastic; head held high I go up to the desk and take my keys and for a moment an Intourist silence falls on two newly arrived groups. And I have overcome once and for all that most humiliating of all dreams: myself in underpants in a square packed with people I know by sight, I cleave through the Sunday crowd and know neither why I am there nor where I shall end up. On my underpants traces of piss and fresh shit mixed with blood and sperm. As if all my humanity were a drip of humours, mine and not mine, the reduction to a liquid anatomy of the deceptive stupor of existence.

Keys in hand, I confront my fate among the tourists, I rush along corridors and stairs and over the party dance-floor, striding like a god, hoping that the price-tag is not showing through my underpants; I seize a cat and take it into my room and we sit and stare at each other on the bed. Then I take it and wear it in front of the mirror: make a stole of it, a hat, a muff, slippers, a bathing costume. At the limits of shamelessness with myself, I pick up my pants and dare to examine them closely – immaculate.

In the street, at the terrace of the cinema, a muscular bravo at a table with two others makes a sign of welcome to me, lifts a cup and invites me to take a coffee. I thank him for his initiative, he sends for the coffee, asks me: One or two lumps? And do I want to make love to him or with one of his friends or with them all? I thank him and decline the offer. Maybe I'm interested in women? He has four under his protection, if I want to sample them they are five minutes away – from the novice to the veteran. No, no. Then let's take a walk, he proposes. I want to hire a car buy a carpet make love with him after all? At the corners of his mouth recent herpes, in the intermittent light of a children's roundabout on the promenade damp patches of coagulated blisters gleam. He take me to a fourth-category boarding house in the kasbah. He bargains with the watchman – it is already 2 in the morning – about the price of the room and I end up by paying for *two* rooms so as not to attract attention. He slips into mine – two metres by a metre and a half. A firm and muscular body, a strong grasp on my hips, I did not know that herpes has a taste of its own – of tarragon. I have to force him to take it in his hand. Then I bend him over the straw mattress, we rustle about a bit before both getting on to it, I put it in his mouth. Resistance but I don't give in. He begins to suck voraciously. I turn him over and begin to lick his arse, he says 'Ooooh!' and I fuck him. I haven't even time to get in properly when he redoubles the 'Ooooh!', he comes in my hand; I give a bored snort. It's time to leave already.

He gets an appointment out of me – what with supper, rooms, tip it has cost me a small fortune and I am left broke.

The next day I go to the appointment with the usual cast-off clothes (three or four months old) and I give him his fee so that he won't follow me, not today, I want to walk alone. He takes it badly – says he really wants to make love to me gratis, promises that this time he will let me go out and in longer but now No, I want to be alone. He insists and I more than he does.

In the Medina a young soldier makes up to me, gives a sign with his head, after a little I speak to him; he invites me to his house which he says is the house of a friend. I go along with this but my eye falls on two sinister-looking characters who begin to behave like vultures circling high over their prey, they disappear and reappear in the crowd. The soldier follows me at a distance – for reasons of caution, he said. Then I stop and tell him I don't want to go on. I give him a banknote for taking up his time, it is not an evening for suffering violent attacks, which have never turned me on. The other two characters are tightening the circle round the two of us. I make off with elusive skill through shops, galleries, baskets, traders, lanes, you would think I had been born in this labyrinth. Then I only want to rest and think about that Tunisian technique, which is so affable – and so far-sighted – that in the plane it had made a certain impression on me: he wanted to know where I was going, to what hotel, how long I was staying. And in the aisle of the plane he said to me without letting two women who had chatted with him all the time hear:

'On Thursday I have to be in Monastir. Perhaps I'll give you a surprise.'

And while they were stamping my passport I passed him a note with my name and address here. He was as tall as me, a certain warmth in his look, well shaved, with a sober elegance . . . Better not to think about it, I am not worth a detour from Monastir, a stay, an unexpected visit. I have never been *premeditated* by anyone, it would be something if it happened to me with an Arab intellectual who looks like some slim athlete before, during and after breaking the tape. I'd have to interest myself in hydraulic engineering and be faithful to Tunis – Jamael lives there. Premeditation leads inevitably to madness in any gender.

In the hotel the evening party atmosphere is typical. The

guests at the tables play at Bingo (tombola in other words) and the 'entertainer' in the middle of the dance-floor draws the numbers and says them into the microphone in five languages. The prizes on offer this evening: a sexy transparent nylon carpet, a pair of camel-skin slippers, a plush camel. I wander about in my room, I get under the sheets, go on to the balcony, can't get to sleep, go back to the dance-floor. There is a parade of leather clothing – the models who parade are the guests of the hotel themselves, all have been offered a hair-set and make-up by The Thousand and One Nights – and here they are, the Ursulas, the Frederikes, a certain Nicolina from Mondovi, parading as best they can. For three days I haven't addressed a word to anyone here – I eat, sleep and get away. Besides, here too, no singles, and even the couples seem to consist of three pieces at least. I look for my cat, it's not there, I wash in my room and sprinkle myself with oil of amber. Round about – the bunches of jasmine I buy in the streets and restaurants from children dressed in dinner-jackets and red bow-ties. I imitate the waltz – the music, always the same each evening and in the same order because it is a tape-recording, there are no discs – which comes in exhaustedly through the windows, I take a few turns between the bed and the commode, bump into a corner, twist my wrist, pursue a mosquito with a cushion, midnight comes. And I am still here, uncertain whether to shut my eyes or keep them open – for ever. Then I go out in my pyjamas, the old watchman with a blanket on his shoulders comes towards me, inclines his head, I offer him the usual cigarette, we have never said a word to each other, I go through the fence, drop into the damp and heavy sand, sit down, look and look, shaking my head as if it were the wind. But what are you looking at since you see nothing? Not even the eye wants to play its part. And I am not good at – I won't say listening to but not even hearing the noise of the sea.

'Do you want to have sex? I have an excellent piston-machine.'

I turn round suddenly with a start; a boy at my shoulders, nestling next to me he looks at me smiling, he takes one of my hands and puts it on his fly – it is very hard. Perfect, like a maintenance mechanic.

'You gave me a heart-attack,' I say to him, squeezing this sort of hand out of good manners.

'Yes, they are all frightened – it's too big.'

'No, I didn't mean . . .' he is feeling the base of my spine, he lifts up a buttock, inserts his right hand in my pyjamas and his forefinger goes its own way. Not even I know what to do, won't I end up being bored? In my doubt I say nothing. It takes more time to say something than do it. Afterwards I go back to my room, take a little money and a pair of trousers, the watchman reappears, taciturnly we go through the rite of the cigarette once more, and under the fence on the beach my handsome whirl-wind is already no longer alone but with a friend who offers himself to me.

'Ah no, good-night and be good boys. I haven't finished spitting out the grains of sand from the first time.'

But I am too good.

~~

Aisha is very nice, the old chambermaid who makes my bed, overcome because I call her *madame* – every day I give her something for her husband and son and then as well a woman's cardigan which I found in the wardrobe. (Every time I must give her a written statement for the overseer who has the job of opening the staff's bags as they finish and go out: *'Ceci est un cadeau de ma part pour Madame Aisha'* and she shouting and gesticulating *'Pas comme ça'* and that I must set out how many buttons, the colour, the cut, and what the garment is called.)

I go to the centre and sit down in a café on the outskirts to write postcards without addresses because I don't remember them. A Tunisian ladykiller who has worked in Sicily starts trying to get off with me from a table in front, he tells me he had to come home, but I don't feel like sitting and listening to him, try in vain to dissuade him. Instead he begins to draw his chair closer ten centimetres at a time. And with him all his numerous comrades round about.

'Italia crisis. Hard to even make cunt work,' he says, a Sicilian proverb perhaps which I haven't heard before. 'All unemployed at sea on land. Not much fish. But Italians good. Cup of coffee too dear. Went and came back again and now after a week no more money – all spent in Italy. Made lots of pizzas and love in Palermo. All nasty – no mafiosi Italy, So much love – mafiosi no.

Sicilian couples? The men all from behind, their wives too. Cunt – not much – difficult. Me very interested cunt – women in Palermo no give cunt. But me satisfied, like arse.'

'Excuse me but I have to send off these postcards and – I'm very sorry.'

'Then fisherman – finish pizzeria. Catania, Siracusa, lots of love on boats, to pass time. Then come away because broke cunt of daughter of boss. She want to marry me, papa no, because I broke his arse as well and daughter's Sicilian mamma's. Always write, never answer. Me thrown in sea by boss, then me save myself. But job finished. Here coffee no dear. What you called, where you stay, we appointment this evening?'

I take myself off and say goodbye to the company. I don't find it much fun any more to walk so many kilometres to go and have a *rest*. Have you ever tried sleeping in Tunisia? There are sand-flies which leave bites like potato scab and if you start scratching you won't rest any more. The sea – limpid. The sky – limpid. The sun – precise. The conversation – the same. The repatriated Tunisian follows me, surprised at my indifference, tries to keep me occupied with other questions at the top of his voice in Italian, 'Like it a lot from behind', I have finished my stock of patience for today. I am off, I must go away. Away away away. 'I am nothing inside me.' I do not feel anything spread out from my system of valves. As if I were not there, as if there had never been anything in me. Outside of me things are not much better, nothing holds my interest, and each ae it is as if, today also having reached evening, I took all the water in today's bucket and threw it over my shoulder along with the bucket. Every time I wake up I have to start again to decorate a desert – with the same lack of coordination of the conditioned reflexes: the palm here, the fountain there, the amphora at its edge, arranging the sun, the shade, and appearing myself at the zenith so as to give a superfluous meaning to the still life.

In fact on waking there is a prick flying about in my thoughts, it traverses them, humiliates a mind already suffering from yet another yawn – precise, identical with that of yesterday's awakening. And there's my mother who says she's sorry to die because she won't ever again eat white grapes and that she would live for ever for a bunch of muscat grapes from autumn to

311

autumn! And is it possible that, inside, I am only these sexual thorns, these tightrope-walking sexes crying for pity and horrifying me? Is it all equally lacerating for all the other men – the fixed pattern of the dream – a sarabande of tits and hairy vulvas which are ensnared in the unforgetfulness between sleep and waking and shoot past, torn from the body of a woman who has disappeared, a desire for sex to the point of dying from it? No longer being even that nothing which you are when you finally feel that you are nothing in yourself? Only love as passion can be rest – a cure that silences for a little time the unwished-for fantasy of being alone, shut up in one's nervous alveolus, the prey to frustrated desires which produce pricks that come out and in of featureless arses, of cunts slashed to pieces and suspended in the head? But you have to be two to reclaim *the heart*. If I were loved where I love, if I were dealing with a man in so far as he is one in our human totality, I would not manage, I would get a dry throat, my stomach would close up from shyness, I would live in a state of terror, my legs would tremble, I would spoil everything. I would not know where to begin except to run off for ever. Exactly.

There they are, striking up that song of Aznavour's – what the devil is 'Venice – how sad' doing here under the palms, which keep losing dates as if they were spitting them down? After the first notes, a miracle: see how the couples automatically run to entwine fingers, how languidly the girls look and how sinuous the movements of the girls who were walking about, how the sexuality of the male and of the woman reasserts itself in its age-old public display, how unnecessary it is to lay Columbus's egg in order to screw in peace. How badly they dance, how excited they are by the pantomime of true happiness! As if everything had been given them for ever. Otherwise they would feel shame at swooning to a twenty-year-old song. They have taken the sun, have eaten to satiety, have put on a fresh bush-shirt, this evening they fuck and tomorrow will be fans for the team closest to their hearts, for the heart does this for anyone who uses it. Then *la boutique des amusements* dresses five of them like desert whores, one more grotesque than the other, and the 'entertainer' throws them on to the dance-floor in a belly-dancing contest. Their respective husbands and fiancés shoot flash after flash, excited by their orientalized female animals – two don't even have a belly, only great pots of cellulitis. The victor is a certain Soline, from Mannheim, who seemed to move her flanks as if, sprung from top to bottom, she were shitting little heaps of Wurstl all round. Then the real Tunisian dancers arrive, one more beautiful than the other, tambourines and bells at their ankles. I don't know why but during an interval I look down from the railing and there is one of them who catches my glance and won't let go of it and I wink to her and she returns it. She looked at me so shamelessly that I could not do anything else, there was no way I could deceive her – and she is the most beautiful of the group. The dancers are usually beautiful and complaisant, exactly like their relatives hereabouts. The tariff: always according to how generous one feels. The moon – a half-moon, confused, with the crack in the middle, orange cloaks. I disappear, from afar I see my dancer scanning the bystanders and searching for me. She will never understand, it has never happened to her before.

The occupants of the rooms to right and left of mine have come back. After ten minutes the bidet symphony begins. I am still there, caught between other people's honeymoons, picking my nose; the seconds it takes to empty the basin are eternal. It oughtn't to be necessary – it is too empty to be considered full but it doesn't matter. Oh Isis, how feline my body is, what refurbished beauty it exhibits from time to time: everything is sculpted in a new way, from the elbow to the jaws it demands a pedestal. And the arch of the back, how interesting it is in the silence which it outlines in the window, how many voices I hear counting my vertebrae. And suppose I kept the water and threw away the basin? Another bidet. The beach; watched over by the police. The streets as well. The little shops, without back-premises. The cinema, without a toilet. The cinema seats, scanned by the usher's torch. The hammams, lit up like day, without a real *séparé*. The public gardens, chained at the first beams of sunset. At the harbour; trucks and trucks of soldiers. The only real possibility – to risk one's skin every time by putting all one's good will into it because *perhaps* it might be possible.

A sullen cat on the swimming-pool trampoline, its front all dappled, as big as a panther cub. And still drums and tambourines and horns from the dance-floor – *arabische Nacht* with hot-dogs and sauerkraut for all after 10 pm. A laugh from the wall on the left. Bidet. A stentorian wail. Shall I go out again? I look at myself in the mirror (the usual rite of recognition and gratitude – today too I have managed to get home in one piece); a little of my coquettish malice has melted in the sun and the cosy heat of the sauna (another sexual going-over). While he was beginning to massage me I felt a great warmth flood my brain, my very brain, the blood that bathed a part in itself insensible and at a constant temperature – a truly new sensation. Malign spirits which issued under pressure from the holes in the head. I am amazed that I was once able to be not bad physically, now I am so ugly – and mad. I shall have to get used to these unexpected circles under the eyes which are full of an unexpressible resentment, the victims' invisible enemy who will raise pockmarks on my looks. The folder says that Gide wrote L'Immoraliste here in Sousse. The tourist organization takes no heed of prejudices in any sense: it makes everything its own, but everything. It is much more advanced than the publicity for aperitifs for instance. Where there is culture or a *past*, no matter of what kind, tourism throws it in your face like make-up – publicity, no – it always maintains the most colourful brand of conformism; what firm producing female lingerie would have the idea of launching its product with a slogan like 'As worn by Barthes in Japan' or 'Our laces – the link between Jean Genet and the Black Panthers'? And so I go about with my big face – the face of a Latin gay with money, with lank and grizzled curls, a big nose between two little eyes with handbags under them. What is a great writer? In the short run – a maker of fireworks who grafts the aesthetic to an 'ambience, a breed and moment' (Hippolyte Taine), in the long run – the artificer of political consciousness of the incidental absolutism of which society is at once victim and executioner. There has always to be an unwished-for participant capable of this new conscious-ness of the same old monstrosity to bear witness to the fact that, in spite of every possible sin, 'Adam is still a miracle'. The great writer covers up man's every despicable action so that life – caught up *for the moment* in the bureaucracy of the formal structures which are suffocating it – may be able once again to have the possibility of smiling at them with fresh irony and turn in a circle on itself. In this sense what is needed is a new masterpiece which, by creating a temporary power vacuum, can stir up the waters and open at least one sluice-gate – contribute to allowing the lazy truths of privileges, by now too stagnant even for the stagnant swamps themselves, to run away. Life knows that it acquires its fullest, mellow quality only if someone arrives to attack it in order to defend it, to provoke it so as to allow it to act anew, to restore its value by scorning its values, which are as *eternal* as they are rotten, to brutalize it in the secret body-bags which *use* it while despising it as a spare part. Someone who every so often displays the by now rotting guts behind the reassuring façade and, in so doing, purges the blocked intestines of the human being, who is social or is nothing. Life therefore exults in the artist who ill-treats it *politically*, doing his job thoroughly – that of ridiculing the dogmas of the culture of death which some castes, sick with immortality, little by little – as they sink into their coffins – impose on the living so as to drag them as quickly as possible with them into their nightmare, which is marketed as a dream. Life delegates art to delude itself into believing that it has the last, intransigent word, not death, not the wise incense-bearers of *mors tua, vita mea* who legislate from a catafalque.

Met a sergeant out walking – we go along the beach early in the night, careful not to let ourselves be seen by the patrols. He is a reassuring sergeant, well-behaved, tall and thin, somewhat serious. He doesn't get excited. He likes to kiss me, loses himself in my mouth, I say to him, 'Give me your tongue,' then, 'Do the same with mine,' and he learns quickly. I try – I teach him the way with my forefinger – it's working better already, even in front. We ejaculate on the sand, not very convinced that it had been a pleasure and not a pang like the Madonna's. It is as if everyone was left extremely surprised by the harshness of my spontaneity, I mean there is nothing complicated in my sexuality, all for real and not at all *psychic*, clearly marked *outside*, in terms of timing and sobriety. I take his hand to guide it over my flesh – men make a point of honour to do things by half, as if yours were a prick with teeth like a saw; but it doesn't bite! Clearing his throat he stresses that the others only turn round and there's trouble if you touch it, they send you away at once. When he has finished excusing himself in monosyllables I say

Right, now you can fuck me. He couldn't make it. No problem, I'll fuck you. Oh no, he says, I'm studying information technology in Tunis, the moment I've finished my military service I'll get my degree. Certain studies exclude certain pastimes. Then since he is really nice and hasn't killed me, I tell him to wait in front of the hotel because I have something for him. Alas, when I got up I noticed I had gone and sat on a piece of shit. I make my way to the water's edge, take off my trousers and with water and sand do a quick wash. That is to say I come back in my underpants for the second time.

I get the keys from the porter and have to repeat the Calvary of the other day: it is as if suddenly two hundred people lost their tongues together. I don't give a damn – awkward moments of the trade because of not being demanding where beds are concerned. I come out again with a little bag, trousers and jerseys, I also give my sergeant money, he seems to blush in the dark, and I become old. I am sanctimonious after scarcely ten minutes of sex. I pay handsomely for every *disinterested* gesture of liking – perhaps in this I am not an ecclesiastic. And when we are at it I also ask him – at midnight – if he has had supper. He says No. Then I say to him let's go and have supper – in the best restaurant. In the restaurant, mute, he looks around with lack of appetite, respectful, I tell him to order whatever he wants. When the elegant boy passes I buy him American cigarettes and jasmine for me. There is no easy conversation between me and Kabir, but his eyes are devoted, I venture to the point where I begin to be interested in him. But he doesn't answer my questions about his family. He orders the cheapest dishes. I insist that he should let himself go and satisfy any whim; nothing doing. It really seems that for him I have nothing to feel sorry about, that he gets along with me as I am and that I do what I do – like the way I kiss him, I think. After supper I hand him a small fortune for having kept me company even if we have spoken so little. He poured me wine, smiled at me and lowered his eyes. No, he doesn't want this extra money – to tell the truth he insisted because he wanted to pay for the cigarettes himself. I tell him to be there tomorrow morning, that he will keep me company because I want to go to Kairouan to buy a carpet or somewhere else to visit a mosque or buy Flit. If he is on duty he should come as soon as he can towards evening. He looks at me in the dark and with a broken voice whispers to me 'I am excited' and clasps me to him so that I can feel it. He is trembling. 'It's late – tomorrow.' 'What if I gave you the money from before?' I laugh and am touched, his style floods my body in a couple of moments. And I break all the rules – I take the keys, walk round the park, open a gap in the wire-netting and take him up to my room and for the first time in his life Kabir gets rid of his prejudices about information technology, to the immense enjoyment of us both. More than loving him, I adore him centimetre by centimetre, someone who made the error of thinking himself a beggar arrives in my room and leaves again feeling himself an idol. And when will anyone else take advantage of him again to cover him with jasmine? Every so often one has to make things happen in life that only happen in novels, otherwise what is the point of reading? I re-accompany Kabir to the same gap, he begins to climb over the wire-netting because we can't find the hole again and then he stops, searches in his pocket, hands me the banknotes. Overcome by this gesture which must have cost him a good deal I take them.

Thank you, patrons and buyers of my novels, for having given me something I have never had, money to throw boomerang-wise at mercenaries.

~

A hitch – the trip by train to Kairouan is postponed. Kabir sent an acquaintance with a message, he says he is on duty but that he will be here tomorrow and that (contradicting himself about being on duty) he is being punished for twenty-four hours for having got in after hours and that, he hopes I will forgive the lie, he isn't really a sergeant but a *full* corporal. I think he deliberately chose as his acquaintance the most gnome-like specimen in the regiment. And so I have to last till evening – beginning from the morning. A little message? The *hammam* is dirty from the grease and hairs of yesterday, still no first client, the attendant hasn't begun to clean it, razorblades sticking to the mouldy walls and on the floor; I stagger in the clumsy wooden sandals; the attendant appears with the brush and I pull out his cock – the

317

attendant is very beautiful and the cock miserable, not in keeping. The hinges of the door creak, fortunately for me, and my handsome masseur appears and salutes me, exulting at the lovely surprise. Since the last time I asked him to give me a sexual massage with the mouth, as a precaution he first of all soaped it well for me, he's afraid I will renew the invitation to him ('*Pas ici,*' he told me). Then he begins to pull at my tendons, to smooth the sciatic nerve, to scrape at the base of the back – says to me 'How tasty you are, Signore' and that with all his heart. He is extremely aroused, I clasp him to me for an instant because we feel we must – but in a sign of brotherhood. There is no use you Tunisians continuing to please me when what I would really like is one of these little French husbands who waggle their bottoms more than their little wives. Since I have been here I haven't stopped admiring the little French arses fresh from the altar. To remain in the realm of accessibility, of those at the hotel an unfortunate French provincial tempts me – not much worse than a big dwarf who has escaped mongolism by a hair's-breadth – no comparison with *Georgina Washington* – I haven't evolved so far: the point is that the young man has an enormous bulge in his bathing slip and the mountainous profile of his cock fully distended is a real bathing-pool skyline, his balls are enormous too, and his deficient expression unspeakably sexy; he is here with a fat old man with a look that is, if possible, still more idiotic or melancholy-greasy, like a good-natured pig. I dream of them with their arses sticking out from the trampoline, I fuck them here and there, there and here, or with their arses one on top of each other, up and down and up . . . I come out of the *hammam* relieved . . . Outside I am greeted by the two watchmen of the other evening – they are standing up on the second floor, they shout something, turning towards the pulley, a dozen happy faces appear at the overhang, they greet me, including one who is apparently the architect, wave their hands, signal to me to come up as if to say: Come on, life is beautiful and we will make you the patron of Tunisian bricklayers during the break. I answer by gesticulating, really no, I wouldn't want to disturb them, and make off towards the centre looking for a jasmine toilet water that is impossible to find and so I find five things in the hands of five different merchants. I don't like perfumes, I'm sorry, but jasmine sends me into ecstasies, I have to find it at all costs – with this excuse I put them all back in their flies, bow and make off from one point to another till dusk. And suddenly there assails me, whispered to me by all the many *Nos* I have had in my life, an immoderate desire for sex right away. I go into the first perfumer's by now prepared for anything – it is a young woman who contents me with a half-litre bottle of amber.

From the opposite side of the street a scruffy and gangling Clark Gable of mixed race is crossing over, he smiles childishly with full lips – says 'Have you a cigarette, Signor italiano? Come with me, I live in a gym, I am the watchman' – he has only one incisor on one side and one canine on the other, he will be about twenty-two, little moustache and big black eyes. On the other side of some railings two teams are indeed playing football in a tiny playing field – but in place of grass the ground is tarred so that if they fall . . . Come, come, Signor foreigner – he speaks makeshift French. He opens a door near the dressing-rooms; there was a large woman lying gracefully on the ground, a little girl – dressed – under the blankets, a corpulent old man sprawled over the double bed and everything was overflowing above and below with rugs, torn blankets, goat- and rabbit-skins, bottles, dozens of shoes, old and dry clothes, the television turned on – a monotonous song being sung by the usual *chanteuse* who seems to be drawing her last breath but instead can go on right up to midnight like this while rocking a cradle. A great to-do over the greetings and signs of deference; when it has died down the girl, sitting down and interested in the subject, explains that they also see Italian programmes of which they mention the unfortunate principals. The first thing I did on entering was to offer the bottle of watered amber to the woman, and the boy, who was very pleased, said something to the old man who, I learn from the girl, who clears a space for herself in the rags, is not the father but the uncle, and is married but in another city and is here in Sousse trying to get fixed up and meantime lives with the three of them. The boy continues to smile in all directions as if he were showing his relatives a chrome mudguard found in the street, I feel like dying and he is off, smiling to me in a sublime manner, like a little angel photographed from life in a little luminous cloud, and it doesn't matter if the old man has begun to shout like one possessed, shaking a bunch of keys which the boy unsuccessfully tries to take from him. We get out quickly and I see the old man has realized what his nephew – penniless but shameless – intended to do with the keys: take me to some comfortable corner with a roof overhead. We leave the building, we skirt the wall and are on the dark sticky beach where low rocks break the waves of the tide, which is beginning to come in. There is a lot of wind too, so much that I don't hear very well what he is muttering, then we find ourselves facing each other and begin to kiss madly – in a few seconds I have the tide up to my knees and he doesn't because, taking precautions, he was no longer standing but crouched on a rock and confined himself to offering his lips comfortably and won't give in. A sensational cock from under his ragged trousers, and he with his Gone with the Wind smile cuts through the dark, he shakes it, provokes with an old, blinding – malicious – light. He sucks my tongue again between the two teeth left to him in front, it seems as if he wants to make it wrap itself round the canine, he furls it round his incisor with his own – saliva sweet with salt, with honey, simply a sweet saliva. I pull it out, he signals to me to move over because we could be seen by anyone who goes into the gym, we go further into the water between the rocks, I am soaked from the waist to the feet but seem to be instantly dried by the wind and by my lazy gaiety which wrings out my repressed laughter. What a nice person! He arranges himself on a rock, I get my trousers well down, I put myself nicely on his cock and begin to fuck myself in an athletic manner, twisting my head with infinite love towards him, famished for kisses – he laughs even when he kisses, indeed even more. At the point when we are most together Ardi suddenly stops my arse at half-mast:

'*Combien tu me donnes?*'

'National rate – five dinars!' I say promptly, and he happily squeezed his cock into me, throbbing with the enthusiastic orgasm of the labourer paid the just price. And I come too, grimacing at the blows which are not new but always stupefying.

Now I come out of contempt, throw away sperm after sperm, my only truly grey matter, nothing can make me stop enjoying myself at all costs, from feeling sentiment and gratitude where a tyro would find only another humiliation. I pay Ardi, who embraces me again, and we say goodbye, reciprocally grateful. And soaking in this way, with the cloth sticking to my legs, I make my usual entrance into the foyer of the hotel with the usual people who, suddenly dumbstruck, line my path in silence without batting an eyelid. The cloth is transparent and I have given away my underpants, sauntering towards the stairs I let off a series of farts with tight buttocks and feel something trickle down my thigh. Ah, if one day these white trousers could talk! I pass the dance-floor which is as crowded as a wake without any corpse in particular. I am completely indifferent to comments. What would I have to say about how *they* pass their time? The entertainment at the Jawhara Club this evening consists in six couples who each have to imitate three animals. A wonderful effort! Meanwhile dead tired as I am, I have to go and mount sentry near the gap in the netting, and Kabir arrives out of breath, he has escaped for a moment from the guardroom to tell me, '*Je vous aime, Monsieur Aldo,*' and I reply '*Moi aussi,*' and, clasped among the bushes which tear at us (they have thorns), we consummate as quickly as possible because he has to get back right away, I slip into his pocket the wherewithal to make sincere declarations for a month, I insist, he doesn't want to accept, but I insist more than he and he is off with a wink – and I shall never see him again. (But in a letter he will tell me that he was about to become a child-father and that he had to get married, that after knowing me he had spent weeks torn between his duty and flight – to Italy – that if I had given him a sign he would have come with me *for ever* because he had never been so happy and will never be so again – I sent him a birthday package with infant clothing, meantime, and the promise that if he marries his child-lover – thirteen years old – and doesn't abandon her I shall give him a big present. But I heard no more of him. He must really have got married.)

Someone last night got it into their head to throw on to my verandah a pair of knickers with lace and menstrual blood. Now they are lying on the ground invaded by ants and licked at by my favourite cat. Warning, insult, promise?

I woke up as always at 6 after an hour during which I kept my eyes quite shut. The cafeteria was already open, I didn't know but it is for tourists leaving early on excursions. I eat something, my knife slips and I am covered with fig jam and, licking my fingers all the way there, I go to the beach to see the sun rise. There it is, the mocking sphere crossed by a little black boat. At first it looks like a hot-air balloon in slow-motion because of the reflection in the water, which elongates the rotundity of the ball, and then a terracotta money-box. A warning to put life away and to capitalize on it for when there will be little of it – a stupid warning; anyone who is sparing with life now not only will never have any later but will always have less the more he increases his savings. Certain treasures are earned only by spending them. And so there it is the light-god who comes here every morning, punctual in his own way, methodical in that he does not let anything stay the way it was – everything must move when he arrives and everything must breathe with open eyes, urged to live because of the attraction of death, which wants to close the cycle quickly, and so goodbye to you all – but not the others.

Creamy-red pigeons on the sand among plastic rubbish, an impotent palm trunk among the calm waves, a runner in the distance. The water is tepid, the coming and going of the low waves a hymn to themselves. And look, it has risen, the dry patches have been redistributed.

Now it is 8 o'clock, the warmth is just right, I shall run calmly to take a train because I know the way they feel you up in second-class Arab compartments – and with a certain *savoir laissez faire* in the first-class ones. I shall put on my green nylon shorts with yellow stripes and, depending on the travellers, will pull them up to bare my thigh or loosen them at the waist. Obviously I take good care not to. Little movement at the station. I look up at the maps painted on the whole wall to left and right. I decide on Kairouan, left-hand map, very well depicted with the Rose of the Winds, camels, warriors painted in many colours, historical ruins, sheep, carpets, pottery, according to the kinds of handi-work and commerce of the places touched by the railway network (the little train runs back and forth among palmettos and prickly pears), then there is a lake and a corner of the Mediterranean. I ask the porter sitting in the newspaper stand, which is still closed or has just closed, if he knows the times for Kairouan. He looks at me perplexed as if to say 'Who are you having on?'

'Kairouan up to last evening was not included,' he says mysteriously and turns his back on me indignantly.

'I'm sorry – isn't that Kairouan up there?'

'Oh that map! First they painted the railway on the wall then they never made it in those parts. So many years ago. But the painting is so nice it was a pity to whitewash it.'

'So Kairouan doesn't – doesn't exist?'

'By train no. By bus yes.'

Right-hand map – direction Sfax/Monastir – little houses, little trees less thick than on the left-hand one. But at El Djem there is a Coliseum no less! And suppose in the meantime it wasn't . . . wasn't there any more.

'Excuse me,' I start up again turning to the porter, who is bored and dozing, or else pretended to be so the moment he saw I was returning to the attack and evidently had no suitcase for him. 'Does El Djem exist?'

'In El Djem they have everything,' he says with a grimace. 'Train, Coliseum, and El Djem as well.'

'Thank you. Ah, the nine fifteen.'

'Track One.'

I look out at the big window which gives on to the platform. It doesn't seem to me that there is more than one track. Second class because I have got into conversation with a student whom I asked the name of the imposing trees in the garden in the station. He does not know, I keep on asking round among the few travellers; no one knows. I resign myself and, shivering with cold, take a walk to look at an abandoned wagon, an orange-tree overladen with wild fruit, to count, without calling attention to myself, the foreheads, the chins, the purple painted cheeks of the traditionalist peasant women, squatting by their baskets of greens. Some youthful soldiers arrive, the same dark green tattered uniform I saw in the military garrisons on the Red Sea years ago, in Egypt, where I had the impression that, until a second before, every soldier on the road had been hidden, weeping.

Train half-an-hour late. I come back again to the name of the trees – nothing doing. I ask a little group of students too – in vain. When the train arrives I shall have to be in ten places at once along with those who don't know the name of the tree and who

323

beg me to tell them something about Italy and of the recent World Cup – I don't know what that is. A student with surly but blue eyes says in a low voice the moment I go off towards the corridor:

'They ought to institute freedom of thought here and of speech as well. Officially politics do not exist in Tunisia, only Bourguiba exists, the Father of the Fatherland. A thoroughgoing egoist and a paternal one, forget about tearful stories. To say how much injustice there is in this country, the political repression there is. You just need to be seen thinking and you are finished.'

Since the conversation attracts all my interest and I am preparing to settle down beside this young man with the revolutionary features – he has a little beard like Lenin's – we are at once surrounded by a little group of curious people and so I pretend not to notice, leaving it to him to take up the conversation again or to cut it short. In fact the boy – whom I find increasingly attractive because severe and idealistic, someone who feels he is a man all of a piece (which is as fascinating in the young as it is ridiculous in grown-ups) ready for action – suddenly is silent, sits there for a little clearly annoyed by this intrusion at his heels, looks at me, smiles bitterly and goes off and I remain where I am. The others immediately begin to talk, I get up too and go away without saying a word. One cannot offend a political poetic at its moment of birth.

El Djem. I go round the Coliseum, go down into the deserted subterranean quarters, come up again, end of visit. The city is all here around the Circus, squeezed by this Roman construction where I have heard the car firms come to shoot their commercials and the gladiators are the custom-built models.

And I walk. A smiling young man is looking out of a door, he welcomes me and strikes up a conversation: he has two children, his wife has just had a natural abortion, he is out of work, the wife arrives, fat, black and sad, not speaking a word of French, and smiles, delighted by the chatter between her husband and me. He explains that his wife because of her illness – unspecified – has no belly any more, they took away a piece of it and some things attached to it and she says 'Oui oui oui.' The children? Oh, they've sold them for the time being but as soon as he has a job and is earning they will go and buy them back for her more than

324

anything because she is suffering too much. He says goodbye to me with a half-bow without asking for anything and the woman too now says a word:

'Merci.'

I shall never know for what. I go off with my hand on my wallet – to go back and empty it? – but I don't have the courage and suppose the message were different? Both have disappeared, everything happened in a second, and it has once again been my fate to arrive at the station as if cheated, upset. Suppose they did not sell children as souvenirs, then it was a *thank you* for something neither given nor requested nor hoped for. Thanks for my having passed that way and that was all.

The train to Sousse is in about three hours; I go from group to group, from driver to driver, to see if I can travel sooner. Nothing doing. By now it is midday. On the open space there appears a big fat man who flourishes a toothpick and then very slowly a crowd with toothpicks in their mouths advance. A sign of social distinction for sure. To show that he too has eaten today. I sit on the terrace of the Hotel Julius; I try with another bus-driver but at my request for a passage he makes fun of me:

'Take a human camel, it's easier.'

'Listen, I'm not English or French or Tunisian.'

'But I didn't mean anything. Only that a human camel costs less than a taxi. What do you think running sixty kilometres means to one of these miserable creatures hereabouts?'

I give him a withering glance for the ambiguity of his sense of humour – a very handsome man with vaguely Turkish features, huge, long sideburns and a high forehead, thinning at the temples, pointed ears, strong white teeth, a prodigy of a tease. I go into the hotel and order a local drink. The waiter, who had begun to have a talk with the driver, arrives.

'Why don't you wait for the train, meantime you will eat and you and I will have a chat. I am called Sahib, I am the Casanova of El Djem. Men and women.'

'Ah!'

I take up the challenge as little as possible even if Casanova Sahib – *maître* Sahib – is of marked (authoritarian) virility if only because of his imposing stature and these little and intensely clouded eyes with their desire, which is contained with difficulty. In fact he looks at me and keeps on winking in a kind of a way and saying to me 'Go in there, there behind you', and I turn round to see that behind me is the toilet. I ask him for the menu, he clears his throat like a head-waiter and tells me what it is. He accompanies me into the restaurant, I sit down and he brings beer and a little vase full of perfumed flowers. He sits beside me, the restaurant is deserted. He presses first with his knee and then with his thigh against my leg, which I shift imperceptibly but firmly. His breath is heavy but intoxicating, it smells of tobacco and powder – of burning or of when you breathe wind and sand. Some gold teeth – he moves his thigh close again.

'Last year we had the Vienna Symphony Orchestra here – the two hundred members of the orchestra stayed here. A lovely concert, the Coliseum lit up like day, unforgettable. It was a week of great love, twenty-four hours out of the twenty-four. The pianist, the woman cellist, the double bass, the harpist oh! But like the oboist . . .'

'Thank you for the flowers,' I'd like to say to him, 'I recognized them among all the others – international rates.'

'I have a nice room here with an anteroom. Do you want to come and see it meantime?'

'And what is the second course?' and I take my leg back.

'Lamb cutlets, salad, chicken cooked in clay, the usual good stuff. You mustn't hurry. It is a nice big room with a bed . . . On the walls wallpaper with red roses.'

'Get me another beer – you have one too.'

'Gladly. What are you doing here in Sousse? Stay here tonight – take the train tomorrow. I have had too many women. They disgust me – they stink of cat shit. Ah, Italian men! Last year as well the director Sergio Leone came here with his crew . . .'

'What was he doing here?'

'A film about a car. A wonderful person. I went to see him in Rome too. Nothing doing.'

'Do you have cigarettes?'

'Tunisian.'

'All right,' and meantime I lean over to take an ashtray from the next table.

He puts a hand on my bottom and gives a long caress, squeezing it.

'It is very romantic here. Aldo Moro too slept here. The meeting with our president, whom God preserve, took place here. A great personality. Then they killed him. He had such wavy hair, really beautiful. Difficulties with him too. All Italian men must be conquered.'

'Really?'

He goes into the kitchen, reappears with a plate of lamb cutlets in one hand and in the other a second vase with three roses – one pink, one yellow, one red.

'All for you, Monsieur. What beautiful lips you have, Monsieur,' he says passing from *tu*, which he had used up to now, to *vous*. 'You like to smell them, eh?'

'Many thanks. What a man!'

'I am a specialist in love. I have also worked in Saudi Arabia, I had a servant, a *little* Filippino boy . . . not bad. To be a good lover is not a question of strength but of rhythms: when, with whom and how. The time of day is very important, at least as much as with whom. I have everything. I have a very well endowed sex. And am not just any Arab – two bangs and off.'

'You are an expert in the erotic.'

'That's right – *je suis un grand baiseur* – I'm good at it. No one has complained ever, I know how to enjoy and make people enjoy. They have a scent, they have a scent, smell them, smell them as much as you like.'

'How old are you?'

'How old do you think?'

'Forty?' I make him much older than me – going on fifty carrying it well.

'Thirty-two,' he says, piqued. 'And you?' he asks, reverting to *tu*.

'Guess.'

'Forty-one?' he says out of pure revenge.

'Thirty-eight. You have a ring as big as an apricot. Let me see it.'

'Because you haven't seen the rest, *mon petit chou* . . . Ah, Sergio Leone! So nice and fat, soft, with his white beard and so polite! He must have been like a featherbed. What a pity! My Filippino boy gave me massages. Every night. Terrible. Muscle by muscle, he dug them all out, one by one, ah what a devil he was, the *little one*! Terrible, terrible! They wouldn't give him the visa for Tunisia, otherwise . . . Oh what massage! he did them for me too with his . . .' and he brings together thumb and first finger in a little circle. 'Ah in Italy you have so many of these crimes. Here, almost none. In Florence a woman cut into twenty-four pieces and thrown down into a river. Why twenty-four? Why do your *Carabinieri* go and count things like that?'

'Yes,' I sigh. 'Why not twenty-three?'

'Women, you see, are like the Filippino boys, they don't deserve any better. First they massage you, then they say they love you and ask for the visa, then you wake up and they are off with the cash and all, a year's newly drawn savings. For a watch they'll cut off your hand. Ah, may Allah protect the Viennese musicians! Yes, tall, blond, nice, available! Nothing ever went missing from my room. And how well they played. I had free tickets . . . Aahaahaah! My red roses on the walls still have all the signs of . . . Ahahah! And every night they even gave me a tip . . . before leaving.'

I go to wait for the train with more tranquillity. Threat of storm. So as not to offend him I have put the roses in my knapsack. A Tunisian mother makes fun of a French mother because of their respective children: the French child, though being the same age as the Tunisian child, is a bit shorter and certainly less beautiful. The French mother is left somewhat perplexed and the other mother hides her laughter behind her veil. Outside the compartment window the whole landscape is swept by rubbish in the wind for kilometre after kilometre: prickly pears, olives, huts, fields, heath, everywhere rags and rusted tins and masses of plastic which roll in the wind. The contempt Muslims nourish for (ungrateful) nature is well known. Even the guide from the travel agency says so. It is as if they delighted in seeing how they have managed to reduce it, to disfigure its arid beauty – and what should other nations say with cultivable areas not even a tenth of this? The train is very silent and there are no level crossings. Toooo, it says, like in the animated cartoons. They are all so beautiful, the inhabitants of this land, and behind their great big black and green eyes you would say there is not *a* pain but *pain*, an absolute feeling of classicism. There is not a man who suffers but the pain of the man who makes him suffer, once and for all. They have grace even when they yawn – look at the refined plasticity of that olive-coloured hand with nails which seem chiselled in plaster and how the two fingers stand straight on the cigarette, the bearing of all the charmed heads which are motionless over their internal landscapes. The girls all wear skirts with big buttons somewhere, it must be the fashion of the moment – and under the veil an extremely old passenger cackled to herself, chewing American gum. In El Djem there was a street with the monitory name 'Rue Alain Carpediem 1948–19 . . .' the last numbers having come off . . .

At the station in Sousse I make for the 'Buvette Union Nationale des Aveugles' (snack-bar of the national union for the blind), take a coffee from the old blind man. Meantime I ask him the name of the trees behind me. He doesn't know, I find it particularly sad that even he doesn't know. I pluck a twig, I shall try again in the hotel.

'How did it go at the Coliseum? A lot of holes, eh Monsieur?'

But it is the same porter as this morning, slow and cunning, with his tortoise profile, who is turning his neck towards me snail-like.

'Oh, well, thanks,' I say waving the twig. 'Listen, can't you tell me what those trees out there are called?' and with my other hand I go for my wallet.

He is thoughtful for a little, draws back his lips, breathes through his teeth.

'*Ah, ça alors! Mais c'est un végétal ça, un arbre végétal!*'

And, taking the twig from my hand, sets off martially in front of me to the door, carrying it as if it were a suitcase.

～

I am at least a millimetre too much above things – alive but floating over situations, sex included. I am more than sexy, terraqueous.

It is as if my lovers when they are fucking me were taking Gaea by the arm – everything is all right with me, I don't lay down conditions, I don't conduct the orchestra, I don't ask for a particular performance. No aggressiveness. I take what is there to be taken. It would be different in a personal relationship. But that presupposes a sensual integrity of character – and one does not come to Africa to find what does not exist even Elsewhere. A male dignified to the touch is a rarity.

Feeling of suffocating in my room, for the nth time I throw off the sheet and wander about the room. It is raining. What could I think of that goes well with rain? Of the speech to be given to the big shots when *Byzantine Dolphin* is launched, some snail is bound to come into the open. I have nothing better to pass through my mind. Another two days and I will no longer be forced to rest here. The telephone rings.

'Monsieur, there is a gentleman asking for you at reception.'

I have not time to ask who it is, my dearly beloved corporal? And who else could want me at this time – and at any time? Not the beautiful bunny with herpes again. When the door is already shut behind me I hear another ring, but I might as well go straight down.

And Jamael is coming out of the telephone booth and, on seeing my face grow pale, his is illuminated. The engineer met on the Milan–Tunis flight! I swallow a couple of times, careful not to betray the sudden emotions which I was unaware had been there for centuries under my skin. He is embarrassed too and all these people looking at us, he was about to tell me not to come down, that he preferred to leave at once, he utters some confused greetings which are immediately cancelled out by an intention and its opposite. How come, I say, how come? He has a room booked in Monastir, there's a plane for Sousse early tomorrow, what is he doing? He wanted to see me but didn't want to stop over, it has been so unexpected, but how unexpected? Stay here, I say, stay here, we'll arrange everything. All right, he says, I'm thirsty, could I drink something? Is it possible? Then we'll see. We'll see, we'll see, the practicalities are so embarrassing, he has to hand over a document just to have access to the bar in the open. Then he draws a deep breath and says: I'll stay. And the clerk asks: Who is paying for the room? I am, I say, put it on my bill. But the guests have no bills, here one pays at once. Oh, all right, how much is it? I am about to pay for the room, that is for the right to stay in mine, Jamael is sweating and shaking his head, no, he can't stay, and the staff come running up to poke their noses in, to aggravate the extent of his

330

surprise. Then finally I manage to drag him on to the terrace, to make him sit down, to order something, aperitifs, seeing that dinner is soon, Jamael keeps on crossing his long legs, looking round and staring at me as if I were a stranger. He is continually on the point of becoming more beautiful because he is here for *me*. What enchanted moments are in store for me tonight? Or even if he has merely come to say Hello and will soon go away, if I had misunderstood, it would still be marvellous, I want no more, the thought of a chat, to break the anguish of this listening which has lasted for five days. If he stays perhaps I shall ask to go with him to Monastir, in short, something will happen, I shall not remain alone. Jamael rests on the seat his travel-bag which he did not wish to get rid of, he kept it in his lap as he sipped a *pastis*, ready to rush off. To feel that it depends on you to keep the ground steady under the feet of someone else who doesn't like to realize that it has never moved . . .

'Is that all your baggage?'

'Yes, pyjamas and toilet things,' he says and looks at me frowning.

'Then do you want to stay or not? I'll take a room for you, a different one, there's no problem. You are my guest.'

'I don't know exactly – I don't understand.'

'What is there to understand *exactly*? Listen, don't worry about things, it isn't necessary to be in my room, the hotel isn't full.'

'Ah no – if I stay I stay in your room. That is what you want, isn't it?'

'I . . .'

'All right, I'll stay but . . . It's difficult. I . . .'

'But what? If you have come to visit me . . . or have you changed your mind already or . . .' I begin to pass from *tu* to the formal mode of address, immensely moved by this *person* who is a handsome living man, disturbing, gnawed by kinds of remorse which I don't understand and which could be a preparation for final physical abandon or anxiety to have everything in black and white first and fix a tip.

We go down to the hall again, particulars definitely entered, my cash paid in advance, and we go to the room, I try to put him at his ease, behaving politely but in a friendly way, he looks around tensely, clenching his jaws, his fist still tight round the handle of his travel-bag. Sweat is pearling his brow again. I have to give him a bit of a tug and put him on the bed.

'Have a shower, here are towels and a dressing gown.'

He undresses, turning his back, and I instinctively look out on to the balcony without letting my eyes rest for a moment on his nakedness. Nothing must be too explicit about things which will either take their own course or have no meaning: to spy on his nakedness would be like profaning the emotion I feel for him, of which nakedness is only a part. And then my surprise is such that I exclude sex *right away* – perhaps he really did come by only to say Hello and . . . I could take advantage of it to rest a little without haste.

He takes a shower and in the bathroom dresses again from head to foot, because at first he had only begun to undress and then preferred to continue under cover – in front of me who was looking outside. He is odd, this boy, and replies to my discretion with an undertone of aggressiveness which is uncalled-for.

'What do you want of me exactly?' he began, slowly opening his little case of which I did not manage to see the contents. I shivered.

'I . . . I don't really know, probably nothing . . . You . . .' I stammer trying to understand, to avoid an imprudent gesture or a gaffe – which is not easy. He takes out something which I don't see, he puts it in his jacket pocket, he shuts the lid again.

'Are you really not hungry?' I start up again. 'Don't you want to eat something? Do you want to go to the restaurant? If you want . . .'

'First you must tell me why you gave me your address in the plane . . . Why are you so pleased to see me?' this character goes on, terrified and terrifying.

'Really it seems to me . . . if I remember rightly . . .' and then gathering courage, 'Look – no one obliges you to do anything, because there is nothing you have to do here. That is to say . . . and then if I am . . . I was pleased to see you because I didn't expect it, because . . .'

Why the devil are you so pleased to see him? Who is he? Is he the definite assassin, a fanatical Muslim integralist, the religious intellectual who has a functioning cock and a culture which compromises sin?

332

'I am just trying to understand,' he says, suddenly closing his jaws and flashing me maliciously neurotic smiles. 'What must I do according to you?' he goes on but without coming any closer, one hand in his pocket on the mysterious object. 'Come on, tell me and let's get it over with once and for all.'

'I want nothing either from you or anyone else. It seems to me it's you who want everything from me.'

'Confess!'

'What am I supposed to confess? Do you want another room? Do you want to leave?'

'No, first I want to see what you are getting at.'

'But I don't want to get anywhere. And not where anyone else doesn't want to go.'

'I am religious . . .'

'I had imagined so.'

'My religion forbids certain bestial contacts. But now, since we are here, I really want to see what it is like. And it was you that got off with me in the plane, provoked me.'

'My God, did I really do that? If that's how it is I'm sorry. I suppose I thought I was simply being well-mannered – as with everyone.'

'I'm not everyone. Come on, why are you still dressed? You with that mouth . . .'

'Look, there's been a misunderstanding. I feel hungry, if you don't mind. Do you want me to call a taxi? I'll pay for it to Monastir. But I'd like to do something so that we part in friendship. But you are so hostile to me and you come so many kilometres to be hostile, like people one meets without wanting to. It all seems so unlikely to me.'

'No, I am staying here, go if you like, I won't move. I'll wait for you here. Why don't you do what you have to do? And is it true that you and people like you take men's sex in their mouths?'

And he sweats, sweats hatred. And I do not, being terrorized but rendered bitter, debased. If he doesn't strangle me, I'll kill him. I have taken to my room a monster who has come two hundred kilometres in an evening and I don't know how he got here, facing what difficulties and obstinacies. A nightmare – and all round the nightmare the pleasing perfume of gleaming skins. And what can a monster in white shirt and tie want from me?

Why is he here? What will he ask of me? What kind of blackmail? Or what excuse is he seeking for carrying out this kind of task?

'I am sure you want me to court you. Is that what one says? *Draguer*? But you're not a girl.'

'No, I'm not a girl and never thought you had to fuck me. But it is absurd, do you understand? Why did you come? Why did you give your identity card to the reception?'

'What is life according to you?'

I reflect for a moment – what is the best answer to a madman?

'A wonderful thing, what else can it be?'

'What does *a wonderful thing* mean?' he asks, not considering himself satisfied.

'Just think for a minute – I go on a journey, by chance you find yourself beside me in the plane, we exchange a couple of words and now you are here isn't that a wonderful thing? Is there anything to add to all that?'

'But you knew – you put a curse on me.'

'Let me take a breath.' I lean on the table, exhausted. 'Knew what?'

'That I would come.'

'I never thought about it even for an instant. The wonderful thing doesn't belong to me. I don't believe it even now.'

'But you knew I wouldn't shut an eye till I came here. You knew. You set this trap for me. You have to pay.'

'Shall we go back over things? Listen I . . . I am like a car, I have two spare wheels and yet it is as if instead of four wheels I had three. I lack something all cars have and have something else there is no use having. I have no illusions about anything. Listen – let's pretend we are on the plane again, you come out now and we say hello, I accompany you down into the hall to the baggage return, I invent an excuse and we shake hands without too much familiarity as if . . .'

'No, I am staying.'

'As you like. But not here. I am telephoning so that you are given another room.'

'That isn't what you want. You want to – with me.'

'Mistake. I want no more from you. Not like this.'

'But you want.'

'Right – I want. What do I want that you want too?'

'You know perfectly well. I just want to see if you have the courage.'

'For what?'

'You know better than me, I don't know anything about these bestial contacts.'

'Do you want me to strip?'

'I didn't mean anything like that. But just suck my sex. You want to suck my sex.'

'Allow me' and I make to seize the handle of the door.

'I will wait for you. Have a nice meal.' But while saying this he blocks the door with one arm. What sense is there in a scuffle with a man who basically wants to experience the intoxication of being sucked off? It's ridiculous.

'All right.' I do an about-turn and take off my trousers and underpants.

'That's enough – you don't need to take off your socks.'

'All this is disgusting.'

And he has already undone his trousers, which slip halfway down his thighs, and he is on top of me with his huge erect prick, at the height of my face.

'You just need to suck here,' he says and moves over, lifts a thigh and fucks me hard with a single thrust, wetting my neck with saliva, wanting to kiss me, I turn my head away in annoyance. Oh how I should like to have a mind in which what is happening to me now would be the most beautiful of phantasms taking bodily shape! Instead no. End.

'If this is what you want,' he says, 'I have a lot of friends.'

'Listen, I could easily have done without this. And now I imagine you will want to go. Come, I'll go with you.'

'Yes,' and as he says Yes extracts a condom from his jacket pocket. 'You didn't even give me time to put it on. Are you sick by any chance?'

'No, I really don't think so. Come on, young man. I'm hungry.'

Crossing the garden he adjusts his tie and trousers for the hundredth time, walks quickly, looks at me as if it was he who had been raped, but I feel that the man must be in a pitiful state and, not to make a mistake, suggest to him to stay and rest in another room, without being bound to see me tomorrow, since I

335

cause him such irresistible disgust, it is right that he should stay and sleep it off and go off calmly to Monastir – also to avoid the nasty reactions of the employees. No, he says suddenly, with the look of a beaten dog. Up at the porter's desk, in order to strike a pose, he rings several numbers, telephones here and there, then has them call the hotel in Monastir, does not even have a taxi called, I try to moderate his reactions and counter-reactions, I accompany him down into the street, I shake his hand almost suffering for him. In the dark he runs off lightly, the Tunisian engineer – the hydraulics expert – who came hundreds of kilometres to learn what life is, who I am supposed to have put a curse on, who hadn't closed an eye until he finished me off like a bad dream to be dreamt to the end so as to be able to eliminate it. And who complained that I didn't keep my leg high enough and apart enough.

This is the speech I shall make to the area reps as the selling line to the bookshops . . . No, not tonight, not now that it is almost dawn, another time. And I begin to laugh, breaking into the noise of the first bidet of the couple to the left of the wall, the good-morning bidet, I laugh because precisely yesterday the *animateur* shouted into the microphone that it would be a memorable *soirée-contact*. Ah, for that yes. And I think still about Jamael perhaps now wandering round Sousse, biting his nails, elegant in the dawn as if for a business meeting, asking himself whatever has he done, his little suitcase in his grip, waiting for a train, for a bus, and why, and with whom, and where is all this wonderful thing.

I am suffocating, I can hardly breathe. Perhaps it is the alcohol – afterwards in the bar I drank a couple of vodkas. He stood in front of me as if at the bar of a court. I feel like vomiting – it would be a good opportunity, this. I have never not managed to give a form to my disgust, to vomit it out brutally. I hold it in, instead, I chew it up, I reduce it to powder, from this powder I draw ink and then literature. Ah, if at least I could have a bowel move-ment. No, instead I feel their sperm spewing in my intestines, I shall lose them in sleep. Suppose you cleaned your teeth? With a less disgusting mouth you could more easily fall asleep. When you get home you could go to the Infectious Diseases Unit in Brescia and ask to be allowed to hold in turn the hands of five people dying of the Final Slimming Cure. It would be like holding my own hand, wouldn't it? – Done. A little washout with an enema is worth five suppositories. That's what was wrong – I hadn't been for five days.

Then the day took fire and it was morning again.

I begin to fill the day by running on the beach, taking care not to step on the syringes. What a lot of dates on the sand, a litter of drowned cats, the swish of a whip in the air, a horse comes up at a trot. Aeroplanes. Three maids with pink dressing-gowns. An immense milk-white sky. A child on a bicycle goes up and down like in a gymkhana. I go back in. Shoe-shuffle of watchmen, greetings from the waiters as they arrive. And there I am smoking on the veranda, dressed in white, awaiting the arrival of Aisha to say good morning to someone; the first guests go past dressed for tennis and the cats, which to me are all deaf-and-dumb so as to conserve energy. And I make a smoke-ring and I think of Valéry and the wise things he said about literature. I'd hand him this piece of paper and he would read:

'Ladies and gentlemen, this page of literature is a page of literature. And good-night to the bucket.'

~

That day – and the way I am reinterpreting it – has brought it about that for a long time I have been going to bed earlier and earlier (yesterday evening I went to bed at 19.30 and fell asleep right away) and I wake up more and more early, in the heart of the night, and go out on to the terrace.

My family moved exactly twenty times from the moment of my birth till five years ago, when we came to this house of mine, modest but finally ours – to be exact mine, but one which I first and foremost consider to belong morally to my mother, of whom I am a proper paying guest. And in our wanderings, first with the household belongings on carts pulled by oxen, I remember, from house to house – to be precise from an inn with kitchen to a lodging house with room for everyone to sleep in – after all my father had to be given what looked like a job which he preferred (but not much) to the too obvious alternative of not doing anything, I developed by myself distrust of any kind of house, because in each of ours instability reigned, the rent hung over us

337

and the damned IOUs and the discord which generates misery and, as far as my case was concerned – the case of a sexual-child and one who was shamelessly autarchic – a hotbed of ancestral prejudices, of arbitrary and hateful worries of beings whom I felt to be inferior and unjustifiably called to sit in judgement on me, a prison of beatings lying in wait from my father, my mother, my two elder brothers. So much so that, the moment I was big enough, I went off and not even on a bench, deprived of sleep, or in the bed of a hairily nice Amphitryon, or alongside a solicitous shit of a saviour, did I ever feel nostalgia for a house, unless for the one I would never be able to have. How surprised I was therefore when I saw that there existed people who, having a house, were fond of it, people who shook their heads when I told them of the magic of my days in the icy cold and certainly thought I had a weakness for fantastic snobberies. Because I have never been a tramp but a perfect wandering gentleman – I always presented myself in the best possible way; as a young person I shaved in the fountains and washed at least once a day in every xenophobic metropolis, I entered houses conscious of being admitted to a space which was at once sacred and ridiculous – I endeavoured not to let it be seen that, all in all, I preferred the open air and ailments and the kerbstones beside the road to embossed sofas. I have aspired very little to look like the poet *maudit* and possess by birth an extraordinary aristocratic instinct for the social forms wherever they manifest themselves and for what they are which, when I took it into my head, transformed me into the best brought-up boy one could ever know – and receive in one's house. 'It pleased me to please' and pleasing was also a form of spiritual subsistence apart from the dinners and the beds – which were much fewer – devoured materially. But the house remained the house of others – since I have lived here in a settled way I have tried to make it sound like a property but I have not succeeded, perhaps because there is no point in possessing a house when there must still be someone who has not even a roof. It is not a house, it is the room where I write and sleep, twenty square metres in all – the rest occupied by my mother in a matronly manner – and to keep up masturbating I use the kitchen.

When I leave here, I forget it every time – I feel I could break away from it without too much fuss, go and live somewhere else so long as it wasn't someone else's house and not another bench either, because they are not well enough upholstered for someone who has a bad back. For example I have tried to see if in me there was some residue of aspiration to mimesis of the petty bourgeois: one day I bought a horrible milk-white crystal lamp and an almost silver six-piece cutlery service. The lamp I never light, and the service has disappeared into some tortuous cranny of my mother's 'in case it gets spoilt'. Thus here, on the furniture, the latest publication of a super-refined American publishing house ends up crowned with a bonbonnière from relatives of my mother, who never throws anything away (I don't know how, but a little red balloon turned up here recently and, after a few days, I found it burst but nicely arranged on a cactus branch) and the enormous black polystyrene phallus which a sculptress friend gave has ended up alongside the bag of balls of old wool with which Maria Busi née Bonora intends to make a blanket, the kind the black pedlars sell, she says, because in any case the colours get mixed. What I like most about these walls and these full floors is their absolute lack of style: but they are nevertheless laden with our brutal, sealed and unpretentious history, one feels good there, like in a chapel of unobvious ex-votos. I don't say anything to her ever since she went furiously to fish out her forks and spoons and knives from when she was married, which I had hidden from her to substitute for them, to be exact, *my* cutlery – a little experimental piece of arse aspiring to something he didn't have.

The thing I remember with most pleasure in Mao is that, in order to be what he was, he needed for himself a very limited apparatus and that he slept and read and wrote in a room like mine. When I have entered some great and rich house I have never been enchanted or fascinated by the display of *taste* and wealth, it seems to me more than anything else to be a waste of time and space to have so much more than necessary, sad that there are still so many people who do not grasp that the true road of sex-appeal begins from stoicism as philosophical frivolity, including furnishings – with that I have also said everything about my extremely weak desire for worldly things, although it may give me some occasion to show my profound sense of *pietas*, aroused in me by every building packed with nothing. Fine houses bore me as much as their masters – if at all I am enchanted by the terraces but they mustn't have many varieties of flowers and definitely no roses, only a few geraniums, of every colour and species, in non-matching vases – those that were there. I too have a little terrace with a little of everything – but they are common-or-garden plants which my mother collects here and there, a *bud* here and a *bud* there, no symmetry, just big bushes, very well looked after and wild.

Once there was a *street*, a life outside, now there is one no longer – it is the greatest loss of our time, *the street*, where no one goes any more or only as much as is strictly necessary to make money or to go and spend it. For me it is a disaster because, for example, it isn't that I don't watch television because I prefer to read, it is simply that it sends me to sleep – quite apart from what it transmits – and I don't tolerate even the shortest commercial. And to stay at home has become more than a habit, a vice of which I am more the victim than the creator. As a boy I too had my fixed abode – it was the River Chiese, I was always there, the only place where there were no removals to be made then and there – and lynchings only occasionally. Now it is full of stray rabid dogs, animals that turn up by the sides of the autostradas which they are made to get out on to by their pained owners with tears in their eyes – and the water is dead, infected, dangerous, another *street* that runs rotten and for no reason, silent, without the cry of someone diving or the squeal of a bicycle's brakes on the gravel.

At night, I was saying, I always wake up more than once and, whether it rains or snows or there is a moon or one to be imagined, go on to the terrace. This winter I let myself fall naked and as if dead on to the snow to see the imprint.

And a little time ago it was a quarter to four in the morning. I went into the kitchen to make myself coffee, scattered garments belonging to Adele, who every so often comes to sleep in her granny's big bed; Adele must have been playing with paper and scissors this evening, pieces of paper everywhere, her little shoes with the holed cotton socks on the chair, her brief knickers, her T-shirt on the table under the four thorn-apple bells, whose whiteish-purple colour and perfume I am mad about. Light, fetish: Adele. Adele who strikes me like a pain. From the other room there penetrates the dizzy effluvium of four stalks of tuberose in the fine crystal vase; the moment they have withered I shall flood the house with chrysanthemums because I love their bitter perfume. I suffered for four years to get my mother to accept chrysanthemums in the house. Odd, but it was the only flower missing from the wreaths when my father died one March years ago. Every flower they brought then I couldn't bear to look at. I managed to feel revulsion also for the people who brought them, who dared to accompany him. For months afterwards his ghost came to sneer in my dreams or else it was a defenceless man who came in at a door, sat at a table and said nothing, look I'm not dead; he began to eat and that was all, while we all stayed with our knives and forks in the air. The hate I felt for him, no longer consuming me by day, came to take its part of me in the night. I forgive only when I have no other choice – and I tear myself to pieces because I have been reduced to forgive.

I take a turn round the terrace, this too is a journey. Just wakened, in front of the mirror I sometimes have the sense of beauty: the belly is still taut, flat, the face, so rested, and the liver in such good shape, relaxed, my hair which I have forgotten to cut for some months, the legs strong, and a general disposition to smile to myself: that arched plant at the other end, black in the night, is a jasmine and that other which leans out from the railings is a mass of pink, purple, cyclamen bells. I gaze towards where the hibiscus is, it has two buds which are there as if lost in thought, not knowing whether, with this weather, it is worth while opening or rotting right away inside the pistils. We have every kind of geranium and several luxurious plants; in the corner of the wall, the rosemary and sage. In the middle of the little terrace my mother has made an altar of flowers, she says they are not there for their beauty but because they are the first which, at the first cold snaps, she brings up to the attic. I drink all the coffee, three cups. Then I go quickly to write something, it is the translation of some verses by Lucan,* for days I have been touching and retouching these fine phrases more or less at this time, breaking the bargain made with her not to type anything

*Pharsalia I. ll. 412–19.

341

between 2200 and 0600. I smoke a second cigarette in the kitchen: it was inevitable that I should end up here and that my corpse should be to hand. Then I go back to the machine to write; yes, I could distribute things better, leave everything to the unauthorized dog's home of that woman on the way to the quarry. I get a lot of fun out of drawing up new wills also because each year my *property* has increased and by now I am very good at surviving the shame of earning the wherewithal to live and die writing.

Then I sit on the step which leads from the kitchen to the terrace. Since the light was on, I have wakened someone in the big bed.

'What a fidget – what are you doing there at this time of night?'

I turn round and it is her in her bare feet in her elastic girdle round that body of hers that seems to contain all my acts of sodomy, her face intact, in a celestial state of inquisitiveness, as if she had always been sleeping or had never closed an eye. And I dare to say to her something I have never said to her or which perhaps I have got tired of saying to her, because in any case she does not believe the truth.

'I'm looking at the moon.'

I have turned towards the sky again, certain that she would go back into her room shrugging and shaking her head. Instead I find her at my back; holding on to the door-jamb with one hand she leans forward, looks to right and to left and as she goes off says:

'But what if it isn't even there, the moon?'

Guess, oh you who are obsessed by the origins of
    things
if the sea rebounds from the furthest point in the
    world
merely to ill-use it before abandoning it
or if it talks cryptically because whipped at certain
    hours by the moon
or if it is the dry earth avid for waves and life
that makes it leap to the stars;
but to me – whatever you are or cause of the
    vicissitudes
between god and earth – never unveil yourself.